GED Connection™

Mathematics

LiteracyLink® is a joint project of PBS, Kentucky Educational Television, the National Center on Adult Literacy, and the Kentucky Department of Education. This project is funded in whole, or in part, by the Star Schools Program of the USDE under contract #R203D60001.

Mathematics: by Cathy Fillmore Hoyt

PBS LiteracyLink®   KET The Kentucky Network   NCAL

Acknowledgments

LiteracyLink® Partners

LiteracyLink® is a joint project of:
Public Broadcasting Service
Kentucky Educational Television
National Center on Adult Literacy
The Kentucky Department of Education

Content Design and Workbook Editorial Development
Learning Unlimited,
Oak Park, Illinois

Design and Layout
By Design,
Lexington, Kentucky

Project Consultant
Milli Fazey, KET,
Lexington, Kentucky

Production Manager
Debra Gibson,
Copywrite,
Lexington, Kentucky

This project is funded in whole, or in part, by the Star Schools Program of the USDE under contract #R203D60001.

PBS LiteracyLink, LitTeacher, LitLearner, LitHelper, and PeerLit are registered marks of the Public Broadcasting Service.

ISBN 1–881020–41–X

Contents

GED Connection Orientation v

How to Use This Book vi

Math Pretest 1
Math Pretest Answer Sheet 7
Math Pretest Answers and Explanations 8

Program 27: Passing the GED Math Test

Before You Watch...13
After You Watch 15
    Calculator Skills for the GED Math Test...16
    Special Formats for GED Items..20

Program 28: Number Sense

Before You Watch...23
After You Watch 27
    Your Approach to Learning Math...28
    Understanding Our Number System...30
    Estimating 34

Program 29: Problem Solving

Before You Watch...41
After You Watch 45
    Basic Operations Review..46
    Solving Word Problems..52
    Solving Multi-Step Problems...56

Program 30: Decimals

Before You Watch...63
After You Watch 67
    Understanding Decimal Values...68
    Basic Operations with Decimals...70
    Everyday Decimals 76

Program 31: Fractions

Before You Watch...85
After You Watch 89
    Basic Operations with Fractions..90
    Problem Solving with Fractions 96
    Everyday Fractions 100

Program 32: Ratio, Proportion, and Percent

Before You Watch...107
After You Watch 111
    Working with Ratios 112
    Working with Proportions 114
    Working with Percent...118

Program 33: Measurement

Before You Watch...129
After You Watch 133
    The English System of Measurement...134
    The Metric System 138
    Finding Perimeter and Area...142

Program 34: Formulas

Before You Watch 149
After You Watch 153
    Using Formulas to Solve Problems 154
    Solving for Other Variables 158
    Using Geometry Formulas 162

Program 35: Geometry

Before You Watch 169
After You Watch 173
    Working with Lines and Angles 174
    Working with Triangles 178
    Working with Circles 182

Program 36: Data Analysis

PART ONE
Before You Watch 191
After You Watch 195
    Reading Tables, Charts, and Pictographs 196
    Understanding Bar and Line Graphs 200
    Understanding Circle Graphs 204
PART TWO
Before You Watch 211
After You Watch 215
    Understanding Data 216
    Mean, Median, and Mode 220

Program 37: Statistics and Probability

Before You Watch 227
After You Watch 231
    Using Statistics to Draw Conclusions 232
    Understanding the Meaning of Chance 234
    Applying Theoretical Probability 238

Program 38: Introduction to Algebra

Before You Watch 247
After You Watch 251
    Working with Signed Numbers 252
    Working with Expressions 256
    Working with Equations 260

Program 39: Special Topics in Algebra and Geometry

Before You Watch 269
After You Watch 273
    Working with Inequalities 274
    Understanding Patterns and Functions 278
    Coordinate Geometry 282

Math Practice Test 297
Math Practice Test Answer Sheet 303
Math Practice Test Answers and Explanations 304

Answer Key 308

Math Handbook

    Common Equivalencies and Measurement 336
    Using the Casio fx-260 Calculator 337
    GED Formulas Page 340

Glossary 341
Index 344

GED Connection Orientation

Welcome to the *LiteracyLink®* system. This workbook is part of a multimedia educational system for adult learners and educators that includes both *GED Connection* for GED preparation and *Workplace Essential Skills*, targeted at upgrading the knowledge and skills needed to succeed in the world of work.

Instructional Programs

GED Connection consists of an orientation program and 38 instructional programs. Each GED topic can be approached in three ways—through video, print, and online. For example, Program 29 is *Problem Solving*. To study this topic, you can watch the *Program 29* video lesson, work in the *Program 29* workbook lesson in this book, and go online to http://www.pbs.org/literacy and then to the GED *Math* module.

Getting Started with the System

You will make the best use of *LiteracyLink* if you use all of the components. At http://www.pbs.org/literacy, you will establish your Home Space, which is your starting point for working through the Internet portion of *LiteracyLink*.

For additional practice, visit *LiteracyLink* online at http://www.pbs.org/literacy.

Making the Best Use of the Workbook

Before you start using this workbook, take some time to preview its features.

1. The **GED Pretest** will help you decide which GED areas you need to focus on. You should use the evaluation chart, provided after the pretest answer key, to develop your study plan.

2. Each workbook lesson corresponds to a video program and Internet activities.

   The **Before You Watch** section orients you to the video program:
   - **Objectives** form the focus for each video, workbook, and online lesson
   - **Sneak Preview** provides an introductory exercise, answers, and feedback
   - **Program Summary** explains what you are about to see in the video
   - **Vocabulary** defines key content area terms

   The **After You Watch** section covers key GED content and skills:
   - **Key Points** to think about and **GED Tips**
   - **Lesson Segments** that provide core instruction
   - **Skill Practice** to reinforce what you have learned
   - **Connection** to another GED subject area
   - **GED Practice** with items similar to those on the GED Test

3. The **GED Practice Test** helps you evaluate your GED readiness.
4. The **Answer Key** consists of answers and explanations.
5. A **Reference Handbook** provides additional resources for GED preparation.
6. The **Glossary** and **Index** help you find the information you need.

For Teachers

Portions of *LiteracyLink* have been developed for adult educators and service providers. LitTeacher is an online professional development system that provides a number of resources including PeerLit, a database of evaluated websites. You can also access LitTeacher at http://www.pbs.org/literacy.

Who's Responsible for LiteracyLink®?

LiteracyLink was developed through a five-year grant by the U.S. Department of Education. The following partners have contributed to the development of the *LiteracyLink* system:

| PBS Adult Learning Service | Kentucky Educational Television (KET) | The National Center on Adult Literacy (NCAL) of the University of Pennsylvania | The Kentucky Department of Education |

All of the *LiteracyLink* partners wish you the very best in passing the GED and meeting all of your educational goals.

Math Pretest—Part I

You may use a calculator for any of the items in Part I, but some of the items may be solved more quickly without a calculator. Use the answer sheet on page 7.

Some of the questions will require you to use a formula. The formulas you may need are given on page 340. Not all of the formulas on that page will be needed.

DIRECTIONS: Choose the one best answer for each question.

1. Lana bought a new washer and dryer for $1062. She paid $150 down and agreed to pay the balance in 12 monthly payments. How much will she pay each month?
   (1) $101.00
   (2) $88.50
   (3) $76.00
   (4) $73.00
   (5) $12.50

Question 2 refers to the following drawing.

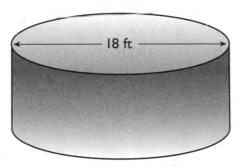

2. The cylindrical storage tank has a height of 12 feet. Which of the following expressions could be used to find the volume of the tank in cubic feet?
   (1) $18(12)$
   (2) $\pi(18)(12)$
   (3) $\pi(9)(12)$
   (4) $\pi(9^2)(12)$
   (5) $\pi(18^2)(12)$

3. Noah spends $\frac{1}{4}$ of his monthly take-home pay on rent and $\frac{1}{5}$ on a car payment. What fraction of his monthly take-home pay does he have left?
   (1) $\frac{1}{20}$
   (2) $\frac{9}{20}$
   (3) $\frac{11}{20}$
   (4) $\frac{7}{9}$
   (5) $\frac{19}{20}$

4. Which of the following expressions is the equivalent of $10 - 3(2x - y)$?
   (1) $10 - 6x + 3y$
   (2) $10 - 6x - 3y$
   (3) $10 - 6xy$
   (4) $-14x + 7y$
   (5) $14x - 7y$

Question 5 refers to the following information.

Frank started a home-based business five years ago. His income and expenses for the five-year period are shown in the table below.

FRANK RAMOS ENTERPRISES Income and Expense Totals by Year		
Year	Income	Expenses
1	$10,500	$12,540
2	$14,215	$6,780
3	$12,562	$4,320
4	$18,920	$5,690
5	$22,378	$3,990

5. To apply for a loan, Frank needs to know his average annual income. What is Frank's mean income for the first five years of his business?
   (1) $78,575
   (2) $15,715
   (3) $14,215
   (4) $9,051
   (5) $6,664

Question 6 refers to the following information.

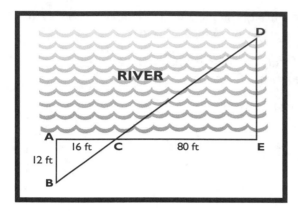

Note: Figure is not drawn to scale.

6. In the diagram, ∠A and ∠E are right angles. What is the distance in feet across the river from D to E?
   (1) 20
   (2) 52
   (3) 60
   (4) 96
   (5) 107

Question 7 refers to the following information.

7. Marilyn plans to buy tomato plants for her home garden. The sale prices for five stores in her area are shown above. Which store is offering the best price per plant?
   (1) Plant Mart
   (2) Garden Center
   (3) KG Nursery
   (4) Outdoor World
   (5) Green House

Question 8 refers to the following information.

8. Crestview Middle School holds a winter carnival every year to raise money for its sports programs. The bar graph shows the ticket sales from 1995 through 2000. In which year was there an increase in ticket sales of approximately 50% from the year before?
   (1) 1996
   (2) 1997
   (3) 1998
   (4) 1999
   (5) 2000

9. Dail needs 8 pieces of electrical wire, each 54 inches long. Which of the following expressions could be used to find how many feet of wiring he needs?
   (1) $8(54)(12)$
   (2) $\frac{(54 \div 8)}{12}$
   (3) $\frac{12(54)}{8}$
   (4) $\frac{54}{8(12)}$
   (5) $\frac{8(54)}{12}$

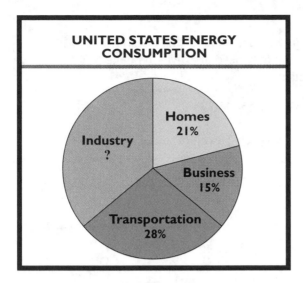

UNITED STATES ENERGY CONSUMPTION

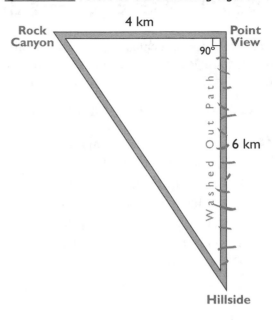

10. The graph shows how energy is used in the United States. What percent of energy is consumed by industry?
    (1) 21%
    (2) 33%
    (3) 36%
    (4) 64%
    (5) 67%

11. Laura, a cyclist, had planned to ride directly from Hillside to Point View; however, a rainstorm has washed out the bike path. She decides to take the path northwest to Rock Canyon first and then ride east to Point View. About how many kilometers will she ride?
    (1) between 7 and 8
    (2) between 9 and 10
    (3) between 10 and 11
    (4) between 11 and 12
    (5) between 12 and 13

12. On a map, the distance between Tampa and Daytona Beach is $\frac{5}{8}$ inch. The actual distance between the two cities is 140 miles. How many miles would a distance of 1 inch represent?

    Mark your answer in the circles in the grid on your answer sheet on page 7.

13. Show the location of a point whose coordinates are $(3, -3)$.

    Mark your answer on the coordinate plane grid on your answer sheet on page 7.

MATH PRETEST

Math Pretest—Part II

You may not use a calculator for the questions in Part II. Some of the questions will require you to use a formula. The formulas you may need are given on page 340. Not all of the formulas on that page will be needed.

DIRECTIONS: Choose the <u>one best answer</u> for each question.

14. Nita and Pat are raising money to start a community theater. Nita raised $500 less than four times as much as Pat. Altogether they raised $3800. Which of the following equations could be used to solve for the amount Pat raised (x)?

  (1) $x + (4x + 500) = 3800$
  (2) $x + (4x - 500) = 3800$
  (3) $4x + 500 = 3800 - x$
  (4) $4x + 500x = 3800$
  (5) $4(x + 500) = 3800$

Question 15 refers to the following drawing.

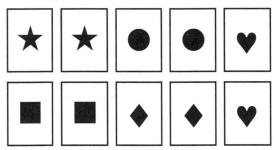

15. During a game, two cards are drawn at random from the cards shown above. A star card is drawn first and removed from the game. What is the probability of drawing either a star or square on the second draw?

  (1) $\frac{1}{9}$
  (2) $\frac{3}{10}$
  (3) $\frac{1}{3}$
  (4) $\frac{2}{5}$
  (5) $\frac{1}{2}$

Question 16 refers to the following figure.

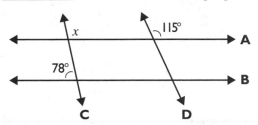

16. Lines A and B are parallel. Lines C and D, which are not parallel, intersect lines A and B. What is the measure of $\angle x$?

  (1) 115°
  (2) 102°
  (3) 78°
  (4) 65°
  (5) Not enough information is given.

17. Two lines intersect at the coordinates $(-2,3)$. Show the location of the point.

Mark your answer on the coordinate plane grid on your answer sheet on page 7.

Question 18 refers to the following figure.

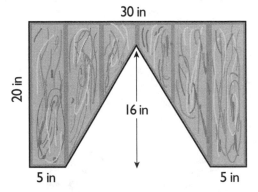

18. A triangular piece is cut from a rectangular piece of plywood. What is the area in square inches of the remaining portion of the plywood (the shaded portion of the figure)?

Mark your answer in the circles in the grid on your answer sheet on page 7.

A parent organization is raising money to remodel a school's library. The frequency table shows the 25 amounts donated during the month.

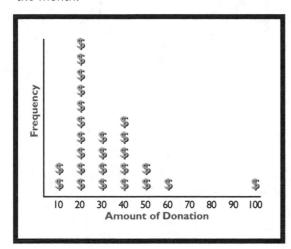

19. For future planning, the parents want to know the typical donation amount. The president suggests that the median will best represent the data. What is the median of the 25 donations?
(1) $20
(2) $30
(3) $32
(4) $40
(5) $55

20. The group also decides to find the mean of the data. The secretary of the organization suggests they should first exclude any outliers. Which of the following should be excluded?
(1) both $10 donations
(2) only one of the $10 donations
(3) the $100 donation
(4) all the $20 donations
(5) the $60 donation

21. Jerry borrows $600 from his brother for six months. He agrees to pay his brother simple interest at the rate of 4% annually. Which of the following expressions could be used to find the total amount he will pay his brother in six months?
(1) $600 \times 0.04 \times \frac{1}{2}$
(2) $600 \times 0.04 \times 6$
(3) $600 + (600 \times 4 \times \frac{1}{2})$
(4) $600 + (600 \times 0.04 \times 6)$
(5) $600 + (600 \times 0.04 \times \frac{1}{2})$

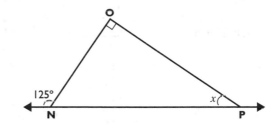

22. A side of a triangle lies along line NP. What is the measure of $\angle x$?
(1) 35°
(2) 55°
(3) 90°
(4) 135°
(5) 155°

23. If $a = 5$ and $b = -2$, what is the value of $\frac{a^2 - b^2}{a + b}$?
(1) -7
(2) -3
(3) 3
(4) 7
(5) $9\frac{2}{3}$

Question 24 refers to the following information.

A	B	C	D	E	F
1	2	3	4	5	6
7	8	9	10	11	12
13	14	15	. . .		

24. If the sequence continues, in which
column will you find the number 200?

    (1) B

    (2) C

    (3) D

    (4) E

    (5) F

Question 25 refers to the graph below.

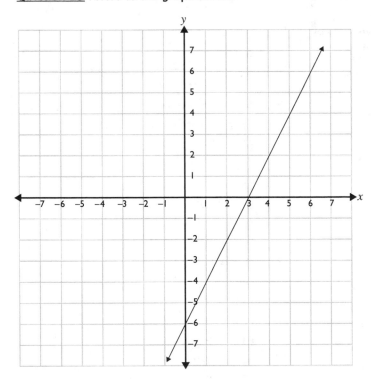

25. Which of the following values represents
the slope of the line shown above?

    (1) −7

    (2) −2

    (3) $\frac{5}{3}$

    (4) 2

    (5) 7

Math Pretest Answer Sheet

Part I

1. ① ② ③ ④ ⑤
2. ① ② ③ ④ ⑤
3. ① ② ③ ④ ⑤
4. ① ② ③ ④ ⑤
5. ① ② ③ ④ ⑤
6. ① ② ③ ④ ⑤
7. ① ② ③ ④ ⑤
8. ① ② ③ ④ ⑤
9. ① ② ③ ④ ⑤
10. ① ② ③ ④ ⑤
11. ① ② ③ ④ ⑤

12.

13.

Part II

14. ① ② ③ ④ ⑤
15. ① ② ③ ④ ⑤
16. ① ② ③ ④ ⑤

17.

18.

19. ① ② ③ ④ ⑤
20. ① ② ③ ④ ⑤
21. ① ② ③ ④ ⑤
22. ① ② ③ ④ ⑤
23. ① ② ③ ④ ⑤
24. ① ② ③ ④ ⑤
25. ① ② ③ ④ ⑤

Math Pretest Answers and Explanations
Part I

1. **(3) $76.00**   Subtract the down payment from the total cost of the washer and dryer: $1062 − $150 = $912. Divide by 12 to find the amount of each monthly payment: $912 ÷ 12 = $76.

2. **(4) $\pi(9^2)(12)$**   Use the formula for finding the volume of a cylinder: $V = \pi r^2 h$. The problem gives you the diameter of the tank. Divide by 2 to find the radius: $18 ÷ 2 = 9$. Substitute the values into the formula.

3. **(3) $\frac{11}{20}$**   Add $\frac{1}{4}$ and $\frac{1}{5}$ to get $\frac{9}{20}$. Subtract $\frac{9}{20}$ from 1 to find the fraction that is left: $1 = \frac{20}{20}$, and $\frac{20}{20} - \frac{9}{20} = \frac{11}{20}$.

4. **(1) $10 − 6x + 3y$**   The number −3 is multiplied by both of the terms in the parentheses.

5. **(2) $15,715**   Add the amounts in the income column and divide by 5: $10,500 + $14,215 + $12,562 + $18,920 + $22,378 = $78,575, and $78,575 ÷ 5 = $15,715.

6. **(3) 60**   The two right triangles are similar. Set up a proportion and solve for DE: $\frac{12}{16} = \frac{x}{80}$. Cross multiply: $12(80) = 16x$, $960 = 16x$, and $\frac{960}{16} = 60 = x$.

7. **(5) Green House**   Find the unit cost of a plant at each store. Using your calculator, divide the group price by the number of plants. The result is the price for one plant. Then compare the results. Green House has the lowest price per plant.

Plant Mart:	$6.50 ÷ 12 ≈ $0.5417
Garden Center:	$0.65
KG Nursery:	$2.26 ÷ 4 = $0.565
Outdoor World:	$1.60 ÷ 3 ≈ $0.533
Green House:	$2.48 ÷ 5 = $0.496

8. **(3) 1998**   In 1997, about 180 tickets were sold. In 1998, 270 tickets were sold, an increase of 90 tickets. Since 90 is 50% of 180, you know the increase was 50%.

9. **(5) $\frac{8(54)}{12}$**   Multiply 8 by 54 to find the total length needed in inches. Then divide by 12 to convert inches to feet.

10. **(3) 36%**   The entire circle represents 100%. Subtract the percents you are given to find the percent that is missing. 100% − 21% − 15% − 28% = 36%.

11. (4) between 11 and 12 Use the Pythagorean relationship to find the distance from Hillside to Rock Canyon:

$$c^2 = a^2 + b^2$$
$$c^2 = 4^2 + 6^2$$
$$c^2 = 52$$
$$c = \sqrt{52}$$

Using your calculator, you can see that the square root of 52 is about 7.2. You can also estimate the square root by thinking that since $7^2 = 49$ and $8^2 = 64$, the distance must be between 7 and 8 kilometers.

Now add the distance from Hillside to Rock Canyon and the distance from Rock Canyon to Point View: $7.2 + 4 = 11.2$.

12. 224

There are several ways to solve this problem. You can set up a proportion and solve: $\frac{5}{8}:140 = 1:x$. You can also reason it out by thinking: Since $\frac{5}{8}$ is 140 miles, $\frac{1}{8}$ must be $140 \div 5$, or 28 miles. 1 inch $= \frac{8}{8}$ inch. If $\frac{1}{8} = 28$ miles, then $\frac{8}{8}$ must equal 8×28 or 224 miles.

13. Your answer is correct if you marked the coordinate plane grid as shown.

Part II

14. **(2)** $x + (4x - 500) = 3800$ If x represents the money Pat raised, then $4x - 500$ represents the amount Nita raised. The total they raised $3800 is equal to the sum of the two expressions.

15. **(3)** $\frac{1}{3}$ After the first card is drawn, 9 cards are left. Of the 9, three have a favorable outcome, either a star or a square. 3 of 9, or $\frac{3}{9}$, reduces to $\frac{1}{3}$.

16. **(2) 102°** The angles formed by line D are not needed to solve the problem. The angle directly to the right of the 78° angle formed by the intersection of lines B and C must measure 102°, since $180° - 78° = 102°$. Angle x is a corresponding angle to the angle that measures 102°, so it must have the same measure.

17. Your answer should appear as shown on the coordinate plane grid below.

18. **440**

The area of the rectangle is $30(20) = 600$ square inches. To find the area of the triangle, first find the measure of its base: $30 - (5 + 5) = 20$ inches. Use the formula: $A = \frac{1}{2}bh = \frac{1}{2}(20)(16) = 10(16) = 160$ square inches. Finally, subtract the area of the triangle from the area of the rectangle: $600 - 160 = 440$ square inches.

19. **(2) $30**   Since there are 25 donations, the middle donation must be the 13th. Counting from either the lowest to the highest or the highest to the lowest, find the 13th value.

20. **(3) the $100 donation**   The $100 donation is separated from the rest of the data by a large gap. Clearly, this outlier does not represent the donations that are usually received by the group. If this outlier is included in the data, the interpretation of the data will be in error.

21. **(5) $600 + (600 \times 0.04 \times \frac{1}{2})$**   Use the formula for finding simple interest. The rate (4%) must be expressed as a decimal, and the time (6 months) must be expressed in terms of years: 6 months $= \frac{1}{2}$ year. The expression $600 \times 0.04 \times \frac{1}{2}$ is equal to the amount of interest Jerry will owe, but he must pay his brother the amount borrowed (600) plus the interest: $600 + (600 \times 0.04 \times \frac{1}{2})$.

22. **(1) 35°**   Angle ONP must measure 55°, since the angle measuring 125° and $\angle$ONP are supplementary.   NOP is a right angle and measures 90°. Since the sum of the interior angles of a triangle equals 180°, $x = 180° - 55° - 90° = 35°$.

23. **(4) 7**   Substitute the values and solve: $\frac{a^2 - b^2}{a + b} = \frac{25 - 4}{3} = \frac{21}{3} = 7$.

24. **(1) B**   The F column always contains the multiples of 6. If 200 is evenly divisible by 6, it will appear in the F column, but $200 \div 6 = 33$ r2. In other words, 198 is a multiple of 6 and will fall in the F column. The number 199 will be in the A column, and 200 will be in the B column.

25. **(4) 2**   Use the formula for finding the slope (m) of a line.

$$m = \frac{y_2 - y_1}{x_2 - x_1}$$
$$m = \frac{-4 - 0}{1 - 3}$$
$$m = \frac{-4}{-2} = +2$$

Using Your Pretest Results

Circle your incorrect answers in Column 1 below. Read across. Column 2 tells you which skills you may still need to work on. Column 3 tells you which program you can use to study those skills.

Pretest Questions	Skills Tested	Program
1	number sense, estimation, problem solving, multi-step word problems	28, 29
7	understanding decimals, decimal applications	30
3	operations with fractions, problem solving with fractions	31
8, 12	ratio, proportion, and percent	32
9	standard English measurements, metric measurements, finding perimeter and area	33
2, 18, 21	using formulas to solve problems, solving for other variables, using geometry formulas	34
6, 11, 16, 22	working with lines, angles, triangles, and circles	35
5, 10, 19, 20	reading tables, charts, and graphs; understanding data; mean, median, and mode	36
15	using data to draw conclusions, understanding chance, applying probability	37
4, 13, 14, 17, 23, 24, 25	signed numbers, expressions, equations, inequalities, patterns and functions, coordinate geometry	38, 39

What do "setting up the problem" and "bubbling in" have to do with the GED Math Test? Find out in this program as test writers, teachers, and GED learners offer information and tips about the types of questions, the answer formats, and the calculator used on the test.

BEFORE YOU WATCH

27

Passing the GED Math Test

OBJECTIVES

1. Know what to expect on Part I and Part II of the GED Math Test.

2. Determine the number of questions and how long you will have to take each part of the test.

3. Explore the math content areas on the test.

4. Discover the calculator skills you will need on the test.

5. Investigate the types of questions on the test, including multiple-choice questions and other formats.

The math skills you will use on the GED Math Test can help you in every aspect of your life. As an adult, you already have a great deal of experience using this kind of math. Paying bills, finding the best buy in a store, measuring the size of a room, and budgeting your money are all examples of the kind of math skills tested on the GED Math Test.

The purpose of the GED Math Test is to assess your ability to apply what you know about math in everyday situations. Some problems can be solved using the four basic operations of adding, subtracting, multiplying, and dividing. Others can be solved by applying the general rules of algebra and geometry. At all times, you will need to apply number sense, the common sense you have about math, to make sure your answers are reasonable.

How can you prepare for the GED Math Test? First, use the videos, workbook lessons, and online lessons to become familiar with the test and the areas of math you will need to know. Use the GED Practice sections of each lesson to practice answering GED-style items. You can also prepare by paying close attention to the math you use every day. Read newspapers and magazines, looking for charts and graphs to analyze. Think about the math you use at work and at home. As you encounter everyday problems, notice the problem-solving approaches you use and think about which are most successful for you.

For additional practice, visit *LiteracyLink* online at http://www.pbs.org/literacy.

GED Math Test Overview

The GED Math Test assesses your ability to understand and apply mathematical procedures correctly, understand and apply basic mathematical concepts, and analyze and solve problems using a variety of strategies.

You will have 90 minutes to answer 50 questions. The test is divided into two parts. For the 25 items in Part I, you will be allowed to use a calculator provided at the GED test site. You will not be allowed to use a calculator for the final 25 items. Many of the items in Part II can be solved using mental math, estimation, and simple paper-and-pencil calculations. About $\frac{1}{2}$ of the questions require you to use some type of graphic.

The questions on the GED Math Test are divided into four main content areas. These correspond to the videos you will see and the lessons in this book.

- **Number Operations and Number Sense (20–30%)** Solving problems using whole numbers, fractions, decimals, signed numbers, ratio, proportion, and percent.
- **Measurement and Geometry (20–30%)** Applying the metric and English systems of measurement, finding the measure of angles, and finding the perimeter, area, and volume of geometric figures.
- **Data, Statistics, and Probability (20–30%)** Analyzing data, drawing conclusions from charts and graphs, and making predictions.
- **Algebra, Functions, and Patterns (20–30%)** Evaluating algebraic expressions, writing and solving equations and inequalities, and applying functional relationships to solve problems.

The items on the GED Math Test can also be classified by the mathematical abilities needed to answer them. The videos and lessons will further explain these types of questions.

- **Procedural (about 20%)** Choosing a correct method to solve a problem and following steps in the correct order.
- **Conceptual (about 30%)** Knowing and applying mathematical principles and concepts.
- **Application/Modeling/Problem Solving (about 50%)** Applying strategies and procedures to solve problems and judging the reasonableness of answers.

Of the 50 items on the test, 40 are multiple choice. Each multiple-choice item has five possible answers, and you must choose the best one. The remaining 10 items will require you to demonstrate or draw an answer. In this workbook, you will receive practice in answering all types of questions.

You will be given a formulas page when you take the GED Math Test. A copy of the formulas page is provided on page 340 of this book.

➡ **NOW WATCH PROGRAM 27:**

In this program you'll have a chance to try sample questions using the three different answer formats on the test. Make sure you understand these formats before test day.

After you watch the program, work on:

- pages 15–22 in this workbook
- Internet activities at http://www.pbs.org/literacy

Passing the GED Math Test

The video program gave an overview of the GED Math Test. The rest of this workbook lesson will give you the opportunity to learn some of the basic skills and concepts that you will apply on the GED Math Test.

Three Types of Math Items

The GED Math Test uses three types of items to assess your math skills. The three item types are explained below.

Procedural These items measure your ability to select and apply appropriate procedures correctly.

Example: Kendall is cutting shelves from a board that is 15 feet long. If each shelf is 4 feet long, what is the greatest number of shelves he can cut?

Answer: 3 You need to know which operation to use (division), and you need to use your common sense to round down to 3 complete shelves.

Conceptual These items measure your knowledge of mathematical principles. Computation skills probably will not be needed to solve these items.

Example: Ann paid $4.14 for 8 cans of dog food. Which of the following equations could be used to find the unit rate per can (r)?

Answer: $8r = \$4.14$ The number of items (8) multiplied by the unit rate, or cost for one item, is equal to the total cost.

Application/Modeling/Problem Solving These items require you to analyze a situation and then choose and apply a strategy for solving the problem.

Example: A box contains 3 white and 2 black marbles. Rosario draws out a white marble and does not replace it. What is the chance that she will draw out a black marble next?

Answer: 50% There are 2 white and 2 black marbles left in the box. Rosario has a 2-out-of-4, or 50%, chance of drawing a black marble.

Calculator Skills for the GED Math Test

For Part I of the GED Math Test, you will be given a calculator that may be helpful for solving some items. Part of your job will be to decide when to use the calculator. A calculator is a useful tool when it saves time by helping you perform difficult computations quickly. However, many of the GED items can be solved using careful analysis and common sense. If you can solve the problem quickly without the calculator, don't waste time using it.

The Casio *fx*-260 will be distributed with the GED Math Test Part I. For more information about this calculator, see pages 337–339. You may want to use this type of calculator to practice for the test. However, you can work with any basic calculator as you do the exercises in this book. Pages 16–19 explain the general calculator skills you will need for the GED Math Test. You will also find calculator work throughout the workbook lessons.

Getting Started with a Calculator

The first step in learning to use your calculator is to become familiar with the placement of the keys. Your calculator may be similar to the one pictured below. **Find the keys in the drawing on your calculator.**

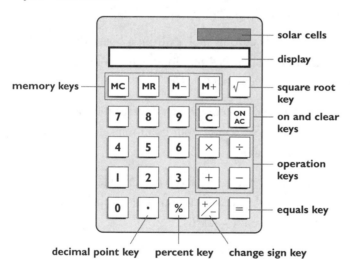

The $\boxed{\text{ON}}$ key activates the calculator. You should see $\boxed{\text{0.}}$ in the display.

The $\boxed{\text{C}}$ (or clear) key erases the display. If you have entered a number incorrectly, press $\boxed{\text{C}}$ and enter the number again. The key is labeled CE for "clear entry" on some calculators.

The $\boxed{\text{AC}}$ (or all clear) key erases the display and all other parts of a calculation stored in the calculator.

> For instruction on using the Casio® fx-260, the calculator distributed with the GED Math Test, see pages 337–339.

▶▶ Use the number pad and operation keys to perform this calculation.

$$486 + 957 + 315 =$$

Enter the key strokes in this order:

$\boxed{4}\boxed{8}\boxed{6}\boxed{+}\boxed{9}\boxed{5}\boxed{7}\boxed{+}\boxed{3}\boxed{1}\boxed{5}\boxed{=}$ The answer display reads: $\boxed{\text{1758.}}$

GED PRACTICE

Sean spent $15 on lawn fertilizer, $22 on grass seed, and $94 on flowers and plants. How much did he spend in all? [*Hint:* Use your calculator to add the amounts.]

(1) $57
(2) $111
(3) $116
(4) $120
(5) $131

Answers and explanations start on page 308.

Number Operations with a Calculator

To perform number operations on your calculator, you will need the number keys, operation keys, equals key, and the display.

The operation keys are:
- +   addition
- −   subtraction
- ×   multiplication
- ÷   division

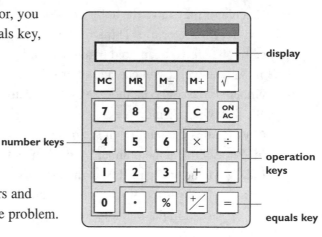

To perform a single operation, enter the numbers and symbols in the order in which they appear in the problem.

▶▶ Try these operations on your calculator.

1. $842 + 1097 =$

2. $540 - 58 =$

3. $76 \times 5 =$

4. $4071 \div 3 =$

5. $22,985 - 3,599 =$

6. $5 \div 8 =$

The answers are **1. 1939; 2. 482; 3. 380; 4. 1357; 5. 19,386;** and **6. 0.625.**

A keying error may prevent you from getting the right answer. Watch the display as you work to catch these common errors.

Common Keying Errors	Examples
Pressing the wrong key.	Pressing $\boxed{8}\,\boxed{3}\,\boxed{2}$ instead of $\boxed{8}\,\boxed{4}\,\boxed{2}$.
Pressing number keys in the wrong order.	Entering $\boxed{6}\,\boxed{7}$ instead of $\boxed{7}\,\boxed{6}$.
Pressing the same key twice.	Entering $\boxed{5}\,\boxed{4}\,\boxed{4}\,\boxed{0}$ instead of $\boxed{5}\,\boxed{4}\,\boxed{0}$.

As you solve problems with your calculator, make sure your answer seems reasonable. Before you solve a GED item with a calculator, quickly estimate an answer. Think about how great or small the answer should be. Then compare the results of your calculations with your estimate. If the number in the display is much less or much greater than your estimate, you may have made a mistake. Key in the problem again to be sure.

> **TIP:** If you enter a number incorrectly, press $\boxed{C}$ or $\boxed{CE}$ once to clear the display. Then enter the number correctly.

You will practice working with a calculator as you work through this book.

GED PRACTICE

The cost of chartering a bus for a school activity is $238. If a school needs six buses for a trip, how much will the bus company charge?

  (1) $40
  (2) $244
  (3) $1,428
  (4) $1,698
  (5) $15,708

Answers and explanations start on page 308.

Advanced Problem Solving with a Calculator

Your calculator may have the ability to store numbers in its memory for later use. Think of the memory as a storage bin where you can hold a number until you need it. As you work, you can add to or subtract from the number stored in the memory. Most calculators have the following memory keys:

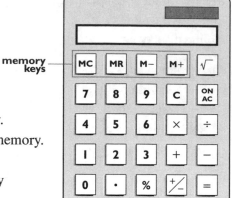

memory keys

M+   Adds the number in the display to the memory.

M−   Subtracts the number in the display from the memory.

MC   Memory Clear: Resets the memory to zero.

MR   Memory Recall: Displays the number currently stored in the memory.

▶▶ Use the memory keys to work sections of a problem separately.

Solve: $(16 \times 12) + (5 \times 19) - 5 =$

Press: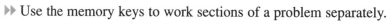

The display should read: ⎣   ᴹ282. ⎦ ◀

> The small M in the display window indicates that a number is stored in the calculator's memory.

Before starting another problem, remember to clear the memory by pressing MC.

▶▶ Use the ⎣M−⎦ key to solve this problem.

Solve: $(4 \times 13) - (180 \div 5) =$

Press: ⎣4⎦⎣×⎦⎣1⎦⎣3⎦⎣=⎦⎣M+⎦⎣1⎦⎣8⎦⎣0⎦⎣÷⎦⎣5⎦⎣M−⎦⎣=⎦⎣MR⎦

The display should read: ⎣   ᴹ16. ⎦

> You will get more practice with the memory keys on pages 73 and 339 of this book.

Like many other scientific calculators, the calculator that you will use when you take the GED Math Test has more complicated memory functions. To learn more about using this calculator, turn to pages 337–339.

GED PRACTICE

Music Central sells CDs for $11 and cassette tapes for $7. How much would it cost to buy 8 CDs and 6 tapes? (*Hint:* Multiply $11 by 8 and $7 by 6. Add the two amounts using the memory function.)

    (1) $40
    (2) $48
    (3) $88
    (4) $125
    (5) $130

Answers and explanations start on page 308.

MATHEMATICS

Special Calculator Keys and Functions

Your calculator has many other special keys and functions that can help you save time when solving math problems. Two common keys are the *percent key* and *square root key*.

If you are using a scientific calculator, you may have more than one function assigned to a key. To use the functions in small print above a key, you must first press the SHIFT key. To learn more about using the SHIFT key, turn to page 338.

Study the examples below to learn how to use the percent and square root keys.

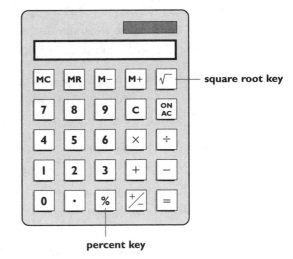

square root key

percent key

1. What is 25% of 200?

    Press: 2 0 0 × 2 5 % The display reads: [50.]

    Answer: 50 is 25% of 200.

2. The number 30 is what percent of 40?

    Press: 3 0 ÷ 4 0 % The display reads: [75.]

    Answer: 30 is **75%** of 40.

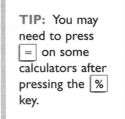

TIP: You may need to press = on some calculators after pressing the % key.

The square root of a number answers the question, "What number multiplied by itself equals this number?" For example, since $4 \times 4 = 16$, the number 4 is the square root of 16.

3. What is the square root of 18?

    Press: 1 8 √ The display reads: [**4.242640687**]

The answer has a whole number and a decimal part. Your calculator will show all the digits it can fit in the display window. The decimal part represents a fraction of a number. Since the whole number part of the answer is 4, you know the square root of 18 is between 4 and 5.

GED PRACTICE

1. A sign above a clothing rack advertises that all items will be discounted 30% at the register. A winter coat found on the rack normally sells for $120. How much is the discount? (*Hint:* Find 30% of $120.)

    (1) $3
    (2) $15
    (3) $30
    (4) $36
    (5) $43

2. The length in inches of the longest side of a right triangle is equal to the square root of 42. Choose the best estimate for the length of the side in inches. (*Hint:* Use the √ key.)

    (1) between 4 and 5
    (2) between 5 and 6
    (3) between 6 and 7
    (4) between 7 and 8
    (5) between 8 and 9

PROGRAM 27: Passing the GED Math Test

Special Formats for GED Items

About 10 out of 50 problems on the GED Math Test are not multiple choice. In this section, you will be introduced to the main formats to expect. You will be able to practice answering items with special formats at the end of the lesson reviews on pages 83, 127, 189, 245, and 295.

For some items, you will be expected to enter your answer by filling in "bubbles" on a number grid. To fill in a grid, first write your answer in the top row of boxes. Write only one number, fraction bar, or decimal point per box. Then fill in the corresponding bubbles below.

Keep these rules in mind:

- Your answer can start in any column.
- For an answer that is not a whole number, you can enter either a fraction or a decimal.
- If the answer is a mixed number, such as $2\frac{1}{2}$, enter it as a mixed decimal (2.5) or an improper fraction ($\frac{5}{2}$).
- If a column is not needed, leave it blank.

▶▶ Study these examples to learn how to record answers in grids.

Fran drove 1608 miles last week and 823 miles this week. How many miles did she drive in all?

Answer: 2431 miles

Name a fraction between $\frac{1}{8}$ and $\frac{1}{2}$.

Answer: Some items can have more than one right answer. One possible answer is $\frac{1}{4}$, or its decimal equivalent 0.25.

GED PRACTICE

Record these numbers in the grids.

1. 394

2. $\frac{5}{8}$

3. 0.07

4. 6.35

Answers and explanations start on page 308.

Filling in Coordinate Grid Planes

A coordinate grid is a system that can be used to write an address for any point within the grid. The grid is formed by two number lines called *x* and *y* that intersect at the 0-point on each line. The coordinates (address) for a point on the grid are written in parentheses. The *x*-coordinate is always shown first; the *y*-coordinate is always second.

Look at the coordinate grid at right. The coordinates of point A are (2,3). Point A is 2 places to the right on the *x*-axis and 3 places up on the *y*-axis. The coordinates of point B are (−4,4). Point B is 4 places to the left on the *x*-axis and 4 places up on the *y*-axis. Notice that a negative *x*-coordinate is to the left of 0 on the *x*-axis. To plot a negative *y*-coordinate, move down the *y*-axis below 0.

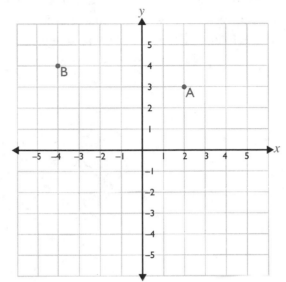

On the GED Math Test, you may be asked to plot points on a coordinate grid. You will learn more about coordinate grids in Program 39.

GED PRACTICE

Plot the following coordinates on the grid shown at right.

1. Plot the point with coordinates (5,1).

2. Plot the point with coordinates (−1,1).

3. Plot the point with coordinates (−3,−5).

4. Plot the point with coordinates (4,−2).

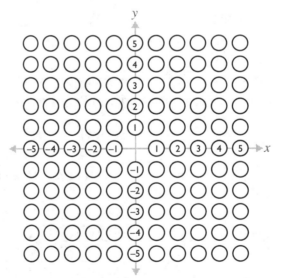

Answers and explanations start on page 308.

Plotting Points to Complete a Figure

The GED Math Test may assess your combined understanding of geometric figures and the coordinate plane. You will learn more about graphing on a coordinate grid in Program 39.

Look at the coordinate grid below. The following points are graphed on the coordinate grid: $(-2,3)$, $(2,3)$, and $(2,-1)$. Suppose a question asked you to graph the coordinate point that would complete the square. You know that a square has four equal sides, so find the distance between two points on a side. In this case, you could count the distance: 5. To complete the square, count down 5 spaces from $(-2,3)$ or count 5 spaces to the left of $(2,-1)$. Fill in the point at the coordinates $(-2,-1)$.

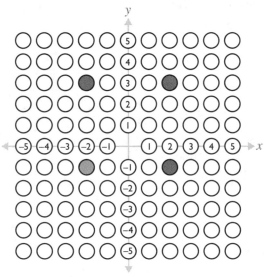

On the GED Math Test, you may be asked to plot points on a coordinate grid. You will learn more about coordinate grids in Program 39.

GED PRACTICE

Graph the point that completes the rectangle on the coordinate plane shown below.

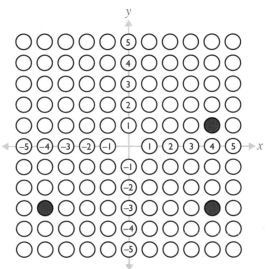

Answers and explanations start on page 308.

From the grocery store to tap dance class, this program explores the meaning and use of numbers. You'll learn about the language of math, how people use common sense about numbers every day, and how you can tap into your own number sense on the GED Math Test.

BEFORE YOU WATCH

28

Number Sense

OBJECTIVES

1. Explore different approaches to problem solving.

2. Understand the relationship between place value and the size of numbers.

3. Know when and how to use estimation.

Number sense is common sense about numbers and their value. You need number sense to understand a bill, find the best value in the grocery store, and apply for a loan. You use number sense to plan your time and manage money. Number sense helps you understand current events, your job, and the world around you.

Number sense is also important to your success on the GED Math Test. As you gain confidence in your ability to estimate answers, you will use number sense to eliminate wrong answer choices and check calculations. You may even find that some items on the GED Math Test can be answered with estimation alone. Number sense is essential in every branch of mathematics. It will help you solve everyday calculations as well as algebra and geometry problems.

On the following pages, you will find a brief exercise called *Sneak Preview*. It is designed to introduce you to the topics that will be featured in the video program and the corresponding lesson. After you complete the exercise and check your answers, turn to the vocabulary page. There you will find terms that will help you better understand the video and the lesson that follow. After reviewing page 26, you will be ready to watch Program 28.

For additional practice, visit *LiteracyLink* online at http://www.pbs.org/literacy.

Sneak Preview

This exercise previews some of the concepts from Program 28. After you answer the questions, use the feedback on page 25 to help set your learning goals.

COMMUNITY LINK: The City Parks and Recreation Department opened a new swimming pool for public use. To use the pool, swimmers must pay a fee. Swimmers can also purchase passes good for 10 or 20 visits to the pool. Monthly passes are also available for individuals and families. The pricing plans are shown below.

C I T Y   P O O L   F E E S

SINGLE USE		PASSES	
Adult	$3	10-Use Pass	$25
Child (12 and under)	$1	20-Use Pass	$40
Senior	$2	Individual Monthly Pass	$38
		Family Monthly Pass	$65

Note: Monthly passes offer unlimited usage.

Answer these questions based on the information given and the city pool pricing plans shown above.

1. Zev bought an individual monthly pass for July. He has already used his pass on July 1, 4, 7, and 10. If he continues this pattern of usage, how many times will he use the pass during the month? (Hint: There are 31 days in July.)

    (1) 18
    (2) 15
    (3) 12
    (4) 11
    (5) 10

2. Tonya spent about $\frac{1}{3}$ of the money she had saved for summer recreation on a 20-use pass. Which of the following statements is true?

    (1) Tonya has about $40 left to spend on summer recreation.
    (2) Tonya saved more than $100 to spend on summer recreation.
    (3) Tonya spent about 50% of the money she saved for summer recreation on the swim pass.
    (4) Tonya has more than $100 left to spend on summer recreation.
    (5) Tonya spent about 10% of the money she saved for summer recreation on the swim pass.

3. Joel plans to take his family to the pool frequently during the summer. He wants to figure out the least expensive option for his family for three months. He thinks his family of two adults and two children will use the pool about 20 times during the summer. The options he is considering are shown below.

Option A — 3 monthly family passes $195
Option B — 4 20-use passes $160
Option C — 8 10-use passes $200
Option D — 12 individual monthly passes $456

Which of the following arranges the options by price <u>from least to greatest</u>?

(1) A, B, C, D
(2) D, C, A, B
(3) B, C, A, D
(4) B, A, C, D
(5) D, A, C, B

4. Alicia swims regularly to keep in shape. She plans to buy six individual monthly passes to use in the fall and winter months. Round the cost of an individual monthly pass to the nearest ten dollars and multiply by six to estimate the cost of the passes. About how much will the six passes cost?

(1) $180
(2) $200
(3) $240
(4) $420
(5) $480

Feedback

- If you got all of the answers right...   you have a good basic understanding of number sense, estimation, and problem solving.

- If you missed question 1...   you need to work on recognizing patterns and trying new strategies to solve problems.

- If you missed question 2...   you need to work with understanding the meaning of numbers and parts of a whole.

- If you missed question 3...   you need to work with place value, ordering, and comparing numbers.

- If you missed question 4...   you need to develop your rounding and estimation skills.

ANSWERS FOR SNEAK PREVIEW:

1. Choice (4)   2. Choice (2)   3. Choice (4)   4. Choice (3)

Vocabulary for *Number Sense*

decimal	part of a whole expressed using digits written after a decimal point; for example, 0.75, 0.5, and 0.825
digit	one of the symbols used to write numbers: 0, 1, 2, 3, 4, 5, 6, 7, 8, and 9
estimate	to find an approximate value
fraction	part of a whole expressed by showing the number of parts being discussed out of a total number of parts; for example, $\frac{1}{2}$, $\frac{2}{3}$, and $\frac{3}{4}$
front-end estimation	a method of estimating by using only the value of the first digits of the numbers in a problem
integer	a signed number (see below); a positive integer is greater than zero, and a negative integer is less than zero
multiple	the product of any number multiplied by another number
number line	a line used to show the order of numbers and their relationship to each other
number sense	common sense applied to mathematics and problem solving
pattern	an organized arrangement of numbers
percent	part of a whole number expressed as a part of 100
place value	a system that shows how much a digit is worth by the location of the digit in the number
rounding	expressing a number to the nearest ten, hundred, thousand, and so on
signed number	a number written with a positive sign ($+$) or a negative sign ($-$); a positive number is greater than zero, and a negative number is less than zero
whole number	a number that is used for counting

MATHEMATICS

➡ **NOW WATCH PROGRAM 28:**

In the program you'll learn how numbers play an important role in how we describe the world, and how we communicate. Think about numbers in your everyday life. You may realize that you have more experience with "math" than you thought.

After you watch the program, work on:

- pages 27–40 in this workbook
- Internet activities at http://www.pbs.org/literacy

Number Sense

On the following pages, you will learn more about the ideas discussed in the video program and have an opportunity to develop and practice your GED math skills.

GED TIPS

When taking the GED Test, you should:

- Think about the situation described in the problem and what size answer would make sense.
- Estimate an answer to each problem *before* calculating the exact answer.
- Use estimation and number sense to eliminate wrong choices.

Key Points to Think About

In the video program, you explored:

- How workers, citizens, and family members use estimation and number sense to approach and solve problems.
- How the size of numbers and number relationships are expressed using place value.
- Different approaches to problem solving and learning mathematics.

On the GED Math Test:

- You will be expected to analyze situations and apply different problem-solving strategies.
- You should know how to use **rounding** and **front-end estimation** to **estimate** answers and to check to make sure your calculations are reasonable.
- You will need to understand the relationships and patterns found among **whole numbers, fractions, decimals,** and **percents.**

As you work through the lesson for Program 28:

- Look for opportunities to try new problem-solving strategies.
- Think about how important place value is in all situations.
- Be aware of the many times that you use number sense and estimation in your daily life, not just studying for the GED Math Test.

Your Approach to Learning Math

WORKPLACE LINK: Evan's boss gives him a map showing which streets to take to reach a meeting that will be held downtown. Although the map is clear, Evan knows that reading a map while he is driving can be confusing. He takes time to rewrite the map as a list of instructions before leaving for the meeting.

Building on Your Experiences

Many people feel anxiety when they are asked to solve math problems in a textbook or on a math test. But these same people use math comfortably in their lives at work and at home. Math is more than memorizing rules and formulas. Math is a tool that we use to make sense of many common life situations.

Everyone has a certain amount of "math intuition" or number sense. **Number sense** is common sense about mathematical ideas. You use number sense when you figure out how much money to leave for a tip or decide whether a new bookcase will fit in your home. You use number sense when you estimate how much money you can spend today and still have enough left to last until the end of the month.

One of the best approaches to increase your understanding of math is to build on the number sense you already have. You will become a better problem solver when you begin to recognize the math in your everyday life. As you refine your approach to problem solving, you will feel greater confidence in your ability to solve problems on the GED Math Test.

Finding Your Own Approach to Learning

Although a math problem may have one right answer, there is rarely one right way to find it. There are many approaches to learning and problem solving. What works for someone else isn't necessarily the best approach for you.

Think about the situation at the top of the page. When you have to find a new place, do you draw a map, or like Evan, do you prefer to have a list of instructions? If you make a list, do you write "Turn *north* on Brand Street" or "Turn *right* on Brand Street"? Maybe you prefer to make a list of landmarks: "Turn *left* at the second light by the car wash." All these approaches work, but some may work better for you than others.

▶▶ Read this list of approaches to learning and problem solving. Some of these approaches may work for you.

1. Make a list of important facts as you listen and read.
2. Create an example to help you remember a new procedure.
3. Discuss what you have learned with a friend or family member.
4. Draw a picture, make a model, or act out a problem-solving situation.

Try more than one approach to see which one works best for you in different situations.

MATHEMATICS

▶▶ Look how different approaches are used in this problem to find the same answer.

Example: Leah is helping her 3rd-grade twins solve a math problem. Her sons need to find how many different outfits they can make from 2 shirts, 2 pairs of pants, and 2 pairs of shoes. Leah knows she can multiply to find the answer: $2 \times 2 \times 2 = 8$, but her sons don't see how multiplication can help. One boy draws the clothes and counts them. The other makes the chart shown at the right.

Shirts: A and B	
Pants: C and D	
Shoes: E and F	

OUTFITS:			
ACE	BCE	ADE	BDE
ACF	BCF	ADF	BDF

Leah and her sons each used different approaches, but they arrived at the same answer. By trying different approaches to problems, you will build number sense and gain confidence in your problem-solving abilities. Once you realize that there is more than one way to approach a problem, your math anxiety will begin to disappear.

SKILL PRACTICE

Answer each question.

1. Math is more than calculations. It includes estimating and making decisions based on mathematical thinking. Think about the past week. List at least five occasions when you used math.

2. Suppose you need to stop at the grocery store for a few items. You plan to pay with cash. Which approach do you use to know that you will have enough money to cover your purchases? Choose one or write one of your own.

   _____ **a.** Round items to the nearest dollar and add mentally.
   _____ **b.** Carry a calculator.
   _____ **c.** Make a list on paper and add.
   _____ **d.** Other _____

3. When you eat at a restaurant, which approach do you use to figure out the 15% tip? Choose one or write one of your own.

   _____ **a.** Look it up on a tip chart.
   _____ **b.** Use a calculator.
   _____ **c.** Mentally find 10%, divide the amount in half, and add the two amounts.
   _____ **d.** Other _____

4. You have to drive to a place that you have never been before. Which approach do you use to find your way? Choose one or write one of your own.

   _____ **a.** Ask a friend for directions and draw a map.
   _____ **b.** Ask a friend for directions and make a list of streets to drive on and where to turn.
   _____ **c.** Write down the address and look it up on a map you have at home.
   _____ **d.** Other _____

Answers and explanations start on page 308.

Understanding Our Number System

COMMUNITY LINK: Sharon has been elected president of the fund-raising organization for her child's elementary school. The parents want to raise $60,000 to put in a new computer lab. Sharon plans three fundraisers. After the first fundraiser, Sharon estimates that they have raised $30,000. Sharon feels confident the parents will reach their goal.

Working with Place Value

Numbers are a way of communicating size and amount. We express the size of numbers through **place value.** In a number, the value or size of a **digit** depends on its place in the number. For example, the digit 3 in the number 30,000 has a greater value than it does in the number 3,000.

To read, write, and compare numbers, you need to understand how place value works. The diagram below shows the names of the first 10 whole number places.

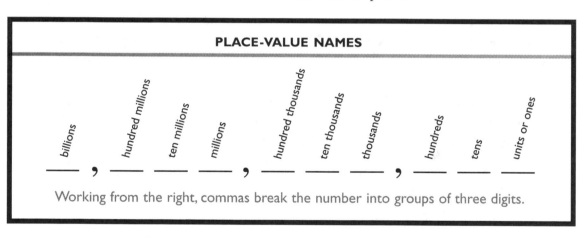

PLACE-VALUE NAMES

billions, hundred millions, ten millions, millions, hundred thousands, ten thousands, thousands, hundreds, tens, units or ones

Working from the right, commas break the number into groups of three digits.

▸▸ Notice how place value is used to find the value of the digits in a number.

Example: What is the value of 3,200,050?

The 3 is in the millions place; its value is $3 \times 1,000,000 = 3,000,000$.
The 2 is in the hundred thousands place; its value is $2 \times 100,000 = 200,000$.
The 5 is in the tens place; its value is $5 \times 10 = 50$.

The number is read **Three million, two hundred thousand, fifty.** The zeros in the number are placeholders. They are not read.

Working with Integers

The numbers that we count with are called **whole numbers.** But many situations cannot be described using whole numbers alone.

Integers, or **signed numbers,** tell a number's relation to 0. Negative numbers are below 0; they must be written with a negative sign ($-$). The temperature $-10°$ means 10 degrees below zero. Positive numbers may be written with a plus sign ($+$) or with no sign at all, such as the temperature $10°$ or 10 degrees above zero.

MATHEMATICS

Example: Celia has $490 in the bank. She writes a check for $500 and deposits $200. If she writes the check in her check register before making the deposit, how can she show the balance?

Answer: When Celia subtracts $500 from $490, she has spent more than she has. At that point, her balance is -$10. After adding the deposit, she will have **$190.**

AMOUNT OF PAYMENT-DEBIT OR FEE (−)	AMOUNT OF DEPOSIT OR CREDIT (+)	BALANCE FORWARD
		490 00
500 00		
	200 00	

Expressing Parts of a Whole

Parts of a whole can be communicated through decimals, fractions, and percents. These three systems are different ways of saying the same thing.

Example: Two quarters are $0.50, $\frac{1}{2}$ of a dollar, or 50% of a dollar.

Fractions are often used when measuring in inches, feet, yards, or miles. Fractions are useful when an object is divided into equal parts.

$\frac{1}{4}$ yard $\frac{1}{2}$ mile $\frac{3}{4}$ inch

Decimals are used with money and metric measurements. Calculators generally show parts of a whole as decimals.

0.01 means *one-hundredth* $0.01 means *one cent*

Percents represent parts of a whole. They compare a part to a whole of 100. Percents are useful in budgeting time, money, and other resources.

If 5% of a job is done, the job has just begun.
If 95% of a job is done, it is nearly finished.

SKILL PRACTICE

Write the value of the underlined digit.

Example: 6,30<u>4</u>,219 _____*four thousand*_____

1. 2,5<u>2</u>1 _____

2. <u>6</u>,702,010 _____

3. 5<u>1</u>,700 _____

4. <u>4</u>55,900,000 _____

5. 13,9<u>6</u>6 _____

6. 12,<u>9</u>04,050 _____

Answer each question.

7. ABM stock fell 5 points on Thursday. Write the change as a signed number.

8. ABM stock rose $3\frac{1}{8}$ points on Friday. Write the change as a signed number.

9. The elevation of a desert is 100 feet below sea level. Write the elevation as a signed number.

10. John estimates that he has finished about $\frac{3}{4}$ or 75% of a project. Which of the following is a true statement?

(1) John has more left to do than he has done.
(2) John is about halfway finished.
(3) John has only about 10% left to do.
(4) John has done more than he has left to do.
(5) John has finished the project.

FAMILY LINK: Jemma was using a calculator to find her checkbook balance. She began with $957.07 in the bank. She wrote checks for $250.00, $16.95, and $420.00. After subtracting the amounts, her calculator display showed $685.92. The number seemed much too high. Immediately, Jemma knew she must have made a mistake when entering a number.

Seeing Number Relationships and Patterns

One of the key ways we use numbers is to represent relationships with other numbers. Kentucky has 40,411 square miles of land. However, that number is even more meaningful when we also know that Kentucky ranks 37th in area in the United States. It means even more when we know that Alaska ranks 1st with an area of 656,424 square miles.

Comparing numbers can help us understand the relationship between numbers. To compare numbers, think about place value. Always work from left to right, comparing digits that have the same place value.

Example: Put these amounts in order from greatest to least: $2419, $1984, and $2014.

- Compare the thousands place first. Clearly, $1984 is the smallest amount.
- Compare the hundreds place in the remaining numbers. Since 4 in 2419 is greater than 0 in 2014, $2419 is the greater number.

> **Answer:** From greatest to least, the amounts are **$2419, $2014,** and **$1984.**

These symbols are used to show number relationships:

>	means *is greater than*	$8 > 6$
<	means *is less than*	$6 < 8$
=	means *equals* or *is equal to*	$6 = 6$
≠	means *is not equal to*	$6 \neq 8$
≈	means *is approximately equal to*	$6.01 \approx 6$

> Notice that the larger, open end of the symbol is next to the greater number.

Recognizing patterns in numbers can also help you solve problems.

Whole numbers are either odd or even. Even numbers can be divided evenly by 2. Odd numbers cannot.

Odd numbers: 1, 3, 5, 7, 9, 11, 13, 15, 17, 19, and so on.
Even numbers: 2, 4, 6, 8, 10, 12, 14, 16, 18, 20, and so on.

> In both sequences, 2 is added each time. To tell whether a number is odd or even, look at the ones place.

A **multiple** is the result of any number multiplied by another number. To find the multiples of a number, multiply by 1, then by 2, then by 3, and so on.

Examples: Multiples of 5: 5, 10, 15, 20, 25, 30, 35, 40, and so on.
  Multiples of 10: 10, 20, 30, 40, 50, 60, 70, and so on.

Knowing the multiples of a number can help you solve problems. For example, the multiples of 5 all end with either 5 or 0. Based on the pattern, any number that ends with 5 or 0 can be divided evenly by 5.

Applying Number Sense

After you work any problem, ask yourself whether your answer seems to be about the right size for the situation. This is especially important when you are using a calculator. Entering numbers in the wrong order or leaving out the decimal point can cause the answer to be off by thousands.

SKILL PRACTICE

Write *True* or *False* for each number comparison.

_____ 1. $418 < 318$

_____ 2. $\$2518 \neq \$2508$

_____ 3. $34 > 33$

_____ 4. $\$5.04 \approx \$5.00$

_____ 5. $45{,}418 = 45{,}814$

_____ 6. $709{,}059 > 705{,}509$

Answer the questions based on a salesperson's expense report.

Food—$97.08, Rental Car—$87.52, Hotel—$238, Parking—$15, Airline Ticket—$437.82.

7. Which of the following lists the expenses in order from largest to smallest?

    (1) parking, car, food, hotel, ticket
    (2) hotel, ticket, car, food, parking
    (3) ticket, hotel, car, food, parking
    (4) food, car, hotel, parking, ticket
    (5) ticket, hotel, food, car, parking

8. The total of the expenses will probably be _____.

    (1) about $100
    (2) between $800 and $1,000
    (3) between $1,000 and $2,000
    (4) about $9,000
    (5) more than $10,000

PROBLEM SOLVER Connection

Creating a number line may help you solve some GED problems. With a number line, you can easily see number relationships and patterns.

Example: Pedro, Tom, Gail, and Sammy are all sales clerks at Garden Nurseries. During one weekend, their sales are as follows: Pedro, $125; Tom, $206; Gail, $132; Sammy, $204. Put the sales clerks' names in order, from the least to greatest sales made.

Step 1. Draw a number line showing the clerks' sales. Label the amounts with the clerks' initials.

Step 2. Find the answer choice that agrees with the order on your number line.

Answer: Sales, from least to greatest, were by **Pedro, Gail, Sammy, and Tom.**

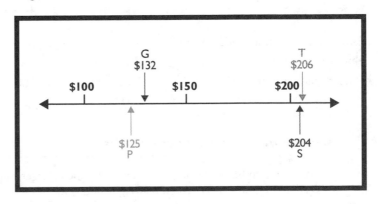

Answers and explanations start on page 309.

Estimating

WORKPLACE LINK: Greg has two job offers. The first job pays $2.18 more per hour than the second, but he would have to spend $42 per month on a bus pass. Greg decides to take the first job. He knows he will work *about* 160 hours per month (40 hours times 4 weeks). At about $2 more per hour, he would earn far more than the cost of the bus pass.

Using Rounding to Estimate

Rounding is a way to make the numbers in a problem easier to work with. When you round, you work with simpler numbers in order to find a solution that is *about equal* to the exact answer.

▶▶ In this situation, rounding makes it easier to do mental math.

Example: Kay is shopping for tires for her car. Each tire costs $68.75. Kay can't afford to spend more than $300. Can she buy 4 new tires for less than $300?

To find an exact answer, Kay needs to multiply $68.75 by 4. This calculation is difficult without pencil or paper, but Kay can mentally estimate the amount.

$68.75 is nearly $70.

Kay thinks: "At $70 each, 2 tires cost $140, so 4 tires would be $280." Kay knows she can afford the tires.

To round numbers, follow these steps:

1. Choose the place value to which you want to round.
2. Look at the place value to its right.
3. If that digit is 5 or more, round up to the next larger number. If it is less than 5, round down to the smaller number.

Examples: Round 3582 to the

Tens Place	**Hundreds Place**	**Thousands Place**
3582 rounds down to 3580.	3582 rounds up to 3600.	3582 rounds up to 4000.

Another way to think about rounding:

- When a number is halfway or more to the next larger number, round up.
- When a number is less than halfway, round down.

Using Front-End Estimation

The value of the first digit of a number gives us the most information about its size. One way to make a quick estimate is to calculate using only the front-end values of the numbers.

▶▶ Look at this example in which front-end estimation is used to estimate the answer.

Example: Lisa is buying 11 printer cartridges for her office. Each cartridge costs $22.90. About how much will she pay for the cartridges?

The problem can be solved by multiplying $22.90 by 11. To use front-end estimation, multiply the *value* of the first digit of each number. Use $20 instead of $22.90. Use 10 instead of 11. **Answer:** Lisa will spend about **$200** on the cartridges.

$$\begin{array}{r} \$20 \\ \times \ \ 10 \\ \hline 200 \end{array}$$

Now compare the estimate to the exact answer: $22.90 × 11 = $251.90. Does the estimate seem close enough to the exact answer? It depends on your needs. If you need a closer estimate, try rounding instead.

SKILL PRACTICE

Estimate to choose the best answer for each item. Do not solve for the exact answer.

1. Max made 47 sales in August. If he continues at the same pace, *about* how many sales should he expect to make in 9 months?

    (1) less than 350
    (2) between 350 and 550
    (3) between 550 and 750
    (4) between 750 and 950
    (5) more than 950

2. Carla is traveling from Las Vegas to Detroit. Her mileage for the trip is shown in the box to the right. Which of the following is the best estimate of her total mileage for the five-day trip?

    (1) 1,000 miles
    (2) 2,000 miles
    (3) 2,300 miles
    (4) 2,500 miles
    (5) 20,000 miles

MILES PER DAY	
Mon.	440
Tues.	495
Wed.	220
Thurs.	660
Fri.	209

3. In 1998, Library Friends, a nonprofit organization, raised $106,782. In 1988, the first year of business, they raised $8,324. Which of the following expressions uses front-end estimation to find the approximate difference in the two amounts?

    (1) $107,000 − $8,000
    (2) $110,000 − $8,000
    (3) $107,000 − $9,000
    (4) $106,800 − $8,300
    (5) $100,000 − $8,000

4. Afton earned $26,948 last year and $28,125 this year. Which of these expressions uses rounding to the thousands place to estimate the total income for the two years?

    (1) $20,000 + $20,000
    (2) $30,000 + $30,000
    (3) $27,000 + $28,000
    (4) $26,000 + $28,000
    (5) $26,900 + $28,100

Answers and explanations start on page 309.

Deciding When to Estimate

In life, an estimate is often all you really need. Since the distance from the earth to the moon changes as the moon orbits the earth, there is no need for Shania's daughter to learn the exact distance. Instead, she learns an approximate distance.

As in life, an approximate answer is sometimes all you need to solve an item on the GED Math Test. Don't spend your time doing unnecessary calculations when a good estimate will do.

▶▶ Working with simpler numbers makes the work go faster.

Example: Marko is silk-screening T-shirts for his son's swim team to help them raise money. The shirt, including ink, costs Marko about $6. If the team sells the shirt for $15 and they sell 48 shirts, about how much will they raise?

   (1)   between $120 and $220
   (2)   between $220 and $320
   (3)   between $320 and $420
   (4)   between $420 and $520
   (5)   between $520 and $620

If you answered **(4) between $420 and $520,** you're right. To solve the problem, you need to find the difference between Marko's cost and his selling price and then multiply by 48.

   ($15 − $6) × 48 = the swim team's profit

Now that you see how to work the problem, estimate. The difference between $15 and $6 is $9, which is close to $10. The number of shirts sold is close to 50. Think: 50 × $10 = $500. Now look at the choices. Only Choice 4 makes sense. There is no need to calculate the exact answer.

Even when you must go on to calculate an exact answer, a good estimate can help you eliminate some answer choices and check your work.

▶▶ Estimate to narrow down possible answer choices.

Example: Felicia had knee surgery. Her hospital bill came to $9,614. Of that, her insurance company paid $8,652. How much did Felicia have to pay?

   (1) $862
   (2) $962
   (3) $1,062
   (4) $1,962
   (5) $18,266

The problem asks you to find the difference between two numbers. You need to subtract to find the difference. Estimate first. Round both numbers to the nearest thousand and subtract.

$9,614 rounds to $10,000 $8,652 rounds to $9,000 $10,000 − $9,000 = $1,000

You know the correct answer is close to $1,000.
You can eliminate choices 1, 4, and 5. Now calculate the exact answer.

$$\begin{array}{r} \$9,614 \\ -\ 8,652 \\ \hline \$962 \end{array}$$

Answer: (2) $962 is correct.

Check: Compare your answer to the estimate.
Since $962 is close to $1,000, you know your answer is reasonable.

SKILL PRACTICE

Estimate to solve each problem.

1. There are 96 fifth-graders at Melrose School. If each child gives $5.25 toward a year-end party, about how much money will the fifth-graders have?

    (1) less than $325
    (2) between $325 and $425
    (3) between $425 and $550
    (4) between $550 and $625
    (5) more than $625

2. A company has 8 computer stations. An upgrade for each station would cost $923. What is the total cost to upgrade the office?

    (1) $116
    (2) $6,424
    (3) $7,384
    (4) $8,114
    (5) $17,230

PROBLEM SOLVER Connection

Clustering is a problem-solving strategy where you use rounding to group numbers of similar value. You then work with the cluster as a unit to figure an estimate of the answer. Clustering can help you eliminate some GED answer choices and check your work.

Example: Martina's daughter Emma has entered a Read-a-Thon to raise money for her school's art supplies. In the first month of the Read-a-Thon, Emma reads books of 205, 198, 188, 218, and 211 pages. About how many pages has Emma read so far?

Step 1. Since all five numbers are close in value, use clustering instead of adding the exact numbers. Think: all of these numbers are close to 200, so I'll multiply 200 by 5.

Step 2. Multiply: $200 \times 5 = 1000$. Eliminate any answer choice that is not close to 1000.

Answer: Emma has read **about 1000 pages** so far.

PROGRAM 28: Number Sense

MATHEMATICS

PART ONE DIRECTIONS: Choose the <u>one best answer</u> to each of the following problems. Use a calculator wherever necessary.

1. Which of the following statements is <u>false</u> concerning this list of numbers?
   10, 30, 40, 80, 120, 370
   (1) All of these numbers can be divided evenly by 3.
   (2) All of these numbers can be divided evenly by 2.
   (3) All of these numbers can be divided evenly by 5.
   (4) All of these numbers can be divided evenly by 10.
   (5) Not enough information is given.

<u>Questions 2 through 5 are based on the</u> following table.

Town	1990 Population	2000 Population
Sunnydale	11,745	15,283
Thorton	38,337	36,849
Winslow	4,009	3,997
Ft. James	44,224	45,670
Payson	102,304	110,050

2. Which town(s) decreased in population between 1990 and 2000?
   (1) Thorton
   (2) Thorton and Ft. James
   (3) Thorton and Winslow
   (4) Sunnydale and Ft. James
   (5) Winslow

3. Which town's population increased by the greatest number from 1990 to 2000?
   (1) Sunnydale
   (2) Thorton
   (3) Winslow
   (4) Ft. James
   (5) Payson

4. What is the 1990 population figure for the town of Thorton, rounded to the nearest thousand?
   (1) 37,000
   (2) 38,000
   (3) 38,300
   (4) 39,000
   (5) 40,000

5. Which town had 1990 and 2000 populations that were <u>approximately</u> equal?
   (1) Sunnydale
   (2) Thorton
   (3) Winslow
   (4) Ft. James
   (5) Not enough information is given.

<u>Question 6 is based on the following diagram.</u>

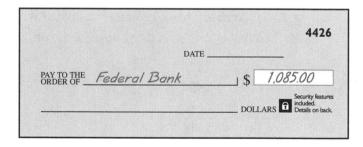

6. How would you write the amount $1,085 in words?
   (1) Ten thousand, eight hundred five
   (2) One thousand, eight hundred fifty
   (3) One thousand eight hundred five
   (4) One thousand eighty-five
   (5) One hundred eighty-five

7. A Japanese export firm can pack about 28 *yukata,* or bathrobes, in one crate. At this rate, <u>about</u> how many *yukata* will be shipped in 8 crates?
   (1) fewer than 150
   (2) between 150 and 325
   (3) between 325 and 450
   (4) between 450 and 600
   (5) more than 600

Question 8 is based on the following sign.

GOLD'S BOX OF CHOCOLATES

Solid Milk Chocolate	$2.80
Dark Chocolate	$3.19
Chewies	$2.90
Nuts	$3.09

8. Jay wants to buy one box of each kind of Gold's Chocolates. Which expression shows how Jay could <u>estimate</u> what the four boxes will cost him?
   (1) 4 × $2.00
   (2) 4 × $3.00
   (3) 4 × ($3.19 − $2.80)
   (4) ($2.80 + $3.19 + $2.90 + $3.09) × 4
   (5) 4 × $4.00

9. Marie's parents have offered her an interest-free loan to buy a car. The car costs $5106. Marie can afford to pay her parents $55 per month. Which of the following expressions could she use to estimate how many months it will take to repay the loan?
   (1) 500 × 50
   (2) 500 ÷ 50 × 12
   (3) 5000 × 100
   (4) 5000 ÷ 5
   (5) 5000 ÷ 50

10. Ms. Yeager is ordering chairs for her new office. She needs to list the prices of the chairs to the nearest $10. A swivel chair costs $198. What amount should she list?
    (1) $10   **(4)** $200
    (2) $190   **(5)** $210
    (3) $198

11. A state plans to spend $53,647,980 to improve public education. Which digit is in the millions place?
    (1) 3   **(4)** 6
    (2) 4   **(5)** 7
    (3) 5

12. Loretta had $2356 worth of dental work done this year. Her insurance company paid for $1884 of the bill. Which expression shows the amount still to be paid?
    (1) $2356 − $1884
    (2) $2356 + $1884
    (3) $1884 − $2356
    (4) $2356 − $472
    (5) Not enough information is given.

13. In York County there were about 1,742,000 registered voters in 1998. This number was about 10,000 more than in 1994. To the nearest <u>hundred thousand</u>, how many voters were registered in York County in 1998?
    (1) 2,000,000
    (2) 1,800,000
    (3) 1,752,000
    (4) 1,700,000
    (5) 1,000,000

Question 14 is based on the following table.

Business	Amount Donated
Lawson's	$1360
Shoe Tree	$1290
Way's Photos	$1305
Café Ritz	$1035

14. Four businesses gave donations to the Pine Tree Boys Home. Which answer choice lists the donations from <u>largest to smallest</u>?
    (1) Café Ritz, Way's Photos, Shoe Tree, Lawson's
    (2) Café Ritz, Shoe Tree, Way's Photos, Lawson's
    (3) Way's Photos, Lawson's, Shoe Tree, Café Ritz
    (4) Lawson's, Way's Photos, Shoe Tree, Café Ritz
    (5) Shoe Tree, Lawson's, Way's Photos, Café Ritz

PART TWO DIRECTIONS: Choose the <u>one best answer</u> to each of the following problems. *You may not use a calculator on these problems.*

15. The village of Santung received $30,430 in small business loans. These loans are to be divided equally among 28 families. Which answer is the most reasonable for how much each family will receive?

(1) less than $800
(2) $812
(3) $1,087
(4) $1,806
(5) $11,003

16. The number 42 will be the next item in which of the following patterns?

(1) 7, 8, 9, 10, 11, ____
(2) 6, 12, 18, 24, 30, ____
(3) 3, 7, 12, 18, 25, ____
(4) 7, 14, 21, 28, 35, ____
(5) 12, 20, 28, 36, 44, ____

17. The land area of Texas is 261,914 square miles. To the nearest <u>thousand</u>, what is the area of Texas?

(1) 300,000 sq mi
(2) 270,000 sq mi
(3) 262,000 sq mi
(4) 261,000 sq mi
(5) 260,000 sq mi

18. What is the value of 8 in the number 14,853,002?

(1) 8 hundred
(2) 8 thousand
(3) 80 thousand
(4) 8 hundred thousand
(5) 8 million

19. After fixing up his car, Willy sold it for $5600. Last year he bought the car for $4450. Which of the following expressions uses front-end estimation to approximate the amount Willy made on the sale of the car?

(1) $6000 − $5000
(2) $6000 − $4000
(3) $5000 + $4000
(4) $5000 − $4000
(5) $4000 − $5000

Questions 20 and 21 are based on the following table.

Employee	Commissions
Karen Hall	$38,450
Rosa Ramirez	$42,190
Ed Racine	$38,054
Tina Bell	$43,010

20. According to the list of commissions, salesperson Ed Racine earned

(1) about as much as Tina Bell.
(2) less than Karen Hall.
(3) more than Rosa Ramirez.
(4) about as much as Rosa Ramirez.
(5) more than Karen Hall.

21. Tina earned <u>approximately</u> how much more in commissions than Rosa?

(1) $190
(2) $200
(3) $1,000
(4) $2,000
(5) $43,010

Answers and explanations start on page 309.

Whether you're looking for a car buyer, planning city neighborhoods, or working on your math, any problem is more manageable if you break it down into steps. In this program you'll see how to use a problem-solving process in a variety of situations.

Problem Solving

OBJECTIVES

1. Use basic operations, estimation, and equations in problem solving.

2. Apply a five-step approach to solving word problems.

3. Apply problem-solving strategies to multi-step problems.

Why do we learn math? Math is an essential problem-solving tool. Through our knowledge of math, we can use numbers, operations, and stcps to translate a situation into a problem to be solved. As we work, we use number sense to make sure our problem-solving approach is on the right track and our answer makes sense.

The ability to choose appropriate problem-solving strategies and apply them is important to your success on the GED Math Test. You will need to know how to analyze a problem, find the necessary facts, perform the correct operations, and decide whether your result seems reasonable. Your knowledge of estimation will help you carry out these steps. Calculator skills are also needed on Part One of the GED Math Test.

On the following pages, you will find a brief exercise called *Sneak Preview*. It is designed to introduce you to the topics that will be featured in the video program and the corresponding lesson. After you complete the exercise and check your answers, turn to the vocabulary page. There you will find terms that will help you better understand the video and the lesson that follow. After reviewing page 44, you will be ready to watch Program 29.

For additional practice, visit *LiteracyLink* online at http://www.pbs.org/literacy.

Sneak Preview

This exercise previews some of the concepts from Program 29. After you answer the questions, use the chart on page 43 to help set your learning goals.

 **FAMILY LINK:** Three families living in the same neighborhood decide to spend their vacation together on a rented houseboat. Phillip volunteers to research rental rates and other information for the trip. He sends for a brochure and rate sheet from Star Resorts, which offers houseboat rentals on Lunar Lake. The three families then meet to discuss their options.

FIVE STAR RESORTS ON LUNAR LAKE

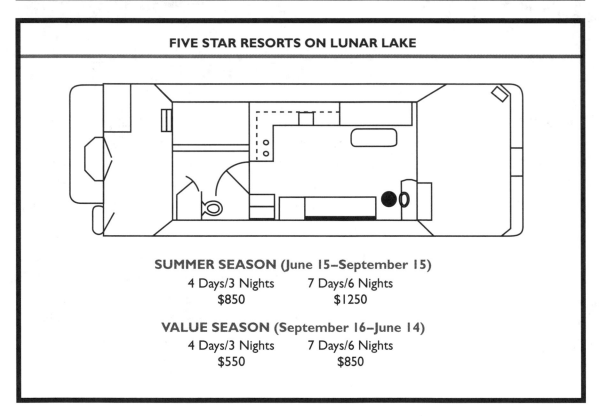

SUMMER SEASON (June 15–September 15)

4 Days/3 Nights	7 Days/6 Nights
$850	$1250

VALUE SEASON (September 16–June 14)

4 Days/3 Nights	7 Days/6 Nights
$550	$850

Answer these questions based on the rate sheet shown above.

1. There are eight adults from the three families who want to rent the houseboat together. Phillip wants to know how much each person will pay if they split the rate equally for 7 days/6 nights in the summer season. Which expression best represents the equation Phillip might use?

   (1) $r = 7 \times 1250$

   (2) $r = \frac{(7 \times 1250)}{8}$

   (3) $r = \frac{850}{8}$

   (4) $r = \frac{1250}{8}$

   (5) $r = 1250 \times 8$

MATHEMATICS

2. How much more would it cost these 8 adults to rent a houseboat in the value season for 6 nights, instead of 3 nights?

   (1) $200
   (2) $300
   (3) $550
   (4) $850
   (5) Not enough information is given.

3. If 10 neighbors decide to rent a houseboat from Star Resorts for 9 days/8 nights in the value season, what could they expect to spend in total?

   (1) $105
   (2) $850
   (3) $850 + 2
   (4) $1250/10
   (5) Not enough information is given.

4. The group decides to vacation from June 15 to June 18. Two of the neighbors will pay $100 each for a deposit to Five Star Resorts, to hold the boat. How much more will the group have to pay for the houseboat rental?

   (1) $1050
   (2) $650
   (3) $350
   (4) $200
   (5) $100

Feedback

- If you got all of the answers right...

  you have a good basic understanding of how to analyze a problem, find the facts, carry out the correct operations, and check the answer for reasonableness.

- If you missed question 1...

  you need to work on setting up equations, variables, and solution set-ups.

- If you missed question 2...

  you need to work on how to analyze a problem or on your subtraction skills.

- If you missed question 3...

  you need to understand when too much or too little information is given.

- If you missed question 4...

  you need to develop your multi-step problem-solving skills.

Vocabulary for *Problem Solving*

associative property	a law that states that when adding or multiplying more than two numbers, you can group the numbers in any order without affecting the result; for example, $2 + (3 + 4) = (2 + 3) + 4$
commutative property	a law that states that the order in which you add or multiply numbers does not affect the result; for example, $2 \times 4 = 4 \times 2$
compatible numbers	numbers that are easy to work with in your mind
distributive property	a law that states that when a number is multiplied by a sum written in parentheses, you can find the result by multiplying the number outside the parentheses by each number in the parentheses and then adding; for example, $3 \times (5 + 6) = (3 \times 5) + (3 \times 6) = 15 + 18 = 33$
equation	a mathematical sentence in which two expressions or numbers are equal
factors	the numbers that are multiplied in a multiplication problem
formula	an equation written with variables that shows the constant relationship among the variables
inverse	opposite; for example, addition and subtraction are inverse, or opposite, operations
order of operations	a set of rules that give the sequence for performing the mathematical operations in an expression
product	the result when two or more numbers (factors) are multiplied together; the answer to a multiplication problem
quotient	the result when one number is divided by another; the answer to a division problem
remainder	the amount left over after dividing two numbers that do not divide evenly
regroup	when adding or subtracting, to carry or borrow a quantity from one place value column to another
variable	a letter or symbol used to hold the place of a number in an expression

---

➡ NOW WATCH PROGRAM 29:

Make a note of the steps in the problem-solving process introduced in the program. Think about whether you've ever used a process like this to solve an everyday problem. Try the process on a math word problem.

PBS LiteracyLink®

After you watch the program, work on:

- pages 45–62 in this workbook
- Internet activities at http://www.pbs.org/literacy

Problem Solving

On the following pages, you will learn more
about the ideas discussed in the video program
and have an opportunity to develop and practice
your GED math skills.

**When taking the
GED Test, you should:**

- Read the problem
  carefully to find the
  question it asks you to
  answer. Make sure your
  response answers that
  question.

- If a problem has more
  than one step, write down
  the result after each step.
  This will save you time if
  you have to go back and
  rework a step.

- Use rounding, front-end
  estimation, and mental
  math to eliminate answer
  choices and check your
  work.

Key Points to Think About

In the video program, you explored:
- How people use math in their daily lives as workers,
  citizens, and family members.
- When to use the four basic operations and strategies
  for applying them to solve problems.
- How to write and solve equations in a problem-solving
  situation.

On the GED Math Test:
- You will need to have the basic addition facts such as
  $4 + 6 = 10$ and $8 + 3 = 11$ memorized.
- You will be expected to read a problem situation and
  decide which operation or combination of operations
  you will need to solve the problem.
- You will need to know the correct equation for solving
  a problem.
- You should apply mental math and estimation strategies
  to save time and check your work.

As you work through the lesson for Program 29:
- Think about the relationships among the four basic
  operations and how they can combine to solve problems.
- Always make sure your answers make sense. Think about
  the size of the numbers and whether they are reasonable
  for the situation.
- Be aware of the problem-solving situations you encounter
  in your daily life and how you go about solving them.

Basic Operations Review

COMMUNITY LINK: Pam is calling community members to raise funds for a homeless shelter. She hopes to raise $1000 during her 4-hour shift. She raises $125 the first hour and $415 the second hour. During a break, she adds $125 and $415, subtracts the sum from $1000, and finds that she needs to raise $460 during the last two hours to meet her goal.

Adding and Subtracting

Adding is combining two or more numbers to find a sum, or total. The procedure we commonly use for adding allows us to add two single-digit numbers at a time.

Follow these steps to add numbers:

1. Write the numbers in a column, lining up like place values.
2. Start with the ones column. Add each column, working from right to left.
3. If the total of any column is more than 9, **regroup,** or carry, the extra digits to the next column on the left.
4. To check your work, estimate an answer and compare.

Daily Transactions	
Mon	209
Tues	84
Wed	330
Thurs	145
Fri	362

Example: Jason works as a bank teller. How many transactions did he process from Monday to Wednesday?

Answer: 623 transactions

Check: Round to the nearest hundred and estimate:
$200 + 100 + 300 = 600$. The answer is reasonable.

$$
\begin{array}{r}
1\,1 \\
209 \\
84 \\
+\ 330 \\
\hline
623
\end{array}
$$

Subtracting is finding the difference between numbers.

Follow these steps to subtract numbers:

1. Write the numbers so that the larger number is on top.
2. Start with the ones column. Subtract, working from right to left.
3. If the digit on the bottom is larger than the digit on top, regroup or borrow from the next column to the left.
4. To check your work, estimate an answer, or add your result to the number you subtracted. The sum should be the number you subtracted from.

Example: How many more transactions did Jason process on Friday than on Thursday?

Answer: 217 transactions

Check: Using estimation, $350 - 150 = 200$. The answer makes sense. You can also check by adding. $217 + 145 = 362$

$$
\begin{array}{r}
5\,12 \\
3\cancel{6}\cancel{2} \\
-\ 145 \\
\hline
217
\end{array}
$$

Multiplying

Multiplying is a way of adding the same number repeatedly. For example, 3×4 means $4 + 4 + 4$ or $3 + 3 + 3 + 3$.

The answer to a multiplication problem is called the **product.** The numbers that are multiplied are called **factors.** The product of the factors 3 and 4 is 12.

We show multiplication with a times sign ($\times$), with a raised dot, or with parentheses: 3×4 $3 \cdot 4$ $(3)(4)$ $3(4)$

TIP: You must have your multiplication facts such as $7 \times 8 = 56$ memorized to solve problems quickly and accurately on the GED Math Test.

▶▶ Study this example to review the steps for multiplying numbers.

Example: If Jason averages 126 transactions per day, how many will he process in 25 working days?

Step 1. Multiply by the ones digit in 25, regrouping as necessary. Multiply the next column, then add the regrouped amount.

Step 2. Multiply by the tens digit in 25, moving the partial answer over one place to the left. Add the partial answers ($630 + 2520 = 3150$).

Answer: 3150 transactions
Check: Estimate an answer. You know 30×100 is 3000. The answer is close to the estimate. It makes sense.

STEP 1
```
  1 3
  126
×  25
  630
```

STEP 2
```
    1
  126
×  25
  630
 2520 ← placeholding zero
 3150
```

When using a calculator to add, subtract, or multiply, press an operations key between each number you enter. Then press the equals key.

Calculator: [2][0][9][+][8][4][+][3][3][0][=] [623.]

[3][6][2][−][1][4][5][=] [217.] ← In subtraction, it is important to enter numbers in the correct order.

[1][2][6][×][2][5][=] [3150.]

SKILL PRACTICE

Solve using pencil and paper. Then check your work with a calculator.

1. $782 + 1050 =$

2. $\$1790 - \$859 =$

3. $128 \times 8 =$

4. A school council figures the cost of planting a tree at $136. How much will it cost a high school to plant 78 trees?

    (1) $2,040
    (2) $7,888
    (3) $9,054
    (4) $10,608
    (5) $20,408

5. $49 + 917 + 6 =$

6. $13,040 - 1,850 =$

7. $512 \times 24 =$

8. To buy a house, the Hills paid $13,940 for a down payment, $1,145 for insurance, and $1,528 for loan fees. How much did they pay?

    (1) $15,085
    (2) $15,468
    (3) $15,503
    (4) $16,613
    (5) $17,513

Dividing

Division is the opposite of multiplication. When we divide, we are trying to find out how many times one number goes into another. The answer to a division problem is called the **quotient.**

On the GED Math Test, division can be written three ways.

With a division symbol: $12 \div 4$ with a slash mark: 12/4   as a fraction: $\frac{12}{4}$

▶▶ Study this example to review the steps for long division.

Example: Cynthia is counting the money received from ticket sales for a benefit performance of a play. If she counts $816 and tickets are $12 each, how many tickets were sold?

Set up the problem using a division bracket. *Think:* About how many times will 12 go into 81, the first two digits? Multiply and subtract.

Think: About how many times will 12 go into 96? Multiply and subtract.

Answer: 68 tickets

Check: Check by multiplying the number you divided by and the quotient. $68 \times 12 = 816$.
The answer is correct.

STEP 1

$$
\begin{array}{r}
6 \\
12\overline{)816} \\
-72 \\
\hline
96 \\
\end{array}
$$

STEP 2

$$
\begin{array}{r}
68 \\
12\overline{)816} \\
-72 \\
\hline
96 \\
-96 \\
\hline
0 \\
\end{array}
$$

Calculator: 8 1 6 ÷ 1 2 = [68.] ◀—— In division, it is important to enter numbers in the correct order.

You can estimate answers to division problems using your knowledge of the multiplication, or times, tables. Instead of dividing 12 into 816, choose a **compatible number,** a nearby number that is easy to work with in your head. You know that $12 \times 7 = 84$, so ask yourself: How many times will 12 go into 840? The answer is 70. Since 814 is less than 840, the answer will be close to, but less than, 70. On the GED, estimating an answer using compatible numbers is a good way to check your work and eliminate answer choices.

Working with Remainders

A remainder is an amount that is left over in the answer to a division problem. To show a remainder in the quotient, use the letter *r.*

    $15 \div 2 = 7 \, r1$ Two goes into 15 seven times with a remainder of 1.

You can express a remainder as a fraction by writing the remainder over the number that you are dividing by.

    $28 \div 3 = 9\frac{1}{3}$ Three will go into 28 exactly $9\frac{1}{3}$ times.

Deciding what to do with a remainder is an important part of problem solving.

▶▶ In this situation, think about the meaning of the numbers to decide how to handle the remainder.

Example: Monica is helping her child's teacher plan a field trip to a museum. Parents from the class have volunteered to drive since no school bus is available. There are 30 children in the class, and Monica figures that each driver can take 4 children. How many cars will they need to make the trip?

The problem is a simple one. Divide 30 by 4. $30 \div 4 = 7$ r2
Monica will have **7 full cars.**

Now think about the remainder. What does it represent? In this situation, the remainder represents children. Monica will have 7 full cars and 2 children left over. To make the trip, Monica needs one more car.

Answer: 8 cars
Check: 8 cars will make room for 32 children ($8 \times 4 = 32$). Monica cannot take the trip with fewer than 8 cars.

SKILL PRACTICE

Solve. Express remainders as whole numbers.

1. $492 \div 6 =$

2. $1600 \div 3 =$

3. $4500 \div 5 =$

4. $12,809 \div 15 =$

A city library is purchasing new furnishings under the direction of Laurie Reese. Use the price list and any of the four arithmetic operations to solve these problems. Check your work with a calculator.

SPACEMISER FURNITURE AND SUPPLIES		
Cat. #	**Item**	**Price**
A4759	Study Station	$223
A2374	All-Wood Side Chair	$89
D1432	Book Cart	$475
Q0492	Standard Book Truck	$189
W2391	Media Display	$32
Q4116	Media Storage Center	$329

5.   Laurie has budgeted $2500 for new chairs. How many All-Wood Side Chairs can she afford?

6.   Laurie plans to spend $1000 to buy a new media storage center and media display units. How much will she have left after buying item Q4116 on the price list?

7.   The library committee wants to encourage students to study at the library. How much will it cost to purchase six study stations?

8.   Book trucks are used for sorting and moving large numbers of books. Laurie wants to purchase one book cart and five book trucks. How much will these items cost?

9.   Laurie also has $12,500 to purchase new books for the children's section. If the average library-bound picture book costs $18, to the nearest ten, how many new books can she buy?

(1)   700   (4)   670

(2)   690   (5)   660

(3)   680

Writing Equations to Solve Problems

An equation states that two expressions or numbers are equal. The two sides of an equation are connected with an equals sign $(=)$.

Examples: $325 + 175 = 500$ $35 = 47 - 12$ $48 \div 6 = 2 \times 4$

Equations can be used to record many mathematical situations.

▸▸ The equations in this situation describe measurements.

Example: Rebecca's son is 60 inches tall. Since there are 12 inches in a foot, Rebecca knows her son is 5 feet tall.   1 foot $=$ 12 inches   60 inches $\div$ 12 inches $=$ 5 feet

Most math problems describe a situation in which one of the numbers in the problem is missing. A letter, called a **variable,** can be used to hold the place of the missing number. Any letter can be used as a variable.

▸▸ The variable takes the place of the unknown amount of money.

Example: After spending $15 on her sister, Marilyn had $38 left. How much did Marilyn have before she bought her sister's gift?

Let the amount before the purchase equal x. Subtract the amount that was spent from the starting amount. The difference is $38. $x - 15 = 38$

Solving One-Step Equations

An equation is solved once we know the value of the variable that will make the equation true. We do this by using the **inverse,** or opposite, operation of the one used in the problem. Adding and subtracting are inverse operations. So are multiplying and dividing. Performing inverse operations can help us get the variable alone on one side of the equation.

An equation is like a balance scale. As long as we add or take away the same amount on both sides, the sides remain balanced. Likewise, as long as we perform the same operation on both sides of the equation, the equation remains true.

Follow these steps to solve equations:

1. Determine the operation used with the variable.
2. Perform the inverse operation on both sides of the equation.

MATHEMATICS

Example: Marilyn had $38 left after spending $15 on a gift. How much did she have before buying the gift?

Write the equation.

Since 15 is subtracted from x, add 15 to both sides of the equation to get x by itself and keep the equation balanced.

$$x - 15 = 38$$
$$x - 15 + 15 = 38 + 15$$
$$x = 53$$

Answer: Marilyn had **$53** before she bought the gift.

Check: Substitute 53 for x and subtract: $53 - 15 = 38$. The solution for x is true.

▸▸ Study how inverse operations are used to find solutions in these examples.

Examples:

Subtract 28 from each side.	Multiply both sides by 3.	Divide both sides by 30.
$x + 28 = 100$	$\frac{z}{3} = 17$	$30b = 120$
$x + 28 - 28 = 100 - 28$	$3 \times \frac{z}{3} = 17 \times 3$	$\frac{30b}{30} = \frac{120}{30}$
$x = \mathbf{72}$	$z = \mathbf{51}$	$b = \mathbf{4}$
Check: $72 + 28 = 100$	*Check:* $\frac{51}{3} = 17$	*Check:* $30 \times 4 = 120$

SKILL PRACTICE

For each situation, write an equation and solve.

1. Dana's electric bill is $36. The sum of her electric and gas bills is $61. How much is her gas bill?

2. Lynn had $624 in her checking account. After writing a check, she had $458 left. Find the amount of the check.

3. Colin worked a number of hours at $9 per hour and earned $342. How many hours did he work?

4. A number of books divided equally among 6 shelves is equal to 42 books per shelf. How many books are there in all?

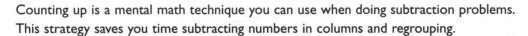

PROBLEM SOLVER Connection

Counting up is a mental math technique you can use when doing subtraction problems. This strategy saves you time subtracting numbers in columns and regrouping.

Example: Three months ago, Timon bought a new car. The car dealer advised him to come back for a service check at 10,000 miles. Today, Timon's car odometer reads 5,380 miles. How many more miles can Timon drive before the service check?

Step 1. Choose the operation: 10,000 − 5,380.
Step 2. Think: 20 gets me to 5,400; 600 gets me to 6,000; and 4,000 gets me to 10,000.
Step 3. Add the differences: 20 + 600 + 4,000 = 4,620.

Answer: Timon can drive **4,620 more miles** before his service check.

Describe how you could find the difference between $185 and $500 by counting up.

Answers and explanations start on page 310.

Solving Word Problems

FAMILY LINK: Ann's bank statement says that she has a $620 balance in her checking account. She thought she only had $520. She reviews each transaction in her check register to see if she made a mistake somewhere. Finally, she realizes that she subtracted a $50 deposit instead of adding it. The mistake caused a $100 error in her records.

A 5-Step Strategy to Problem Solving

To solve problems in everyday life, we have to search for information. We ask a question, then we have to find the facts that will help us answer it. In test-taking situations, we are asked a question. We are also given an assortment of facts. To solve the problem, we must choose the facts we need and then use them to answer the question. Many people use a 5-step approach to problem solving. These steps are the key to understanding and solving word problems.

The 5-Step Strategy to Problem Solving

1. Understand the question.
2. Find the facts you need to answer the question.
3. Choose the correct operation(s).
4. Solve the problem.
5. Check to make sure your answer is reasonable.

▶▶ See how the 5-step strategy is applied in this situation.

Example: Matt is driving 504 miles from San Francisco to San Diego. After driving about $6\frac{1}{2}$ hours, Matt decides to spend the night in Santa Barbara. If the distance from San Francisco to Santa Barbara is 332 miles, how many miles does Matt have left to drive?

 (1) 172 miles   **(4)** 4 hours
 (2) about 50 miles per hour   **(5)** 2158 miles
 (3) 836 miles

Step 1. Understand the question. The question asks how many *miles are left* to drive in the trip.

Step 2. Find the facts you need to answer the question. To find how many miles are left, you need the total miles (504) and the miles driven (332).

Step 3. Choose the correct operation. The amount driven plus the amount left equals the total trip. You can write an equation to represent the problem.

$332 + x = 504$
$x = 504 - 332$
Subtract to find the difference.

Step 4. Solve the problem. $504 - 332 = \textbf{172 miles}$

Step 5. Check the answer. $332 + 172 = 504$ miles

MATHEMATICS

Too Much or Not Enough Information

Many situations have more information than you will need to solve a specific problem. Tables, maps, and graphs usually have many numbers. On the GED Math Test, you will need to select the information needed to solve problems.

A few problems on the GED Math Test will not give you all the numbers that you need for a solution. You may be able to find the information you need by reading a table or graph or doing some calculations. If not, choose **(5) Not enough information is given.**

▶▶ Use the information from the graph to solve this problem.

Example: The Neighborhood Association is raising money to build a baseball diamond. The graph shows the receipts for this year. How much more money was raised from candy sales than from T-shirt sales?

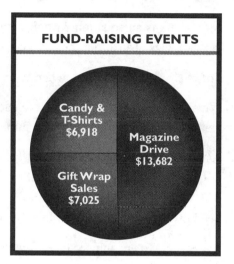

(1) $6,918	**(4)** $107
(2) $6,764	**(5)** Not enough
(3) $6,657	information is given.

You're right if you chose **(5) Not enough information is given.** The graph shows the combined total for the two events. It doesn't give separate amounts for those sales, so there is not enough information.

SKILL PRACTICE

The questions below are based on the graph above. Use the 5-step plan to solve each problem.

1. How much did the Neighborhood Association raise from the magazine drive and gift wrap sales?

(1) $6,657	**(4)** $27,625
(2) $13,943	**(5)** Not enough information is given.
(3) $20,707	

2. The association is planning to hold a fall festival on the vacant lot. The goal for the festival is to raise $5,000. If this goal is met, how much more will the association need to raise this year to reach its annual goal?

(1) $32,625	**(4)** $8,682
(2) $18,682	**(5)** Not enough information is given.
(3) $22,625	

3. How much more did the association raise from the magazine drive than from the candy and T-shirt sales?

(1) $6,918	**(4)** $107
(2) $6,764	**(5)** Not enough information is given.
(3) $6,657	

Answers and explanations start on page 310.

FAMILY LINK: Natalie is ordering clothes for her child from a catalog. Denim jeans for children are $16 per pair. Natalie orders 3 pairs for her daughter. On the order form, she copies the description of the jeans and writes 3 under *Quantity* and $16 under *Unit Cost.* Finally, she multiplies 3 × $16 and writes $48 under *Total Cost.*

Applying Formulas

A **formula** is an equation written with variables that shows the mathematical relationship among the variables. To fill out the catalog order form, Natalie applied the formula for finding total cost.

Total Cost $c = nr$ where c = total cost, n = number of units, and r = cost per unit

When variables are written next to each other, they are to be multiplied. So the formula states that the total cost is equal to the number of items multiplied by the cost of one item.

As applied to Natalie's order: $c = nr$
$$\$48 = 3 \text{ pairs of jeans} \times \$16 \text{ per pair}$$

▶▶See how the formula is used to solve for r, the cost of one item.

Example: To encourage students to use the new school library, Arturo bought 6 banners to decorate the school hallways. If the total cost of the banners was $348, how much did he pay per banner?

Read and Succeed

Step 1. Write the formula. $c = nr$
Step 2. Substitute known values for the variables. $348 = 6r$
Step 3. Divide both sides by 6. $\frac{348}{6} = \frac{6r}{6}$
$$58 = r$$

Answer: The cost of one banner is **$58.**
Check: Substitute $58 for r: $58 × 6 = $348.

You can also estimate to check answers. Use compatible numbers: $348 is close to $360, and $360 ÷ 6 = $60. Since $58 is close to $60, the answer makes sense.

Another useful formula is the distance formula.

Distance $d = rt$ where d = distance, r = rate, and t = time

In other words, multiply the rate of travel by the time traveled to find the distance traveled.

▶▶ See how the distance formula is applied to find time in this situation.

Example: Wanda hauls goods by truck from Savannah to Nashville, a distance of 495 miles. Because of bad weather, Wanda expects to average 45 miles per hour. How long will it take her to make the trip?

Step 1. Write the formula.

Step 2. Replace the variables with the known values.

Step 3. Divide both sides by 45.

$$d = rt$$
$$495 = 45t$$
$$\frac{495}{45} = \frac{45t}{45}$$
$$11 = t$$

Refer to page 340 for a copy of the GED formulas page.

Answer: Wanda can drive the distance in **11 hours.**

Check: Substitute 11 for *t*. 45 × 11 = 495

SKILL PRACTICE

Use the cost and distance formulas to help solve each problem.

1. For an after-school program, Eunsook bought 36 board games. Each game cost $9. What was the total cost for the games?

2. A computer repairer bought 8 hard drives at a total cost of $1432. How much did she pay for each hard drive?

3. A grocery store bought a case of shampoo for $432. If the store paid $3 per bottle, how many bottles were in the case?

4. John is planning a trip cross country. If he drives 8 hours a day at an average rate of 55 miles per hour, how many miles can he drive per day?

5. A plane travels 1725 miles in 3 hours. What is the plane's rate of travel?

   (1) 575 miles per hour
   (2) 625 miles per hour
   (3) 3450 miles per hour
   (4) 5175 miles per hour
   (5) Not enough information is given.

SCIENCE Connection

Engineers use formulas to find out whether a structure can support the required amount of pressure. Think of the floor of your living room. It has to support the pressure from furniture and people in the room. This pressure, also called the floor's design live load, is measured in pounds per square foot (psf).

In science, this formula is written: $p = \frac{F}{A}$, where p = pressure (or design live load), F = force or weight, and A = surface area.

Example: The surface area of a living room is 300 square feet. If the estimated weight of the furniture and the maximum number of people in the room are about 2400 pounds, what is the floor's design live load?

Step 1. Substitute the values from the problem into the formula.
$$p = \frac{F}{A} \qquad p = \frac{2400}{300}$$
Step 2. Divide: $\frac{2400}{300} = 8$ psf

Answer: The room's live load is **8 pounds per square foot.** Since the building codes require that the floor supports at least 40 pounds per square foot, the floor is not in any danger of collapsing.

Try this one: A room has an area of 180 square feet. The furniture and occupants weigh about 1620 pounds. **What is the floor's live load in psf?**

Answers and explanations start on page 310.

Solving Multi-Step Problems

FAMILY LINK: Jein is buying a new washer and dryer. After paying $150 as a down payment, she will make 24 monthly payments of $34 each. Jein calculates that she will pay a total of $966 for the new appliances.

Breaking the Problem into Steps

Many problems have more than one step. Usually, the additional steps involve finding some of the facts needed to answer the question asked in the problem.

In the situation above, Jein has to find the total of the down payment and the monthly payments to know how much she will spend for the washer and dryer. She knows the amount of the down payment, but she has to calculate the total of the monthly payments. She does this by multiplying $34 by 24 months.

Step 1. First find total of monthly payments. $34 × 24 = $816
Step 2. Add monthly payments to down payment. $816 + $150 = **$966 total**

You can apply the 5-step plan to multi-step problems. Once you identify the question you have to answer, look for the facts you need to answer it. Do you have all the facts? If not, look for a way to calculate one or more of the numbers you need.

▸▸ In this distance problem, an extra step is needed to calculate one of the needed facts.

Example: Max drove from Lincoln to Norfolk and back in 4 hours. If the distance from Lincoln to Norfolk is 124 miles, what was Max's average rate of travel?

     (1)   31 miles per hour   **(4)**   62 miles per hour
     (2)   38 miles per hour   **(5)**   64 miles per hour
     (3)   54 miles per hour

You're right if you chose **(4) 62 miles per hour.** Find the total distance; $d = rt$
Max drove twice the distance given in the problem, or 248 miles. $248 = r \cdot 4$
Use the distance formula with 248 miles as the total distance. $\frac{248}{4} = \frac{r \cdot 4}{4}$
Check: 62 × 4 = 248 $62 = r$

Using the Order of Operations

When a problem has more than one step, the order in which you perform operations could affect the answer.

Consider this expression: $8 + 4 × 5$
If you add first, the answer is 60. $(8 + 4) × 5 = 12 × 5 = 60$
If you multiply first, the answer is 28. $8 + (4 × 5) = 8 + 20 = 28$
Both answers can't be correct.

MATHEMATICS

To avoid these kinds of issues, mathematicians have agreed upon a correct order to perform operations. The steps are shown below. You will need to know these steps to solve multi-step problems and to evaluate expressions on the GED Math Test.

The Order of Operations

FIRST   Do operations that are grouped in **parentheses.**
SECOND   Do **multiplication** and **division** steps from **left to right.**
LAST   Do **addition** and **subtraction** steps from **left to right.**

Some calculators (such as the calculator provided for Part I of the GED Math Test) are programmed to use the order of operations. However, many are not. Try this experiment with your calculator.

Calculator: $\boxed{8}\boxed{+}\boxed{4}\boxed{\times}\boxed{5}\boxed{=}\boxed{\qquad\qquad ?}$

Using the order of operations, you need to multiply 4 and 5 before you add 8. Now, enter the numbers and operations in the order shown above. If the result is 28, your calculator performed the multiplication step first even though the addition step was entered first.

If the result is 60, your calculator added before it multiplied: $8 + 4 = 12$ and $12 \times 5 = 60$.

If your calculator does not follow the order of operations, enter the problem according to the order of operations.

Calculator: $\boxed{4}\boxed{\times}\boxed{5}\boxed{+}\boxed{8}\boxed{=}\boxed{\qquad 28.}$

To learn more about the capabilities of your calculator, turn to page 337.

SKILL PRACTICE

Use the order of operations to find the value of the following expressions.

1. $9 \times 6 \div 2 - 10$

2. $(62 \times 5) \div (8 + 2)$

3. $100 - (90 \div 2)$

4. $50 \div 5 + 20$

5. $7(14 - 8 + 3)$

6. $(3 \times 42) + (60 \div 4)$

Questions 7 and 8 are based on the diagram below. You may use your calculator.

7. Rachel drives from home to work and back on Monday, Tuesday, and Wednesday. How many miles does she drive on those days altogether? (*Hint:* Start by finding the distance she drives to work and back each day.)

8. On Thursday and Friday, Rachel drives from home to work at 8 A.M. Then she drives from work to school at 6:30 P.M. She returns home from school at 9:30 P.M. How many miles does she drive on Thursday and Friday combined?

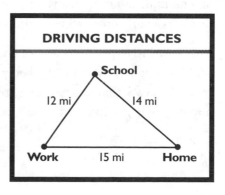

DRIVING DISTANCES

Solving Set-up Problems

Some items on the GED Math Test ask you to select a correct method for solving a problem instead of finding the solution. These problems do not require calculations. Instead, you need to find an expression that shows the correct numbers, operations, and order of steps.

▸▸ Think about the method you would use to solve this problem.

Example: Marie earns $16 per hour for overtime hours. She worked 8 hours overtime last week and 6 hours overtime this week. Which expression could be used to find Marie's overtime pay for the two-week period?

    (1) $16 × 8 × 6   **(4)** 6($16 + 8)

    (2) $16(8 + 6)   **(5)** 8(6) + 8($16)

    (3) 8(6) + $16

You're right if you chose **(2) $16(8 + 6).** In this expression, $16 (the overtime hourly wage) is multiplied by the sum of 8 and 6 (the total overtime hours worked).

There is another way to work the problem. You could find the overtime pay for each week and add: $16(8) + $16(6). Both choice (2) and this expression yield the same result. Both are correct.

$16(8 + 6) = $16(14) = $224 $16(8) + $16(6) = $128 + $96 = $224

To solve GED set-up problems, think about how you would calculate an answer to the problem. Put your ideas into words. Then substitute numbers and operations symbols for the words.

Properties of Operations

To recognize the correct setup, you should be familiar with these important properties.

The **commutative property** applies only to addition and multiplication. It means that you can add or multiply numbers in any order without affecting the result.

    8 + 9 = 17 OR 9 + 8 = 17

    7 × 6 = 42 OR 6 × 7 = 42

The **associative property** works only for addition and multiplication. It means that when you add or multiply more than two numbers, you can group the numbers any way that you like without affecting the result.

    (5 + 8) + 10 = 13 + 10 = 23

                OR

    5 + (8 + 10) = 5 + 18 = 23

    (6 × 2) × 3 = 12 × 3 = 36

                OR

    6 × (2 × 3) = 6 × 6 = 36

MATHEMATICS

The **distributive property** says that a number outside parentheses can be multiplied by each number inside the parentheses. Then the products are added or subtracted according to the operation symbol.

$$8(8 + 6) = 8(8) + 8(6)$$
$$8(14) = 64 + 48$$
$$112 = 112$$

On the GED Math Test, your setup may not seem to be among the answer choices. Try applying these properties to the choices to see whether the setup is written a different way.

$$5(12 - 3) = 5(12) - 5(3)$$
$$5(9) = 60 - 15$$
$$45 = 45$$

SKILL PRACTICE

Solve each problem.

1. In January, 58 parents attended the PTA meeting. In February, 72 parents attended, and 113 in March. Which expression represents the total attendance for the 3 months?

   (1) $\frac{58 + 72 + 1133}{3}$
   (2) $3(58 + 72 + 113)$
   (3) $113 + 72 + 58$
   (4) $58(72 + 113)$
   (5) $3(113 - 58) + 72$

2. Which of the following expressions is the same as $(5 \times 15) - (5 \times 8)$?

   (1) $5 \times (15 - 5)\ 8$
   (2) $5(15 \times 8)$
   (3) $5(15 + 8)$
   (4) $(5 \times 8) \times 15$
   (5) $5(15 - 8)$

3. Lamar earned $20,800 last year, and his wife, Neva, earned $22,880. Which expression could be used to find the amount they earned per month last year?

   (1) $2(\$22,880 + \$20,800)$
   (2) $(\$22,800 - \$20,800) \div 12$
   (3) $12(\$22,880 - \$20,800)$
   (4) $(\$22,880 + \$20,800) \div 12$
   (5) $(\$20,800 + \$22,800) \div 2$

4. Alexa sold 12 sweatshirts at $23 each and 28 T-shirts at $14 each. Which expression represents total sales?

   (1) $12(\$23) + 28(\$14)$
   (2) $12(\$23 + \$14)$
   (3) $28(\$14 + \$23)$
   (4) $12 + \$23 + 28 + \$14$
   (5) $28(12) + \$23(\$14)$

CALCULATOR Connection

Suppose you are solving a set-up problem. You know how to do the math, but you don't recognize any of the setups offered as answer choices. You may have used a correct, but different, approach. Your calculator can help.

Example: Phyllis buys two software programs, each costing $150. There is a $25 rebate on each program. Which expression shows the combined cost?

(1) $2(\$150)(\$25)$ (4) $\$150 - 2(\$25)$
(2) $2(\$150) + 2(\$25)$ (5) $2(\$150) - \$25$
(3) $2(\$150) - 2(\$25)$

Step 1. Think about how you would solve this problem. Perhaps you would add and subtract: $150 + $150 - $25 - $25. Your approach is not among the choices, however.

Step 2. Do the math using your approach: $150 + $150 - $25 - $25 = $250. Now use your calculator to evaluate each setup until you find the one that yields your answer. Which expression is correct?

Answers and explanations start on page 310.

PART ONE DIRECTIONS: Choose the <u>one best answer</u> to each of the following problems. Use a calculator wherever necessary.

1. Lucia spent $84 for 4 shirts and $66 for 2 pairs of jeans. If each shirt cost the same amount, what was the price of one shirt?
   (1) $84
   (2) $65
   (3) $42
   (4) $33
   (5) $21

Questions 2 and 3 are based on the following situation.

The Primo Camping Supply Company is holding a team-building seminar for its 84 employees. There will be 4 to 7 employees on each team. The teams will work on Saturday, for $2\frac{1}{2}$ hours in the morning and 4 hours in the afternoon.

2. A manager suggests putting 6 employees on each team. Which of the following expressions could be used to find how many teams the employees would form?
   (1) $84 \div 6$
   (2) $(84 \div 7) + (84 \div 4)$
   (3) 7×4
   (4) $84 \div (7 - 4)$
   (5) 84×6

3. The entire seminar will last for 8 hours. Based on the information given, which expression best represents how much time will be left for lunch and breaks?
   (1) $8 - 2\frac{1}{2} - 4$
   (2) $2\frac{1}{2} + 4 - 8$
   (3) $8(2\frac{1}{2} + 4)$
   (4) $8(2\frac{1}{2}) - 8(4)$
   (5) Not enough information is given.

Questions 4 and 5 are based on the sign.

Plant Depot Trees	
Plum trees	$35
Orange trees	$46
Lemon trees	$28

4. Before tax, how much more will Warren spend for a plum tree than a lemon tree?
   (1) $0.70
   (2) $7.00
   (3) $11.00
   (4) $18.00
   (5) Not enough information is given.

5. Warren brought $100 with him to buy trees. Which trees can he buy with this money and still have at least $10 change?
   (1) two plum trees and one orange tree
   (2) two orange trees
   (3) three lemon trees
   (4) four lemon trees
   (5) three plum trees

6. For a school trip to a museum, the school pays $135 for a bus which holds up to 50 students and $3 per student for admission. How much will it cost for 80 students?
   (1) $240   **(4)** $476
   (2) $270   **(5)** $510
   (3) $375

7. Eva spent $102 for six tickets to a baseball game and souvenirs. If the souvenirs cost a total of $24 and the tickets all had the same price, which expression could be used to find the cost of one ticket?
   (1) $102 - 6 + $24
   (2) $102 \div 6 - $24
   (3) $102 \times $24 \div 6
   (4) ($102 - $24) \div 6
   (5) ($24 \div 6) + ($102 \div 6)

MATHEMATICS

8. The attendance at the Maine South football game was 3450 last Friday. This Friday's attendance was 4126. How many fans attended the games in all?

   (1) 676
   (2) 1676
   (3) 3450
   (4) 7276
   (5) 7576

Questions 9 and 10 are based on the following information.

9. Anna decides to take her nephews to the water park. She plans to buy 4 children's all-day passes. Which of these expressions could be used to find how much Anna will pay for the children's passes?

   (1) 4($8)
   (2) 4($12)
   (3) 4($14)
   (4) $20 ÷ 4
   (5) ($20 + $14) ÷ 4

10. If Anna decides to buy half-day passes, how much will 4-hour passes for 1 adult and 4 children cost her?

    (1) $32
    (2) $44
    (3) $48
    (4) $76
    (5) Not enough information is given.

11. The distance from Kuala to Meising is 140 kilometers. A freight train makes the round trip in 7 hours. What is the average number of kilometers the train travels an hour?

    (1) 20
    (2) 24
    (3) 30
    (4) 40
    (5) 48

12. Marina's gross pay for one pay period is $852. Her take-home pay for the same period is $696. Approximately how much is deducted from Marina's pay for taxes and insurance?

    (1) less than $50
    (2) between $50 and $100
    (3) between $100 and $200
    (4) between $200 and $250
    (5) between $250 and $300

13. On a trip to Lake Spencer, Theo makes two stops. He drives 220 miles before making the first stop, an additional 280 miles before the second stop, and an additional 175 miles before arriving at Lake Spencer. How many miles per hour did he drive on the trip?

    (1) 55
    (2) 225
    (3) 455
    (4) 675
    (5) Not enough information is given.

14. Which pair would represent compatible numbers for the expression 1388 ÷ 69?

    (1) 1400 and 70
    (2) 1380 and 70
    (3) 1400 and 69
    (4) 1300 and 70
    (5) 1300 and 60

15. Decide which of the following operations you should perform first in the expression: $60 - \frac{32}{8} - 5 \times 3 + 10$.
    (1) $60 - 32$
    (2) $\frac{32}{8}$
    (3) $8 - 5$
    (4) 5×3
    (5) $3 + 10$

16. Phil repairs VCRs for an appliance store. He is paid $50 for each repaired VCR. In June he repaired 8 VCRs. In July he repaired 12. Which of the following expressions could be used to find how much he was paid for the repairs during the two months?
    (1) $\$50(8) + 12$
    (2) $\$50(12) + 8$
    (3) $\$50(8 + 12)$
    (4) $\$50(12)(8)(2)$
    (5) $\frac{\$50(12)(8)}{2}$

17. Bella drove 340 miles in 5 hours. In miles per hour, what was Bella's average rate of speed for the trip? (*Hint:* Use the distance formula from the GED formulas page.)
    (1) 15
    (2) 55
    (3) 60
    (4) 64
    (5) 68

18. What is another way of writing the expression 137×6?
    (1) 1376
    (2) $137 + 6$
    (3) $\frac{1}{137} \times \frac{1}{6}$
    (4) $137(6)$
    (5) $\frac{137}{6}$

Questions 19 through 21 are based on the following table.

Mixture	Amount (in ounces)	Boiling Point (in minutes)
A	8	8
B	5	4
C	5	10
D	4	6

19. The table states the amount (in ounces) and boiling points (in minutes) of four chemical mixtures. What is the difference in minutes between the fastest and the slowest boiling points?
    (1) 2
    (2) 4
    (3) 6
    (4) 8
    (5) 14

20. Mixtures B, C, and D are poured into a 20-ounce jar. The mixtures do not change in amount. Which expression states the amount of room left in the jar?
    (1) $5 + 5 + 4$
    (2) $2(5) + 4$
    (3) $20 - 2(5 - 4)$
    (4) $20 - 5 - 4$
    (5) $20 - 5 - 5 - 4$

21. According to the table, which mixture would reach freezing point first?
    (1) A
    (2) B
    (3) C
    (4) D
    (5) Not enough information is given.

Answers and explanations start on page 310.

Using money and writing checks, filling up at the gas tank, and checking out the size of the federal budget are some of the examples of using decimals shown in this program. You'll find out what decimals mean and review how to read them and calculate with them.

BEFORE YOU WATCH

30

Decimals

OBJECTIVES

1. Explore the meaning and value of decimals.
2. Add, subtract, multiply, and divide decimals.
3. Solve problems with everyday decimals.

The next time you go to the grocery store or the gas station, take a close look at the numbers around you. Notice how many are actually decimal numbers. At the gas station, the *price per gallon,* the *number of gallons* pumped, and the cost of the gas all use decimals to show amounts. At the grocery store, hundreds of prices and even many of the weights are listed as decimals.

The ability to work with decimals is important to your success on the GED Math Test. Most important will be your ability to perform the basic operations with decimals—adding, subtracting, multiplying, and dividing. By estimating with decimals, you can find approximate answers, narrow down answer choices, and check the accuracy of your work. Being comfortable with decimals will help you with other math skills such as fractions, percents, measurement, and geometry.

On the following pages, you will find a brief exercise called *Sneak Preview*. It is designed to introduce you to the topics that will be featured in the video program and the corresponding lesson. After you complete the exercise and check your answers, turn to the vocabulary page. There you will find terms that will help you better understand the video and the lesson that follow. After reviewing page 66, you will be ready to watch Program 30.

For additional practice, visit *LiteracyLink* online at http://www.pbs.org/literacy.

63

Sneak Preview

This exercise previews some of the concepts from Program 30. After you answer the questions, use the feedback on page 65 to help set your learning goals.

 **WORKPLACE LINK:** Rachel works for a small cheese company that provides cheese to restaurants in the region. The company itself manufactures three different kinds of cheese, but it also distributes other cheeses for different cheese makers. Rachel's job involves preparing the customers' invoices.

the CHEESE SHOP

C 103001

DATE: *7-10*

SOLD TO: *Al Dente*

Joliet, IL

INVOICE PAID ON ACCOUNT

LB		AMOUNT	
190.70	Mozzarella @ $1.70		
19.25	Baby Swiss @ $2.82	54	29
85.40	Mild Cheddar @ $1.97	168	24
10.70	Mild Brick @ $1.92	20	54
100.00	Shredded Cheddar @ $2.12	212	00
		$1055	56

Answer these questions based on the invoice shown above.

1. The price per pound of each type of cheese is listed after the @ (at) symbol. Which of the following shows the cheeses on the invoice listed from <u>least to most expensive</u> per pound?

   (1) Baby Swiss, Shredded Cheddar, Mild Cheddar, Mild Brick, Mozzarella
   (2) Mozzarella, Shredded Cheddar, Mild Cheddar, Baby Swiss, Mild Brick
   (3) Mild Cheddar, Mild Brick, Shredded Cheddar, Mozzarella, Baby Swiss
   (4) Mozzarella, Mild Brick, Mild Cheddar, Shredded Cheddar, Baby Swiss
   (5) Mozzarella, Mild Brick, Mild Cheddar, Baby Swiss, Shredded Cheddar

MATHEMATICS

2. Given the number of pounds delivered and the price per pound, how much will the customer be charged for mozzarella?

    (1) $32.42
    (2) $112.18
    (3) $324.19
    (4) $1121.80
    (5) $3241.90

3. The customer decides to substitute American cheese for the mild brick cheese. If American cheese costs $1.80 per pound, which expression represents how much less the new cost will be?

    (1) $($1.92 \times 10.70) - \$1.80$
    (2) $($0.80 \times 10.70) - \$1.92$
    (3) $\$1.92 - \$1.80 \times 10.70$
    (4) $($1.92 + \$1.80) \times 10.70$
    (5) $($1.92 - \$1.80) \times 10.70$

4. If the price of mild cheddar cheese goes up $0.02 this month and $0.05 next month, what will be the price of mild cheddar cheese next month?

    (1) $2.67
    (2) $2.17
    (3) $2.04
    (4) $2.02
    (5) $1.99

Feedback

- If you got all of the answers right...   you have a good basic understanding of decimal calculations and problem solving.

- If you missed question 1...   you need to learn more about the values of decimals and how to compare those values.

- If you missed question 2...   you need to work on your decimal multiplication skills.

- If you missed question 3...   you need to work on how to set up multi-step problems.

- If you missed question 4...   you need to develop your decimal addition skills.

Vocabulary for *Decimals*

calculations	math processes—such as adding, subtracting, multiplying, and dividing—carried out to solve a problem
decimal point	the point that separates whole numbers from parts of a whole or dollars from cents
dividend	the number being divided in a division problem; the number inside the long division bracket
divisor	the number you are dividing by
partial product	the answer to part of a multiplication problem involving numbers with two or more digits; the sum of the partial products is the answer to the multiplication problem
perimeter	the measure of the distance around the boundary of an object or figure
place value	a system that shows how much a digit is worth by the digit's location in the number
placeholder zero	a zero written to hold a place value open; for example: 4.02

➡ **NOW WATCH PROGRAM 30:**

Pay close attention to the explanations of how decimals relate to fractions and percents. This is a key concept that will help you understand all three.

After you watch the program, work on:

- pages 67–84 in this workbook
- Internet activities at http://www.pbs.org/literacy

30

Decimals

On the following pages, you will learn more about the ideas discussed in the video program and have an opportunity to develop and practice your GED math skills.

GED TIPS

When taking the GED Test, you should:

- Use common sense as a way to check the reasonableness of your answers.

- Skip any problem you are having difficulty with and come back to it after you have completed the rest of the test. **Answer every question on the test.**

- Make sure what you mark on the answer sheet matches the number of your answer choice.

Key Points to Think About

In the video program, you explored:

- How people use decimals in their daily lives as workers, citizens, and family members.

- How the values of decimals are used to identify and order objects and amounts.

- Everyday decimals such as those that deal with money, time, and measurement.

On the GED Math Test:

- You will be expected to know how to add, subtract, multiply, and divide with decimals.

- You will need to know how to compare and order decimals.

- You will work with decimals a great deal, especially when working with money amounts and with measurement and geometry problems.

As you work through the lesson for Program 30:

- Concentrate on the correct placement of the decimal point in all of your **calculations.**

- Use estimation wherever possible—to find answers, eliminate answer choices, and check calculations.

- Be aware of the decimal skills you can use in your daily life, not just on the GED Math Test.

Understanding Decimal Values

FAMILY LINK: June is using a calculator to figure out how much sales tax she owes on a catalog order. After punching in the numbers, she reads 4.375 in the calculator display. June rounds up and writes $4.38 in the blank for sales tax.

The Meaning of Decimal Values

Decimals are a way of expressing an amount less than one. When you read a price tag, you know that the number to the left of the **decimal point** represents whole dollars. The number to the right represents cents, a fractional part of a dollar.

In our number system, the placement of a digit tells you its value. To understand a decimal number, you need to pay attention to the place each digit occupies.

The first three decimal places are tenths, hundredths, and thousandths. Each digit to the right is ten times smaller than the digit on its left.

decimal point → • ☐ ☐ ☐
tenths hundredths thousandths

A leading zero may be written before the decimal point to show that there is no whole number part. **Placeholder zeros** may be written between the decimal point and the start of the decimal number. Ignore leading zeros when you read a number.

0.205
leading zero   placeholder zero

To read a decimal, say the number plus the **place value** of the last digit on the right.

Examples: 0.8 is read *eight-tenths*.   0.04 is read *four-hundredths*.
0.015 is read *fifteen-thousandths*.   6.4 is read *six and four-tenths*.

Rounding Decimals

Rounding is a way to work with easier numbers. Rounding is useful for estimating. When an exact answer is not needed, calculating with simpler numbers saves time.

Rounding decimals is much like rounding whole numbers:

STEP 1. Choose the place value to which you want to round.
STEP 2. Look at the place value to its right. If that digit is 5 or more, round up to the next larger number. If the digit on the right is less than 5, round down. The digit stays the same.
STEP 3. Drop any digits to the right of the place value you rounded to.

Examples: To the nearest tenth: 9.654 rounds up to 9.7
To the nearest hundredth: 8.753 rounds down to 8.75
To the nearest whole number: 9.502 rounds up to 10
To the nearest whole number: 9.489 rounds down to 9

Comparing and Ordering Decimals

Follow these steps to compare decimals:

STEP 1. Write the numbers in a column, lining up the decimal points.

STEP 2. If needed, add one or more zeros to the right of the last digit so that you have the same amount of digits in each number.

STEP 3. Compare the whole numbers, then the decimal digits, working from left to right.

▶▶ Look at the following sign from a shelf of library books.

Example: Dillon is looking for a library book with the call number 812.841. This sign shows the range of call numbers found on a shelf. If the call number for Dillon's book is between or equal to one of the numbers, it can be found on the shelf. Does Dillon's book belong on this shelf?

Call Numbers
812.8–923.0

Step 1. Compare the book call number with the numbers on the sign.

Step 2. Write the numbers in a column. Add zeros so that all the numbers have the same number of digits.

812.841
812.800
923.000

Step 3. Compare digits from left to right. 812.841 is greater than 812.8 *but* less than 923.0. **The book belongs on this shelf.**

SKILL PRACTICE

Use rounding, comparing, and ordering to answer the following questions.

1. Which is greater: 0.08 or 0.018?

2. Which is greater: 5.05 or 5.2?

3. Which is less: 12.65 or 11.95?

4. Which is less: 0.169 or 0.17?

5. A centimeter is equal to 0.394 inches. What is that amount to the nearest tenth?

6. Art is helping his son Colin with his homework. Colin needs to find his height to the nearest centimeter. Measured with a meter stick, Colin's height is 132.4 centimeters. What is his height to the nearest whole centimeter?

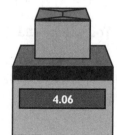

7. Carol estimates the total weight of a package at 4.5 pounds. The digital scale gives the weight as 4.06 pounds. Is the weight of the package greater or less than Carol's estimate?

8. A plumber has to join four lengths of copper pipe. On the plans, the lengths are labeled A, B, C, and D. The lengths are A = 1.85 m, B = 1.775 m, C = 1.255 m, and D = 1.8 m.

   Which of the following arranges the sections in order from <u>shortest to longest</u>?

   (1) C, B, A, D
   (2) D, C, A, B
   (3) C, B, D, A
   (4) A, D, B, C
   (5) D, A, C, B

Answers and explanations start on page 311.

Basic Operations with Decimals

COMMUNITY LINK: John is helping his son complete a 10-hour community service project. On Saturday, they worked 3.75 hours cleaning up an empty lot in their neighborhood. John subtracted 3.75 from 10 to find out how many hours they had left to work.

Adding and Subtracting Decimals

Performing operations with decimals is similar to working with whole numbers. For both whole numbers and decimals, place value matters. If you carefully align the place value columns before you add and subtract, you will avoid many errors.

Follow these steps to add or subtract decimals:

STEP 1. Write the numbers in a column, aligning the decimal points.
STEP 2. If needed, you can add zeros to the right of the last digit in a decimal number so that you have the same number of digits in each number.
STEP 3. Add or subtract as you would with whole numbers.
STEP 4. Put the decimal point in the answer below the decimals in the problem.

▶▶ Look at the following information from the weather page of a newspaper.

Example: Kim has recently moved to Los Angeles. She wonders what kind of weather to expect. While reading the newspaper, she finds the chart shown here. How can she use the information to find the average rainfall for Los Angeles for one year?

You need to add the amounts to find the average for one year.

$$
\begin{array}{r}
{\scriptstyle 1\ 1} \\
3.80 \\
0.25 \\
2.80 \\
+\ 8.00 \\
\hline
14.85
\end{array}
$$

Line up the decimal points.

Add zeros to the right to make the columns even.

Add to find the sum.

LOS ANGELES AVERAGE RAINFALL BY SEASON (IN INCHES)	
Spring	3.8
Summer	0.25
Fall	2.8
Winter	8

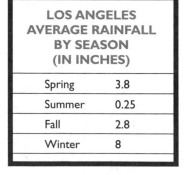

Calculators always display a leading zero when the decimal number has no whole number part. Most don't display zeros added to the right of the last decimal digit. When using a calculator, you do not have to enter leading zeros. Just make sure that you enter the decimal point in the exact place that it appears in the number.

Calculator: [3] [.] [8] [+] [.] [2] [5] [+] [2] [.] [8] [+] [8] [=] | 14.85 |

Answer: 14.85 inches

Check: Use front-end estimation to see if your answer is reasonable. Add the front-end digits of the decimal numbers: 3 + 0 + 2 + 8 = 13. Since 14.85 is close to 13, your answer makes sense.

MATHEMATICS

▶▶ Use your knowledge of place value in this situation.

Example: Fabio has the flu. His temperature is 103.2 degrees. A normal body temperature is 98.6 degrees. How many degrees above normal is his temperature?

    (1) 0.046   **(4)** 46

    (2) 0.46   **(5)** Not enough information is given.

    (3) 4.6

$$\begin{array}{r} {}^{9}\!\!\!\not{10}{}^{1}2 \\ \not{1}0\not{3}.2 \\ -\ 98.6 \\ \hline 4.6 \end{array}$$

You're right if you chose **(3) 4.6.** The difference between 103.2 and 98.6 is 4.6 degrees. You needed to subtract to find the answer. If you line up the decimal points in the numbers before subtracting, you can see that the answer will have exactly one decimal digit. Only choice (3) makes sense. *Check:* 98.6 + 4.6 = 103.2

SKILL PRACTICE

Add or subtract as indicated.

1. Find the sum of 0.4, 1.55, and 0.648. Begin by writing the numbers in a column, lining up the decimal points.

2. Find the difference between 18.56 and 10.9.

3. 104.5 − 95.25 =   5. 105.9 + 16.47 + 82 =   7. 100.765 + 48.9 + 22.5 =

4. 3.625 − 0.775 =   6. 1.005 − 0.75 =   8. 98.7 − 29.683 =

Choose the best answer for each item.

9. Anna is weighing items to estimate shipping charges. The digital scale shown here gives the weight of two items in pounds. Which of the following is the best estimate of their total weight in pounds?

    (1) 1   **(4)** 4

    (2) 2   **(5)** 5

    (3) 3

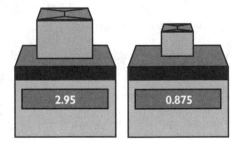

10. Craig is helping his daughter with a science project for school. From a wooden dowel that is 30 centimeters in length, he cuts a piece that measures 16.72 centimeters. How many centimeters long is the remaining piece?

    (1) 1.328   **(4)** 14.38

    (2) 1.438   **(5)** 46.72

    (3) 13.28

11. At the start of a trip, a car's odometer read 41,253.6 miles. At the end of the trip, the odometer read 41,839.2. How many miles long was the trip?

    (1) 83092.8   **(4)** 585.6

    (2) 1092.8   **(5)** 586.4

    (3) 586.6

Answers and explanations start on page 311.

Multiplying Decimals

To multiply decimals, set up the problem just as you would when working with whole numbers. Remember that you can multiply numbers in any order without changing the product, or result. Usually, it makes sense to set up the problem by writing the number with more digits first.

Then multiply as you would whole numbers. To place the decimal point in the answer, add the number of decimal places in the factors, the numbers being multiplied. The product will have that same number of decimal digits in the answer.

▶▶ Use your knowledge of decimals to calculate cost.

Example: Alana bought a 12.5-pound turkey. At $.69 per pound, how much did she pay for the turkey?

Step 1. Set up the problem and multiply. Ignore the decimal point as you find the **partial products.**

Step 2. Now count the decimal places in the factors. 1 + 2 = 3. Count 3 places from the right and insert the decimal point in the answer.

$$
\begin{array}{r}
12.5 \quad \leftarrow \text{1 decimal place} \\
\times\ .69 \quad \leftarrow \text{2 decimal places} \\
\hline
1125 \\
750 \quad\ \\
\hline
8.625 \quad \leftarrow \text{3 decimal places}
\end{array}
$$

After using a calculator to solve a problem, check your work using front-end estimation. If the number in the display seems much too large or too small, you probably made a mistake while entering a number.

Calculator: | 1 | 2 | . | 5 | × | . | 6 | 9 | = | ⌷ 8.625 |

Since you are working with money, round up to the nearest cent.

Answer: Alana paid **$8.63** for the turkey.
Check: Use front-end estimation. You know that 10 pounds at 60 cents is $6.00. Since the actual weight and price per pound are greater numbers, you know the correct answer must be a little more than $6.00. Your answer makes sense.

Solving Multi-Step Problems

Many problems that you encounter in life require more than one operation to reach a solution. To answer multi-step problems, focus on the question asked in the problem. Think: *What facts do I need to answer this question?*

Choose the operations needed to solve a problem. There may be more than one way to solve it. Decide what you will do. Then record the results of each step. When working on paper, label each step. Using a calculator, either record the results of each step or use the memory keys as shown in this example.

MATHEMATICS

▶▶ Apply your calculator skills in this situation.

Example: Matt's Little League team needs uniforms. He needs a shirt, pants, a cap, and socks for 12 children. The shirts cost $5.45 each. The pants are $4.95. Caps and socks are $5.25 per child. How much will 12 uniforms cost?

 One way to solve the problem is to multiply each price by 12 and then add to find the total cost for the uniforms. The memory key on your calculator can make the work easier.

Calculator: $\boxed{5}\ \boxed{.}\ \boxed{4}\ \boxed{5}\ \boxed{\times}\ \boxed{1}\ \boxed{2}\ \boxed{=}\ \boxed{\qquad 65.4}\ \boxed{\text{M+}}$

$\boxed{4}\ \boxed{.}\ \boxed{9}\ \boxed{5}\ \boxed{\times}\ \boxed{1}\ \boxed{2}\ \boxed{=}\ \boxed{\qquad 59.4}\ \boxed{\text{M+}}$

$\boxed{5}\ \boxed{.}\ \boxed{2}\ \boxed{5}\ \boxed{\times}\ \boxed{1}\ \boxed{2}\ \boxed{=}\ \boxed{\qquad 63.}\ \boxed{\text{M+}}$

Press $\boxed{\text{MR}}$, which stands for Memory Recall.
The display will show $\boxed{\qquad 187.8}$.

> The $\boxed{\text{M+}}$ key adds the amount in the display to the calculator's memory.
>
> Press $\boxed{\text{MC}}$ to clear your calculator's memory.

Answer: The uniforms will cost **$187.80.** Note that if your calculator does not have memory keys, you can write the results of each step and then add.

Check: Estimate the cost of one complete uniform ($15) and multiply by 12. 15 × 12 = 180. Your answer is reasonable.

SKILL PRACTICE

Use the advertisement to answer the questions below. Use your calculator when necessary.

1. Kim needs 48 feet of lumber. Would it be less expensive to buy 8-inch wide poplar or 6-inch wide oak boards?

2. Maggie needs 7 boards, each 8 feet in length, to build a bookshelf. What will it cost her to build the bookshelf out of poplar boards that are 8 inches wide? *Hint: Figure out how many feet in length Maggie needs in all. Then multiply by the cost per foot.*

HOME WAREHOUSE BOARDS			
Price per Foot			
for Length of Board			
Width	**4-inch**	**6-inch**	**8-inch**
Pine	$0.39	$0.63	$0.79
Oak	$1.80	$2.80	$3.80
Poplar	$1.25	$1.90	$2.65

3. Ray needs 24 feet of lumber to build a printer stand for his home office. He doesn't want to spend more than $70. Can he afford to build the stand out of 8-inch-wide poplar?

4. Pine boards come in 12-foot lengths. A contractor orders 50 pine boards that are 6 inches wide. Which expression could be used to find the total cost of the order?

   (1) 12 × 0.63
   (2) 50 × 0.63
   (3) 12 × 50 × 0.63
   (4) (12 × 0.63) + 50
   (5) (50 × 0.63) + 12

Answers and explanations start on page 311.

WORKPLACE LINK: Neil is checking his pay stub to make sure he was paid the correct wage. He received $308.75 for 32.5 hours of work. To find out how much he was paid per hour, Neil uses his calculator. He enters: 308.75 ÷ 32.5. The display reads 9.5. Neil was paid $9.50 per hour.

Dividing Decimals

The process for dividing decimals is the same as the long-division process you have learned for whole numbers. But before you begin dividing, you need to figure out where to place the decimal point in the quotient.

Use these steps to divide with decimals:

STEP 1. If there are decimal places in the **divisor,** move the decimal point to the right, making the divisor a whole number. Then move the decimal point the same number of places to the right in the **dividend.** Add zeros where needed in the dividend.

STEP 2. Align the decimal point in the quotient with the decimal point in the dividend.

STEP 3. Divide as you would with whole numbers.

▶▶ Study these examples to learn how to place the decimal point in the quotient.

Example 1: The decimal points in the quotient and the dividend are aligned.

$$
\begin{array}{r}
2.7 \\
6\overline{)16.2} \\
-12 \\
\hline
42 \\
-42 \\
\hline
\end{array}
$$

Example 2: Move both decimal points. The quotient is a whole number.

$$
\begin{array}{r}
21. \\
1.4\overline{)29.4} \\
-28 \\
\hline
14 \\
-14 \\
\hline
\end{array}
$$

Example 3: Add zeros to move the decimal point to the right in the dividend.

$$
\begin{array}{r}
120 \\
.05\overline{)6.00} \\
-5 \\
\hline
10 \\
-10 \\
\hline
\end{array}
$$

Add a zero in the quotient to complete the division process.

To divide using a calculator, enter the dividend <u>first</u>.

Example: To divide 6 by 0.05, enter: `6` `÷` `.` `0` `5` `=` [120.]

Decimal division often continues beyond the last digit in the dividend. You bring down the last digit, divide, and still have a remainder. You can continue dividing by adding zeros to the right of the decimal point in the dividend.

But when should you stop dividing? Some decimal divisions go on infinitely. How you handle a remainder depends on the problem you are trying to solve.

To work with decimal remainders:

---

1. Figure out how many decimal places you need in your answer.
2. If you're using paper and pencil, carry out the division one additional place.
3. Round your answer to the place value you need.

Example: The Grahams are trying to save $200 for a family trip that they plan to take in 12 weeks. To the nearest whole dollar, about how much do they need to save each week?

You need to divide 200 by 12 to solve the problem.

After dividing, you have a remainder of 8. Add a 0 after the decimal point in the dividend and continue dividing.

Do you see the pattern in the division? It will continue infinitely.

Answer: Round to the nearest dollar. The Grahams need to save about **$17 per week.** *Check:* Multiply: 12 × $17 = $204. The answer is reasonable.

$$
\begin{array}{r}
16.6 \\
12{\overline{\smash{\big)}\,200.0}} \\
\underline{-12} \\
80 \\
\underline{-72} \\
80 \\
\underline{-72} \\
8
\end{array}
$$

SKILL PRACTICE

Answer the questions. Use your calculator to check your work.

1. Maria drove 210 miles in 3.5 hours. On average, how many miles per hour did she drive? *Hint:* Divide the miles she drove by the time it took to drive them.

2. Reggie is starting his own clothing design company. It takes 2.75 yards of fabric to make one of his new shirt designs. If he has 45 yards of fabric on hand, how many shirts can he make?

3. A 16-acre piece of land is being divided for a housing project. Each building lot will be four-tenths of an acre. How many building lots can be made from the land?

CALCULATOR Connection

When working with decimals, you may sometimes make an entry mistake on your calculator. Do you have to start over again?

Example: You are entering the expression 64.75 + 6.65 − 34.5 into your calculator when you notice on the display that you entered "3.45" instead of "34.5." What is the quickest way to correct your error?

Step 1. Press the CE key or the C key, depending on your calculator. This clears the number being entered but does not clear previously entered numbers.

Step 2. Enter 34.5. Continue with your calculation.

When you take the GED Math Test, a calculator will be provided. You can run this quick test to see how the calculator works. Enter the subtraction problem 10 − 5. Don't press the equals = key. Instead press CE or C and the number 6 . Finally, press = . If the display reads 4, the CE or C key can be used to clear errors. If the display reads 5, the calculator does not clear errors. Try this test now using your own calculator. See pages 337–339 for more help on calculator use.

Answers and explanations start on page 312.

Everyday Decimals

FAMILY LINK: Michael returns from running an errand for his mother. "How much did everything cost?" his mother asks. Michael looks at the receipt and replies, "$14.78." "I would like to have the change back from the $20 bill I gave you," his mother says. "That's about $5!"

Working with Money

Money—we use it almost every day and always wish we had more. Let's take a closer look at the decimals involved as we spend and save money.

dimes   pennies

$14.78

dollars cents

$0.25 = quarter of a dollar
$0.50 = half of a dollar
$0.75 = three-quarters of a dollar
$1.00 = one dollar

Performing calculations with money is the same as working with other decimals:

1. Align the decimal points when adding, subtracting, and dividing.
2. Count the number of decimal places when multiplying.

▶▶ Look at the following information taken from a grocery advertisement.

Example: How much does each of the two boxes of cereal cost? Although the ad says that one box is free, you split the cost between the two boxes to find how much each box cost. Divide the total cost by two since there are two boxes. $3.70 ÷ 2

CRUNCH CEREAL
Buy One
at $3.70,
Get One FREE

When using a calculator, leave off the dollar sign.

Calculator: | 3 | . | 7 | 0 | ÷ | 2 | = | ⟶ | 1.85 |

Answer: At the sale price, each box of cereal costs **$1.85.**
Check: Do the two amounts add up to $3.70? Yes: $1.85 + $1.85 = $3.70.

Working with Time

You can also express time using decimal amounts. Parts of an hour can be broken down into quarters just like money.

0.25   quarter of an hour = 15 minutes
0.5   half an hour = 30 minutes
0.75   three-quarters of an hour = 45 minutes
1.00   one hour = 60 minutes

Decimals are often used to track the amount of service time spent on the installation or repair of items in various service industries. It may help you to remember that every 6 minutes is 0.1, or one-tenth, of an hour.

MATHEMATICS

▸▸ Keep decimal equivalents in mind as you read the following situation.

Example: Mario has his own plumbing business. He charges $38.50 an hour for labor plus materials. His minimum charge is for half an hour's worth of work. His first call was to 346 E. Lansing to take care of a clogged drain. It took him only 15 minutes, and no additional materials were needed.

Which expression shows how Mario could write up the invoice?

    (1)   0.25 + $38.50

    (2)   0.25 × $38.50

    (3)   0.5 + $38.50

    (4)   0.5 × $38.50

    (5)   15 × $38.50

You're right if you chose **(4) 0.5 × $38.50.** It took Mario only 15 minutes to unclog the drain, but his minimum charge is always half an hour. Since the $38.50 rate is for an entire hour, Mario would write the invoice to reflect half that amount: 0.5 × $38.50. (**Note:** $\frac{1}{2} = \frac{5}{10} = 0.5$ hour.)

SKILL PRACTICE

Answer the questions. Use a calculator when necessary.

1. Star Accounting paid $568.75 for computer repairs. If the repair person charges $65 per hour, for how long did she work?

    (1) 6 hours 30 minutes   **(4)** 8 hours 75 minutes

    (2) 8 hours 45 minutes   **(5)** 84.5 hours

    (3) 8.45 hours

2. A repair person charges $70 per hour for labor. Choose the expression that best represents the labor cost for a 45-minute job.

    (1) 45 × 70   **(4)** 0.75 × 70

    (2) 45 + 70   **(5)** 0.75 + 70

    (3) 0.45 × 70

3. Three service calls required the following amounts of labor, respectively: 24 minutes, 2 hours and 30 minutes, and 1 hour and 15 minutes. Which of the following expressions correctly lists these times in decimal form?

    (1) 0.2, 2.3, 1.15   **(4)** 0.4, 2.5, 1.25

    (2) 0.4, 2.3, 1.15   **(5)** 0.5, 2.5, 1.15

    (3) 0.5, 2.5, 1.25

4. Choose three tasks that you do every day. Estimate how much time each task takes. Write each task and the estimated time as a decimal part of an hour.

Answers and explanations start on page 312.

WORKPLACE LINK: As a volunteer with Senior Citizens Services, you track your car's mileage so you can be reimbursed. At the beginning of the day, your car's odometer read 87,659.3. By the end of your volunteer shift, the odometer read 87,731.5. That's 72.2 miles for one shift.

Working with Distance

You will find that many measurements and distances are represented as decimal amounts. For example, the odometer on a vehicle tracks whole miles and tenths of a mile. Metric measurements often use decimal amounts as a means of accurately recording distance.

▶▶ Look at the example of distance and decimals shown below.

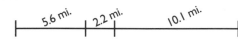

Example 1: This figure shows the length of each segment of a route. The lengths are labeled in miles. To find the total length of the route, add 5.6 + 2.2 + 10.1.

Calculator: $\boxed{5}\,\boxed{.}\,\boxed{6}\,\boxed{+}\,\boxed{2}\,\boxed{.}\,\boxed{2}\,\boxed{+}\,\boxed{1}\,\boxed{0}\,\boxed{.}\,\boxed{1}\,\boxed{=}$ ☐ 17.9

The length of the route is **17.9 mi.**

The measure of the distance around the boundary of an object is called the **perimeter.** If you wanted to fence in a yard or put up a border along the top of the walls of a room, you would need to measure the perimeter.

▶▶ Look at the example of finding the perimeter shown below.

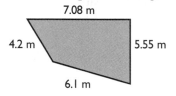

7.08 m
4.2 m
5.55 m
6.1 m

Example 2: This figure is labeled to show the length of each side. In order to find the perimeter of the figure, you add the lengths of the sides together. This gives you the total distance around the figure.

Calculator: $\boxed{4}\,\boxed{.}\,\boxed{2}\,\boxed{+}\,\boxed{7}\,\boxed{.}\,\boxed{0}\,\boxed{8}\,\boxed{+}\,\boxed{5}\,\boxed{.}\,\boxed{5}\,\boxed{5}\,\boxed{+}\,\boxed{6}\,\boxed{.}\,\boxed{1}\,\boxed{=}$ ☐ 22.93

The perimeter is **22.93 m.**
Check: Estimate to see if the answer is reasonable.
4 + 7 + 6 + 6 = 23 Yes, the answer is reasonable.

SKILL PRACTICE

Answer the questions below. Use a calculator when necessary.

1. Write an expression to represent each figure's perimeter. *Do not solve.*

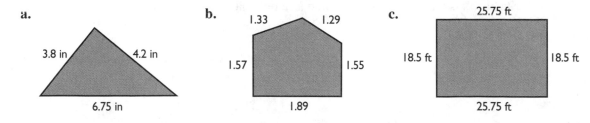

a.
3.8 in   4.2 in
6.75 in

b.
1.33   1.29
1.57   1.55
1.89

c.
25.75 ft
18.5 ft   18.5 ft
25.75 ft

MATHEMATICS

Use the map to answer questions 2 through 5. Distances on the map are given in miles.

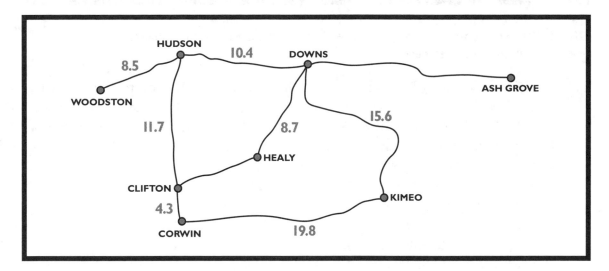

2. Driving through Hudson and Downs, the distance from Woodston to Ash Grove is 39.1 miles. How many miles is it from Downs to Ash Grove?

3. Lee lives in Corwin and works in Kimeo. She works five days a week. How many miles does she drive going to and from work each week?

4. Seung needs to drive from his home in Healy to a job interview in Hudson. If the distance from Healy to Clifton is 7 miles, how much shorter is the route through Clifton than the route through Downs?

5. Using the information from the map and the preceding items, find the shortest route from Downs to Corwin.

PROBLEM SOLVER Connection

Sometimes it helps to **draw a picture** when solving a problem. That way, you have a concrete example that helps you see what you have to do.

Example: On a repeat service call, the repair person took a route different from the original route to the service call. The distance of the original route was 15.8 miles on one road and 3.6 miles on another road. The route taken for the repeat call was 10.9 miles on one road and 11.1 miles on another road. How much longer was the route for the repeat service call?

Step 1. On another sheet of paper draw a picture to show the service call routes. Be sure to label each segment of the route. (The beginning of a drawing is shown here.)

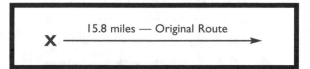

X ———— 15.8 miles — Original Route ————▶

Step 2. Use the picture to organize the information. Then use a calculator to solve the problem. Hint: You need to combine the distances for the repeat call route (10.9 + 11.1), and then subtract the combined distance of the original route (15.8 + 3.6).

How much longer was the route for the repeat service call?

DIRECTIONS: Choose the <u>one best answer</u> to each of the following problems. Use a calculator wherever necessary.

1. In her job at the library, Shaunte put books back on a shelf according to the Dewey Decimal Numbers on their spines. Which of the following lists arranges the numbers from <u>least to greatest</u>?
   (1) 9.13, 9.135, 9.043, 9.058
   (2) 9.043, 9.058, 9.13, 9.135
   (3) 9.135, 9.13, 9.043, 9.058
   (4) 9.13, 9.043, 9.058, 9.135
   (5) 9.135, 9.13, 9.058, 9.043

2. Janelle spent $12.45, $5.92, and $7.02 while shopping. How much did she spend altogether?
   (1) $14.39
   (2) $15.39
   (3) $24.19
   (4) $24.39
   (5) $25.39

3. When Kathy packs grocery bags at Convenience Foods, she knows that the heaviest items should be placed on the bottom of the bag. Based on weight in pounds, in what order should Kathy place items in the bag?
   (1) 0.5, 0.75, 1.1, 1.5, 2.0
   (2) 1.1, 1.5, 2.0, 0.5, 0.75
   (3) 0.5, 1.1, 1.5, 2.0, 0.75
   (4) 0.75, 0.5, 1.1, 1.5, 2.0
   (5) 2.0, 1.5, 1.1, 0.75, 0.5

4. Nathan bought a case of oil as labeled below. If there are twelve quarts in the case, <u>approximately</u> how much did he pay per quart?
   (1) $8.00
   (2) $5.00
   (3) $3.00
   (4) $2.00
   (5) $0.20

5. Claire's boss asked her to cut two equal lengths of pipe 2.2 meters long off a piece of pipe that measures 5 meters long. How many meters of the original pipe is left?
   (1) 7.2
   (2) 4.4
   (3) 2.8
   (4) 2.2
   (5) 0.6

6. Samly bought 20 blank nametags at $0.29 apiece. After adding $0.41 in sales tax, what was the total of the purchase?
   (1) $62.10
   (2) $58.00
   (3) $6.21
   (4) $5.80
   (5) Not enough information is given.

Question 7 is based on the following drawing.

23.9 mi.   7.8 mi.   ?

7. If the total distance shown here is 58.6 mi., how many miles long is the missing distance?
   (1) 7.8
   (2) 23.9
   (3) 26.9
   (4) 31.7
   (5) 58.6

8. A rectangle has a width of 7.8 cm and a length of 11.5 cm. Which expression represents the perimeter of the rectangle?
   (1) 7.8 + 11.5
   (2) 7.8 × 11.5
   (3) 7.8 + 7.8 + 11.5
   (4) 7.8 + 11.5 + 11.5
   (5) 7.8 + 11.5 + 7.8 + 11.5

HIKER	TIME TO WALK PATH
George	3.55 hours
Lucinda	2.25 hours
Drew	2.5 hours
Cessie	3.25 hours
Tyrone	1.75 hours

9. What is the difference in the time Drew and Cessie took to walk the path?
   (1) 0.75 hour
   (2) 1.75 hours
   (3) 3.25 hours
   (4) 5.75 hours
   (5) 7.5 hours

10. Who hiked <u>approximately</u> twice as fast as George?
    (1) Lucinda
    (2) Drew
    (3) Cessie
    (4) Tyrone
    (5) Not enough information is given.

11. If Tyrone began walking at 1:30 P.M., what time did he finish the path?
    (1) 2:45 P.M.
    (2) 3:05 P.M.
    (3) 3:15 P.M.
    (4) 3:25 P.M.
    (5) Not enough information is given.

12. Sally and her nine co-workers gave a party for their boss's birthday. Their expenses totaled $170.10. How much money does each person need to pay as his or her equal share?
    (1) $1701.00
    (2) $170.10
    (3) $18.90
    (4) $17.01
    (5) $1.89

13. The distance between Caitlin's home and work is 4.6 miles. If Caitlin drops her son off on the way to work, she has to drive 3.4 miles to her son's school and then 2.8 miles to work. Which expression shows how much farther she has to drive if she has to drop off her son at school?
    (1) 4.6 − 2.8
    (2) 4.6 − 3.4
    (3) 4.6 + 3.4 + 2.8
    (4) 4.6 − (3.4 + 2.8)
    (5) (3.4 + 2.8) − 4.6

14. Paul runs 45 minutes per day for 5 days per week. How many hours does Paul run per week?
    (1) 1.25
    (2) 2.25
    (3) 3.75
    (4) 4.5
    (5) 5.45

Question 15 is based on the following information.

DONUT DEPOT SPECIAL

I dozen assorted doughnuts
$3.95
Today Only

15. Mark has to buy 60 doughnuts to serve at his store's grand opening. If he shops at Donut Depot, how much will he pay for the doughnuts?
    (1) $11.85
    (2) $19.75
    (3) $23.70
    (4) $24.75
    (5) $27.00

16. Chick paid for 10 large cans of cat food with a $20 bill. Each can cost $0.89. How much change should Chick receive?
    (1) $1.10
    (2) $1.11
    (3) $8.90
    (4) $11.01
    (5) $11.10

Question 17 is based on the following drawing.

17. Jack takes two tablets of the medication shown three times a day. How many milligrams (mg) of the medication does he take in one day?
    (1) 150
    (2) 15
    (3) 7.5
    (4) 6
    (5) Not enough information is given.

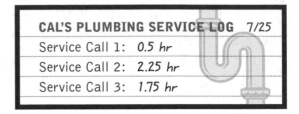

ANTIBIOTIC
60 tablets
2.5 mg each

18. Eva's sailboat travels at a constant speed of 17 miles an hour. <u>Approximately</u> how long in hours would it take to sail 60 miles?
    (1) 0.35
    (2) 2
    (3) 2.5
    (4) 3.5
    (5) 35

19. Tim charges $16 an hour for teaching piano. How much will he be paid for teaching without any breaks from 11:30 A.M. to 1:15 P.M.?
    (1) $24
    (2) $28
    (3) $32
    (4) $44
    (5) Not enough information is given.

Questions 20 through 23 are based on the following table. These are notes from a plumber's log.

CAL'S PLUMBING SERVICE LOG 7/25
Service Call 1: *0.5 hr*
Service Call 2: *2.25 hr*
Service Call 3: *1.75 hr*

20. Altogether, how many hours did the plumber spend on the first three service calls of the day?
    (1) 0.5
    (2) 1.25
    (3) 2.25
    (4) 4.5
    (5) 9

21. If the plumber charges $60 per hour for service, what will be the charge for the third service call?
    (1) $87
    (2) $90
    (3) $102
    (4) $105
    (5) $135

22. The plumber left for the second service call at 9 A.M. If it took 20 minutes to drive to the site of the repair, at what time was the second service call completed?
    (1) 11:25 A.M.
    (2) 11:35 A.M.
    (3) 11:45 A.M.
    (4) 12:05 P.M.
    (5) 12:15 P.M.

23. Service calls 4 and 5 took 0.75 hour each, and service call 6 took 2.25 hours. Which expression could be used to find the total hours spent on service calls 4, 5, and 6?
    (1) 2 × (0.75 + 2.25)
    (2) 0.75 + 2.25 + 2.25
    (3) (2 × 2.25) + 0.75
    (4) 3 × (2.25 + 0.75)
    (5) (2 × 0.75) + 2.25

Answers and explanations start on page 312.

Alternate Math Formats

The questions below are based on the math skills in Programs 28–30.
For more information on answering alternate format items, review pages 20–22.

Grid in the answers to questions 24 through 35.

Question 24 refers to the following information.

COPIER PAPER (price per ream)	
white	$3
color, pastel	$5
color, bright	$8

24. Yael bought 8 reams of white paper and 3 reams of bright blue paper. What was the cost of her purchase before tax?

25. Arie cut two lengths of tubing each 1.3 meters long from a length measuring 4.5 meters. Disregarding waste, what is the length in meters of the remaining piece?

26. Kellie drove 202 miles on 11 gallons of gasoline. To the nearest tenth, how many miles on average did Kellie drive per gallon of gasoline?

Questions 27 and 28 refer to the following information.

THE GREAT LAKES		
Lake	Area (sq mi)	Depth (ft)
Superior	31,700	1,333
Michigan	22,300	923
Huron	23,000	750
Erie	9,910	210
Ontario	7,340	802

27. How much deeper in feet is Lake Superior than Lake Huron?

28. What is the area of Lake Superior rounded to the nearest thousand?

29. Name a decimal that is between 6.4 and 6.5.

30. A calculator display reads 5.59432. Round to the nearest tenth.

31. Lee drove 28 miles each way to and from work. If he worked 5 days last week, how many total miles did he drive to and from work?

32. Hanna is a basketball referee at a city park. She is paid $15 per game. If she works 3 games on Saturday and 4 games on Sunday, how much will she earn?

33. A calculator display reads 0.09375. Round the number to the nearest hundredth.

Questions 34 and 35 refer to the following information.

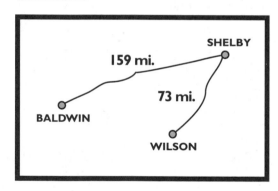

34. Oscar drove from Shelby to Baldwin in 2 hours and 30 minutes. To the nearest whole number, how many miles per hour did he average for the trip? (*Hint:* Use the formula $d = rt$.)

35. Oscar lives in Shelby and works in Wilson. He makes the commute from Shelby to Wilson and back five days a week. How many total miles does he drive each week going to and from work?

Answers and explanations start on page 313.

MATHEMATICS

Afraid of fractions? As you'll see in this program, there's no reason to be. They're just another way to write number values. A chef, musicians, math teachers, and GED learners help you understand and use fractions, common denominators, and factors.

Fractions

OBJECTIVES

1. Explore the meaning and size of fractions.
2. Add, subtract, multiply, and divide fractions.
3. Solve problems with everyday fractions.

The next time you go to a store, read a newspaper, or follow the instructions on a food package, think about the fractions you see each day. A product label advertises "$\frac{1}{3}$ More Free." A sale rack boasts "All Items— $\frac{1}{2}$ price." You measure $1\frac{3}{4}$ cups of flour for a recipe. In each of these examples, the fractions show part of something.

The ability to work with fractions is important to your success on the GED Math Test. You will need to know how to perform basic operations with fractions—adding, subtracting, multiplying, and dividing. Your knowledge of decimals will help you estimate answers and check your work using a calculator. Your understanding of fractions will help you master other math skills in the areas of percent, ratio and proportion, measurement, and algebra.

On the following pages, you will find a brief exercise called *Sneak Preview*. It is designed to introduce you to the topics that will be featured in the video program and the corresponding lesson. After you complete the exercise and check your answers, turn to the vocabulary page. There you will find terms that will help you better understand the video and the lesson that follow. After reviewing page 88, you will be ready to watch Program 31.

For additional practice, visit *LiteracyLink* online at http://www.pbs.org/literacy.

Sneak Preview

This exercise previews some of the concepts from Program 31. After you answer the questions, use the feedback on page 87 to help set your learning goals.

COMMUNITY LINK: Tom and Joe volunteer to build six lounging chairs for the Sycamore Recreation Center. Looking for ideas in a hobby magazine, Tom finds a plan for building a sling chair out of plastic pipe and canvas. The brothers will follow the materials list and diagrams in the magazine.

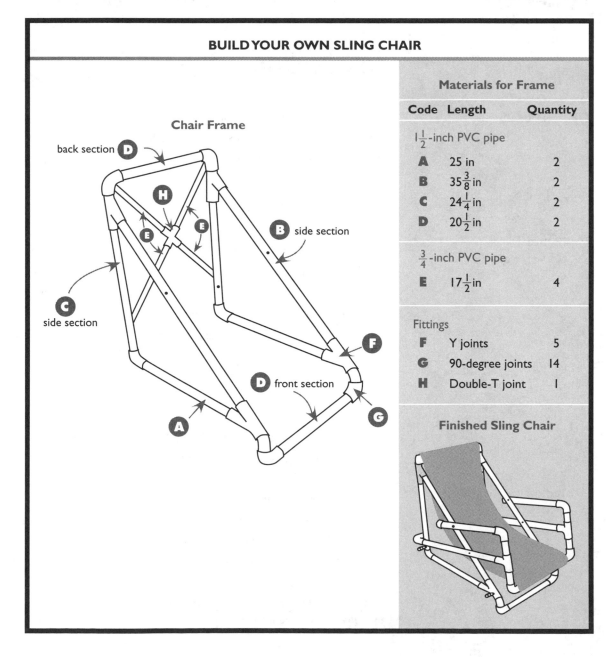

BUILD YOUR OWN SLING CHAIR

Chair Frame

back section **D**

H

E

E

B side section

C

side section

A

D front section

F

G

Materials for Frame

Code	Length	Quantity
$1\frac{1}{2}$-inch PVC pipe		
A	25 in	2
B	$35\frac{3}{8}$ in	2
C	$24\frac{1}{4}$ in	2
D	$20\frac{1}{2}$ in	2
$\frac{3}{4}$-inch PVC pipe		
E	$17\frac{1}{2}$ in	4
Fittings		
F	Y joints	5
G	90-degree joints	14
H	Double-T joint	1

Finished Sling Chair

Answer these questions based on the information shown.

1. Joe needs enough $\frac{3}{4}$-inch pipe for six chairs. Which expression represents how much $\frac{3}{4}$-inch pipe he should buy?

   (1) $\frac{3}{4} \times 4 \times 6$
   (2) $\frac{3}{4} \times 17\frac{1}{2} \times 6$
   (3) $\frac{3}{4} \times 17\frac{1}{2} \times 4 \times 6$
   (4) $17\frac{1}{2} \times 4$
   (5) $17\frac{1}{2} \times 4 \times 6$

2. After cutting some $1\frac{1}{2}$-inch pipe, Tom has a leftover piece that is 42 inches long. Which pipe or pipes can Tom cut from this piece, resulting in the least amount of waste?

   (1) One "A" pipe
   (2) One "B" pipe
   (3) Two "C" pipes
   (4) Two "D" pipes
   (5) Not enough information is given.

3. At a plumbing supply store, Joe finds some double-T joint fittings for 1/3 off the original price of $3.12 each. <u>Approximately</u> how much will Joe pay for each double-T joint at the sale price?

   (1) $2.50
   (2) $2.00
   (3) $1.50
   (4) $1.00
   (5) $.50

Feedback

- If you got all of the answers right...   you have a good basic understanding of fraction calculations and problem solving.

- If you missed question 1...   you need to work on your understanding of multiplication skills and solution setups.

- If you missed question 2...   you need to work on your fraction subtraction skills and multi-step problem solving.

- If you missed question 3...   you need to work on how to estimate with fractions and how to find discounts.

Vocabulary for *Fractions*

canceling	a shortcut procedure for multiplying fractions in which you factor out the same number from a numerator and denominator to make the multiplication simpler
common denominator	a number that each denominator in a problem can divide into evenly
denominator	the number on the bottom of a fraction; tells into how many parts the whole has been divided
equivalent fractions	different fractions that name the same number; for example, $\frac{3}{6}$ and $\frac{1}{2}$
improper fraction	a fraction that names a number equal to or greater than 1; the numerator is equal to or greater than the denominator; for example, $\frac{7}{6}$
like fractions	fractions that have the same denominator
lowest common denominator	the smallest number that two or more denominators will divide into evenly
mixed number	a number that has both a whole number and a fractional part; for example, $1\frac{1}{2}$
numerator	the number on the top of a fraction; tells how many parts of the whole are used
proper fraction	a fraction that names a number less than 1; the numerator is less than the denominator; for example, $\frac{1}{2}$
raising to higher terms	finding an equivalent fraction with a higher numerator and denominator by multiplying by a fraction equivalent to 1; for example, $\frac{2}{3} \times \frac{4}{4} = \frac{8}{12}$
reciprocal	the result of inverting the numbers in a fraction; for example, the reciprocal of $\frac{3}{4}$ is $\frac{4}{3}$
reducing to lowest terms	writing an equivalent fraction using smaller numbers so that the numerator and denominator of the fraction have no common factors other than 1; for example, $\frac{6}{12} \div \frac{6}{6} = \frac{1}{2}$

➡ **NOW WATCH PROGRAM 31:**

The program concentrates on helping you understand what fractions represent. The host and interview subjects will help you review how to calculate with fractions—but extensive practice is up to you.

After you watch the program, work on:

- pages 89–106 in this workbook
- Internet activities at http://www.pbs.org/literacy

MATHEMATICS

31

Fractions

On the following pages, you will learn more about the ideas discussed in the video program and have an opportunity to develop and practice your GED math skills.

Key Points to Think About

In the video program, you explored:
- How people use fractions in their daily lives as workers, citizens, and family members.
- How fractions are used to represent the dividing of objects or groups into parts.
- Everyday fractions such as those that deal with money, time, and measurement.

On the GED Math Test:
- You will be expected to know how to add, subtract, multiply, and divide with fractions.
- You should know how to write equivalent fractions and change fractions to decimals.
- You will work with fractions a great deal, especially when working with ratio and proportion and measurement problems.

As you work through the lesson for Program 31:
- Think about the relationship between the numbers in a fraction to understand the size of the fraction and the quantity it represents.
- Make sure to reduce your answers to lowest terms, since all answer choices on the GED Math Test are written in lowest terms.
- Be aware of the fraction skills you can use in your daily life, not just on the GED Math Test.

Basic Operations with Fractions

WORKPLACE LINK: Robert works for a restaurant. His manager wants to know what fraction of the restaurant's customers pay with a credit card. Of the 24 customers during Monday's dinner hour, 12 paid with a credit card. Using his knowledge of fractions, Robert reports that $\frac{1}{2}$ of the customers paid with a credit card.

Understanding Fractions

A fraction can show part of a whole, part of a group, or a division problem.

$\frac{5}{8}$ of the rectangle is shaded.

$\frac{2}{5}$ of the circles are shaded.

$\frac{3}{4}$ means $3 \div 4$.

$\dfrac{3}{4}$ The fraction bar means "divided by."

The two numbers in a fraction are called terms. The bottom term, called the **denominator,** tells you how many parts an object or group is divided into. The top term, or **numerator,** tells you how many of those parts are represented by the fraction.

$\dfrac{5 \longleftarrow \text{numerator}}{6 \longleftarrow \text{denominator}}$

Reducing Fractions

Fractions are easier to understand when they are written with smaller numbers. At the restaurant, Robert knew that $\frac{12}{24}$ of the customers used a credit card, but he reported the fraction as $\frac{1}{2}$.

$\frac{12}{24}$ and $\frac{1}{2}$ are **equivalent fractions** because they have the same value. Of the 24 circles shown here, 12 are shaded. As you can see, the shaded portion is $\frac{1}{2}$ of the total.

Reducing to lowest terms means writing an equivalent fraction with a numerator and denominator that have no common factors other than 1. Robert reduced $\frac{12}{24}$ to $\frac{1}{2}$.

> **To reduce a fraction to lowest terms:**
>
> 1. Divide both the numerator and the denominator by the same number.
> 2. Will another number divide evenly into both terms in the new fraction? If the answer is yes, repeat step 1. If not, the fraction is in lowest terms.

Examples: $\dfrac{12 \div 12}{24 \div 12} = \dfrac{1}{2}$ $\dfrac{4 \div 2}{6 \div 2} = \dfrac{2}{3}$ $\dfrac{24 \div 2}{42 \div 2} = \dfrac{12 \div 3}{21 \div 3} = \dfrac{4}{7}$

On the GED Math Test, the answer choices are written in lowest terms. If you finish your calculations and don't find your answer among the choices, make sure your answer is reduced to lowest terms.

Adding and Subtracting Like Fractions

Before you add or subtract whole numbers or decimals, you have to line up the columns so that you are adding ones to ones, tenths to tenths, and so on. In the same way, you have to make sure that when adding or subtracting fractions, the denominators are alike. **Like fractions** have the same denominator.

To add or subtract like fractions:

1. Add or subtract the numerators of the fractions.
2. Write the sum or difference over the denominator.
3. Reduce the result if you can.

▶▶ Look at the following sign posted for bird-watchers.

Example: Omar plans to take Trail 1 in the morning and Trail 2 in the afternoon. How far will he walk in all?

Step 1. Add the numerators: $\frac{1}{10} + \frac{3}{10} = \frac{4}{10}$

Step 2. Reduce the answer: $\frac{4}{10} \div \frac{2}{2} = \frac{2}{5}$

Omar will walk a total of $\frac{2}{5}$ **of a mile.**

SUN CREEK TRAILS

Trail 1: $\frac{1}{10}$ mile

Trail 2: $\frac{3}{10}$ mile

Trail 3: $\frac{9}{10}$ mile

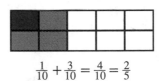

$\frac{1}{10} + \frac{3}{10} = \frac{4}{10} = \frac{2}{5}$

▶▶ Subtraction works the same way.

Example: Find the difference in miles between Trail 3 and Trail 1.

Step 1. Subtract the numerators: $\frac{9}{10} - \frac{1}{10} = \frac{8}{10}$

Step 2. Reduce the answer: $\frac{8}{10} \div \frac{2}{2} = \frac{4}{5}$

The difference is $\frac{4}{5}$ **of a mile.**

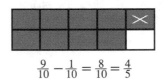

$\frac{9}{10} - \frac{1}{10} = \frac{8}{10} = \frac{4}{5}$

SKILL PRACTICE

Solve each problem. Reduce your answers to lowest terms.

1. $\frac{1}{4} + \frac{2}{4} =$

2. $\frac{3}{5} + \frac{1}{5} =$

3. $\frac{2}{9} + \frac{4}{9} =$

4. $\frac{11}{12} - \frac{7}{12} =$

5. $\frac{7}{8} - \frac{3}{8} =$

6. $\frac{11}{20} - \frac{6}{20} =$

7. Chris has to drive from Fort Wayne to Danville, a distance of about 200 miles. She stops after 50 miles to fill up her car with gasoline. What fraction of the trip has she driven?

8. Bill bought 2 gallons of enamel paint for trim and 10 gallons of exterior latex paint. Of his total purchase, what fraction was enamel paint? (*Hint:* First find the total number of gallons purchased. Then write the fraction.)

FAMILY LINK: Fabio bought one pound each of ground beef and ground turkey to make hamburgers for his family. Afterwards, he estimated that he had $\frac{1}{3}$ pound of ground beef left and $\frac{1}{4}$ pound of ground turkey. To find out how many pounds of meat are left over, he needs to add $\frac{1}{4}$ and $\frac{1}{3}$.

Adding and Subtracting Unlike Fractions

You can't add $\frac{1}{3}$ and $\frac{1}{4}$ as written because the parts aren't the same size.

To add $\frac{1}{3}$ and $\frac{1}{4}$, you need to write the fractions with a **common denominator,** a number that each denominator in the problem can divide into evenly. The **lowest common denominator** is the smallest number that both denominators will divide into evenly.

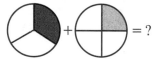

You can find the lowest common denominator by thinking of the multiples of the denominators.

- The multiples of 3 are 3, 6, 9, **12,** 15, and so on.
- The multiples of 4 are 4, 8, **12,** 16, and so on.
- The *first* (or *lowest*) multiple that both numbers have in common is 12.

Now you need to change $\frac{1}{3}$ and $\frac{1}{4}$ to fractions with a denominator of 12. You need to raise both fractions to higher terms.

> **Raising to higher terms is the opposite of reducing. Follow these steps:**
>
> 1. *Think:* By what number do I need to multiply the old denominator to get the new denominator?
> 2. Multiply both the numerator and the denominator by that number.

Step 1. Raise $\frac{1}{3}$ and $\frac{1}{4}$ to equivalent fractions with a denominator of 12.

$$\frac{1 \times 4}{3 \times 4} = \frac{4}{12} \qquad \frac{1 \times 3}{4 \times 3} = \frac{3}{12}$$

Step 2. Now you can add.

$$\frac{4}{12} + \frac{3}{12} = \frac{7}{12}$$

Answer: The sum of $\frac{1}{3}$ and $\frac{1}{4}$ is $\frac{7}{12}$.

Remember this important principle: If you multiply or divide both terms in a fraction by the same number, the result will always be an equivalent fraction.

▶▶ Use the same rules to solve a subtraction problem.

Example: A cookie recipe calls for $\frac{7}{8}$ cup of sugar of which $\frac{1}{4}$ cup is used to make a cream filling. The rest is put into the cookie dough. What fraction of a cup of sugar is used in the dough?

Step 1. Find the common denominator for 4 and 8.

Step 2. Raise $\frac{1}{4}$ to a fraction with a denominator of 8.

Step 3. Subtract: $\frac{7}{8} - \frac{2}{8} = \frac{5}{8}$.

Since 8 is a multiple of 4, 8 is the lowest common denominator.

$$\frac{1 \times 2}{4 \times 2} = \frac{2}{8}$$

Answer: $\frac{5}{8}$ **cup** of sugar is used in the dough.

MATHEMATICS

Improper Fractions and Mixed Numbers

The fractions you have seen so far are proper fractions. A **proper fraction** is less than 1. In a proper fraction, the numerator is less than the denominator.

An **improper fraction** is equal to or greater than 1. In an improper fraction, the numerator is equal to or greater than the denominator. You can rewrite an improper fraction as either a whole number or a mixed number. A **mixed number** has both a whole number and a fraction.

Examples:  $\frac{8}{8} = 1$ 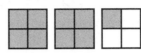 $\frac{9}{4} = 2\frac{1}{4}$

If the answer to a problem is an improper fraction, you will probably need to rewrite it as a mixed number. Follow these steps:

1. Divide the numerator by the denominator.
2. If there is a remainder, write it over the denominator.
2. Always reduce fractions to lowest terms.

Example: Teresa has $\frac{7}{8}$, $\frac{3}{4}$, and $\frac{5}{8}$ yards of fabric. How many yards does she have in all?

Step 1. Raise the fraction $\frac{3}{4}$ so that it has a denominator of 8. $\frac{3}{4} \times \frac{2}{2} = \frac{6}{8}$

Step 2. Add the three amounts. $\frac{7}{8} + \frac{6}{8} + \frac{5}{8} = \frac{18}{8}$

Step 3. Rewrite $\frac{18}{8}$ as a mixed number. Divide. $18 \div 8 = 2\ r2$

Step 4. Write the remainder 2 over the denominator 8 and reduce. $2\frac{2}{8} = 2\frac{1}{4}$

Answer: Teresa has **$2\frac{1}{4}$ yards** of fabric.

SKILL PRACTICE

Solve each problem. Reduce your answer to lowest terms.

1. $\frac{1}{2} + \frac{3}{10} =$

2. $\frac{5}{8} + \frac{1}{3} + \frac{1}{6} =$

3. $\frac{2}{3} + \frac{5}{6} + \frac{3}{4} =$

4. $\frac{5}{8} - \frac{1}{4} =$

5. $\frac{4}{5} - \frac{1}{3} =$

6. $\frac{7}{9} - \frac{1}{2} =$

7. Arlene adjusted the size of a border for a picture until it looked right to her. Using the information in the table, what was the <u>total width</u> of the border?

   (1) $+2\frac{3}{8}$
   (2) $+2\frac{3}{16}$
   (3) $+2$
   (4) $+1\frac{11}{16}$
   (5) $+1\frac{1}{2}$

CHANGE
$+\frac{5}{16}$
$+\frac{1}{4}$
$+\frac{3}{8}$
$+\frac{3}{4}$

COMMUNITY LINK: Lydia is gathering the materials she needs to help her local Cub Scout troop learn to tie knots. She plans to buy enough cotton rope so that each scout will have $\frac{3}{4}$ yard of rope. The den leader tells Lydia to buy enough for 32 scouts. Lydia multiplies 32 by $\frac{3}{4}$ to find out how many yards of rope to buy.

Multiplying Fractions

Multiplying fractions is simpler than adding or subtracting fractions because you don't need to find a common denominator. Just multiply the numerators, then the denominators, and reduce your answer.

> Problems that ask for a "fraction of" require you to multiply.
>
> $\frac{1}{2}$ of 4 means $\frac{1}{2} \times 4$

Example: What is $\frac{1}{2}$ of $\frac{2}{3}$?

$$\frac{2}{3} \times \frac{1}{2} = \frac{2 \times 1}{3 \times 2} = \frac{2}{6} = \frac{1}{3}$$

Did you notice that the answer $\frac{1}{3}$ is smaller than either of the numbers in the problem? When you multiply a number by a proper fraction, the answer is smaller than the number.

You may remember a shortcut called **canceling** for multiplying fractions. To cancel, look for opportunities to divide a numerator and a denominator by the same number *before multiplying*. Sometimes you can cancel several times within the same problem.

Example: Find the product of $\frac{3}{8}$ and $\frac{1}{9}$.

$$\frac{\overset{1}{\cancel{3}}}{8} \times \frac{1}{\underset{3}{\cancel{9}}} = \frac{1}{24}$$

3 goes into 3 one time
3 goes into 9 three times

The answer is the same even if you don't cancel: $\frac{3}{8} \times \frac{1}{9} = \frac{3}{72}$, which reduces to $\frac{1}{24}$.

You can also multiply fractions by whole numbers and mixed numbers. To multiply a fraction by a whole number, rewrite the whole number as a fraction with a denominator of 1.

Example: Find out how much rope Lydia bought by multiplying 32 by $\frac{3}{4}$.

$$32 \times \frac{3}{4} = \frac{32}{1} \times \frac{3}{4} = \frac{\overset{8}{\cancel{32}}}{1} \times \frac{3}{\underset{1}{\cancel{4}}} = \frac{24}{1} = 24$$

Answer: Lydia bought **24 yards** of rope.

Before multiplying by a mixed number, rewrite it as an improper fraction. Follow these steps:

1. Multiply the whole number part by the denominator of the fraction.
2. Add the result to the numerator of the fraction.
3. Write the result over the denominator.

Example: What is $\frac{1}{4}$ of $3\frac{1}{2}$?

Step 1. Change $3\frac{1}{2}$ to an improper fraction

$$3\frac{1}{2} = \frac{(3 \times 2) + 1}{2} = \frac{7}{2}$$

Step 2. Multiply to find $\frac{1}{4}$ of $\frac{7}{2}$.

$$\frac{7}{2} \times \frac{1}{4} = \frac{7}{8}$$

Dividing Fractions

Before dividing by a fraction, you need to rewrite the problem as multiplication.

To divide by a fraction:

1. Write the problem so that the number being divided comes first.
2. Change any mixed numbers or whole numbers to improper fractions.
3. Change the division sign to multiplication *and* invert the second fraction to form its **reciprocal.** To invert a fraction, turn it upside down.
4. Multiply. Then reduce the answer to lowest terms.

▶▶ See how multiplication is used to solve this division problem.

Example: How many people will 6 large pizzas feed if each person eats about $\frac{1}{4}$ of a pizza?

Step 1. Write the problem. You need to divide 6 by $\frac{1}{4}$ $6 \div \frac{1}{4} =$

Step 2. Change mixed or whole numbers to improper fractions. $6 \div \frac{1}{4} = \frac{6}{1} \div \frac{1}{4}$

Step 3. Change $\times$ to $\div$. Invert the second fraction to form its **reciprocal.** $\frac{6}{1} \div \frac{1}{4} = \frac{6}{1} \times \frac{4}{1}$

Step 4. Multiply and reduce. $\frac{6}{1} \times \frac{4}{1} = \frac{24}{1} = 24$

Answer: Six pizzas will feed **24** guests.

SKILL PRACTICE

Solve each problem. Reduce your answer to lowest terms.

1. $\frac{5}{6} \times \frac{4}{15} =$

2. $\frac{7}{8} \times \frac{2}{7} =$

3. $\frac{2}{3} \times \frac{5}{6} \times \frac{9}{10} =$

4. $\frac{5}{8} \div \frac{1}{4} =$

5. $10 \div \frac{1}{3} =$

6. $6\frac{1}{2} \div \frac{1}{4} =$

Refer to page 339 to learn how to use the fraction keys on the Casio *fx*-260.

---

7. How many $2\frac{1}{2}$-foot lengths can be cut from a 16-foot board?

SCIENCE Connection

Compatible numbers can help you quickly form an estimate.

Example: The Eagle Watch Project bands eagles to monitor migration patterns. At the Alpine Station, scientists observed 12 out of 25 banded eagles had returned to their station. About what fraction of the eagles had returned?

The fraction $\frac{12}{25}$ is very close to the fraction $\frac{12}{24}$, which equals $\frac{1}{2}$. About $\frac{1}{2}$ of the eagles returned to the station.

Try this: At Sundance Station, 39 out of 50 eagles returned. **What common fraction could be used to express about what fraction of the eagles returned?** *Hint:* Look for numbers close to 39 and 50 that are easier to work with.

Problem Solving with Fractions

 **FAMILY LINK:** For one of her night classes, Nita had to choose a stock and follow its value over two weeks. On Monday, Nita read in the newspaper that the stock she chose was $18\frac{3}{8}$ per share. On Tuesday, the stock dropped $2\frac{3}{4}$ points. To find out her stock's new value, she needs to subtract.

Working with Mixed Numbers

A mixed number has both a whole number and a fraction part. When you add or subtract mixed numbers, you work with each part separately. Finally, you combine and simplify the results. Sometimes, you will need to regroup, meaning to carry or borrow a quantity from one column to another.

$$\begin{array}{r} 13\frac{3}{8} \\ + 5\frac{1}{8} \\ \hline 18\frac{4}{8} = 18\frac{1}{2} \end{array}$$ ←— Reduce.

↑ ↑
Add whole   Add fractions.
numbers.

▶▶ Read the steps for adding mixed numbers. Then study the example.

Example: $9\frac{5}{6} + 2\frac{3}{4} =$

$$\begin{array}{r} 9\frac{5}{6} = 9\frac{10}{12} \\ + 2\frac{3}{4} = 2\frac{9}{12} \\ \hline 11\frac{19}{12} = 11 + 1\frac{7}{12} = 12\frac{7}{12} \end{array}$$

The improper fraction $\frac{19}{12}$ is equal to $1\frac{7}{12}$.

To add mixed numbers:
1. If necessary, find the common denominator and rewrite all fractions as like fractions.
2. Add the whole numbers and fractions separately.
3. If the sum of the fractions is an improper fraction, change it to a mixed number and add it to the whole number sum.
4. Make sure your answer is reduced to lowest terms.

Answer: $12\frac{7}{12}$

Check: You can estimate an answer by adding the whole numbers. Since $9 + 2$ is 11, the answer should be close to 11. The answer $12\frac{7}{12}$ makes sense.

▶▶ Apply the rules for subtracting mixed numbers in Nita's situation.

Example: To find the price per share of her stock at the end of Tuesday, Nita needs to subtract $2\frac{3}{4}$ from $18\frac{3}{8}$.

Regroup by borrowing 1 from 18.
Think: $1 = \frac{8}{8}$. $\frac{3}{8} + \frac{8}{8} = \frac{11}{8}$

$$\begin{array}{r} 17\frac{11}{8} \\ 18\frac{3}{8} = 18\frac{3}{8} = \cancel{18}\cancel{\frac{3}{8}} \\ - 2\frac{3}{4} = - 2\frac{6}{8} = - 2\frac{6}{8} \\ \hline 15\frac{5}{8} \end{array}$$

To subtract mixed numbers:
1. Change to like fractions, if necessary.
2. If the fraction being subtracted is the greater fraction, regroup. Borrow 1 from the top whole number. Write it as an improper fraction with the same denominator. Add it to the top fraction.
3. Subtract the fractions first, then the whole numbers. Reduce if necessary.

Answer: The current value of Nita's stock is **$15\frac{5}{8}$ per share.**

Check: Subtract the whole numbers: $18 - 2 = 16$. Your answer is reasonable.

You have already learned to change mixed numbers to improper fractions before you multiply or divide them. If you need to review, the steps for changing a mixed number to an improper fraction are given on page 94.

Choosing the Correct Operation

Now that you know how to add, subtract, multiply, and divide fractions and mixed numbers, you need to focus on learning when to use each operation. Sometimes, the fractions make it difficult to see which operation is needed.

▶▶ Think about which operation you would use in this situation.

Example: For a community party, Nell is filling bags with candy for party favors. Which expression could you use to find out how many $\frac{1}{4}$-pound bags she can make from a $10\frac{1}{2}$-pound bag?

(1) $10\frac{1}{2} + \frac{1}{4}$ (4) $10\frac{1}{2} \div \frac{1}{4}$

(2) $10\frac{1}{2} - \frac{1}{4}$ (5) $\frac{1}{4} \div 10\frac{1}{2}$

(3) $10\frac{1}{2} \times \frac{1}{4}$

You're right if you chose **(4) $10\frac{1}{2} \div \frac{1}{4}$**. You need to divide $10\frac{1}{2}$ by $\frac{1}{4}$ to find the answer. But how do you know to divide?

A situation is sometimes easier to analyze when you replace the fractions with whole numbers. *Think: How many 2-pound bags could Nell make from 10 pounds?* You can easily see that she could make 5. *Now ask yourself: What operation did I use to solve that?* You divided 10 by 2, so you know that this problem can be solved by dividing. Do the work with the original numbers.

$$10\frac{1}{2} \div \frac{1}{4} = \frac{21}{2} \div \frac{1}{4} = \frac{21}{2} \times \frac{4}{1} = \frac{84}{2} = \frac{42}{1} = 42 \text{ bags}$$

SKILL PRACTICE

Choose the expression that could be used to answer each item.

1. Shipping charges are based on weight. Max is shipping 4 items, each weighing $2\frac{5}{8}$ pounds. What is the total weight of the shipment in pounds?

   (1) $4 + 2\frac{5}{8}$ (4) $4 \times 2\frac{5}{8}$

   (2) $4 - 2\frac{5}{8}$ (5) $4 \div 2\frac{5}{8}$

   (3) $4\frac{5}{8} - 2$

2. Jan is making cloth picture frames for gifts. If each frame requires $\frac{3}{4}$ yard of fabric, how many frames can she make from $30\frac{1}{2}$ yards of fabric?

   (1) $30\frac{1}{2} + \frac{3}{4}$ (4) $30\frac{1}{2} \div \frac{3}{4}$

   (2) $30\frac{1}{2} - \frac{3}{4}$ (5) $30 \times (\frac{1}{2} + \frac{3}{4})$

   (3) $30\frac{1}{2} \times \frac{3}{4}$

3. At a hardware store, a spool of metal chain holds 50 yards. After sales of $2\frac{3}{4}$ yards and $5\frac{2}{3}$ yards, how many yards of chain remain on the spool?

   (1) $50 + 2\frac{3}{4} + 5\frac{2}{3}$ (4) $50 \times 2\frac{3}{4} \times 5\frac{2}{3}$

   (2) $50 - (2\frac{3}{4} + 5\frac{2}{3})$ (5) $50 \div (2\frac{3}{4} + 5\frac{2}{3})$

   (3) $50 \times (2\frac{3}{4} + 5\frac{2}{3})$

FAMILY LINK: Kina is preparing a budget for her family. She wants to spend no more than $\frac{1}{5}$ of her income on food for her 3-person family. She brings home $449.50 each week. To figure out how much of her check she can spend on food, she needs to find $\frac{1}{5}$ of $449.50.

Equivalent Fractions and Decimals

Fractions and decimals are both ways of expressing part of a whole. Understanding how fractions and decimals are related can make your work easier.

Example: Kina needs to multiply $449.50 by $\frac{1}{5}$. If Kina knows that $\frac{1}{5}$ is equal to 0.2, she can easily do the work on the calculator.

Calculator: | 4 | 4 | 9 | . | 5 | × | . | 2 | = | [89.9]

Answer: $\frac{1}{5}$ of $449.50 is **$89.90.**

You can change a fraction to a decimal by dividing the numerator by the denominator. Think of the fraction bar as a division sign. $\frac{5}{8}$ means $5 \div 8$.

Changing fractions to decimals is an ideal use for your calculator. The long-division process takes time and your time on the GED Math Test is limited. If you need to change a fraction to a decimal, use your calculator to do the division whenever possible.

$$
\begin{array}{r}
0.625 \\
8\overline{)5.000} \\
-4\,8 \\
\hline
20 \\
-16 \\
\hline
40 \\
-40 \\
\hline
0
\end{array}
$$

Calculator: | 5 | ÷ | 8 | = | [0.625]

You can also change a decimal to a fraction. Use the decimal number without the decimal point as the numerator; use the name of the place value of the last digit as the denominator. Finally, reduce the fraction.

▶▶ Changing the decimal to a fraction makes the work easier in this situation.

Example: Mike earns about $20,000 per year before taxes. He read in a magazine article that he should expect to spend about 0.25 of his income on housing. According to the article, what amount should he spend on housing?

Instead of multiplying 20,000 by 0.25, change 0.25 to a fraction.

$0.25 = \frac{25}{100}$ ◀———— The number without the decimal point
◀———— The last digit of the decimal is in the hundredths place.

Reduce: $\frac{25}{100} = \frac{1}{4}$

Mike can easily find $\frac{1}{4}$ of 20,000 by dividing by 4: $20,000 \div 4 = 5,000$.
Answer: $5,000

Check: Does $5,000 \times 4$ equal 20,000? Yes.

> Refer to page 336 of the Math Handbook for common fraction and decimal equivalences.

The table below shows the fractions that you will use most often in life and on the GED Math Test. Memorize their decimal equivalencies. Then you can decide whether a problem can be more easily solved by using fractions or decimals. Always choose the way that seems easier to you.

Common Fractions and Decimal Equivalencies

$\frac{1}{8}$	$\frac{1}{5}$	$\frac{1}{4}$	$\frac{1}{3}$	$\frac{3}{8}$	$\frac{2}{5}$	$\frac{1}{2}$	$\frac{2}{3}$	$\frac{5}{8}$	$\frac{3}{4}$	$\frac{4}{5}$	$\frac{7}{8}$	$\frac{9}{10}$
0.125	0.2	0.25	about 0.33	0.375	0.4	0.5	about 0.67	0.625	0.75	0.8	0.875	0.9

▶▶ In this situation, decimal equivalencies are used to compare fractions.

Example: Which is greater, $\frac{5}{16}$ or $\frac{1}{3}$?

Use a calculator to convert $\frac{5}{16}$ to a decimal.

Calculator: 5 ÷ 1 6 = 0.3125

You can see from the table that $\frac{1}{3}$ is equal to about 0.33.

Answer: $\frac{1}{3} > \frac{5}{16}$ because 0.33 > 0.3125.

> For a review of inequality signs, refer to page 32.

SKILL PRACTICE

Solve each problem. Use your calculator when necessary.

1. Which is greater? $\frac{3}{4}$ or $\frac{5}{7}$?

2. Which is less? $\frac{1}{3}$ or $\frac{3}{10}$?

3. At Ray's company, 16 out of 20 workers ride in a carpool to work.

   a. What fraction of the workers carpool?
   b. Write the decimal equivalent.

4. Is the decimal $\frac{4}{7}$ closer in value to $\frac{1}{2}$ or $\frac{7}{8}$? *Hint:* Change the fractions to decimals and compare decimals.

5. Sharon worked 12 hours to paint her garage. She estimates that she spent $\frac{3}{4}$ of her time patching and sanding. How could you find $\frac{3}{4}$ of 12 using a calculator?

CALCULATOR Connection

You can use your calculator to solve many problems involving fractions.

Example: During the week, Marisol worked $\frac{3}{4}$ hour of overtime on Monday and $1\frac{3}{8}$ hours of overtime on Thursday. What was the total amount of overtime?

Step 1. Change $\frac{3}{4}$ to a decimal. $3 \div 4 = 0.75$
Step 2. Change the fractional part of $1\frac{3}{8}$ to a decimal. $3 \div 8 = 0.375$. The mixed number would be written 1.375.
Step 3. Use your calculator to add the decimals: $0.75 + 1.375 = 2.125$.
Step 4. Using the table above, $0.125 = \frac{1}{8}$, so the answer is $2\frac{1}{8}$ hours.

The next week Marisol worked $1\frac{1}{2}$ hours of overtime on Monday and $2\frac{7}{8}$ hours on Friday.
Find the total overtime for that week.

Everyday Fractions

WORKPLACE LINK: Marcus works as a salesperson at Pelts' Electronics. The store is currently having a $\frac{1}{3}$-off sale on all computer monitors and printers. A customer asks Marcus how much she will save on a monitor with a regular price of $582. Marcus uses a calculator to find the amount of the discount and the sale price.

Finding Discounts and Sale Prices

Fractions are often used to describe a discount. A discount is an amount that is subtracted from an item's regular price. The result is the sale price. In other words, the discount and the sale price are both fractions of the regular price. We can write these equations.

Discount + Sale Price = Regular Price   **Regular Price – Discount = Sale Price**

Finding a sale price is a 2-step problem. First multiply to find the discount. Then subtract the discount from the regular price to find the sale price.

▶▶ Apply your knowledge of fractions in Marcus's situation.

Example: The regular price of the monitor is $582. The discount is $\frac{1}{3}$ of the regular price, so Marcus needs to multiply $582 by $\frac{1}{3}$ to find the discount.

$$\frac{\overset{194}{\cancel{\$582}}}{1} \times \frac{1}{3} = \$194$$

Multiply to find the discount: $582 $\times$ $\frac{1}{3}$

Answer: The customer will save **$194** off the regular price.
Check: Round $582 to $600. $\frac{1}{3}$ of $600 is $200.
Your answer is reasonable.

Subtract the discount from the regular price $582 - $194 = $388
to find the sale price.

Answer: The sale price of the monitor is **$388.**
Check: $388 + $194 = $582.

> **Did you notice?**
> Multiplying by $\frac{1}{3}$ is the same as dividing by 3. To find $\frac{1}{3}$ using a calculator, divide by 3.

Working with Finances

Fractions are useful when making a financial decision. Many people use fractions to help them develop a budget. By comparing your actual spending to your budget, you can identify problem areas in your financial situation.

▶▶ Notice how fractions are used to make this financial decision.

Example: The Kangs live in California. They want to buy a new car. After talking to a loan officer, they decide to develop a budget. To qualify for a car loan, they need to spend no more than $\frac{1}{3}$ of their income on housing and $\frac{1}{4}$ on credit card bills. They decide to use these fractions to evaluate their financial picture.

The Kangs' total monthly income is $3336. They currently spend $900 on rent and $1050 on credit card bills. Are the Kangs spending within their budget limits?

Step 1. Find the maximum amount the Kangs want to spend on housing by multiplying $3300 by $\frac{1}{3}$. Then compare to their actual spending.

$3300 \times \frac{1}{3} = 1100
$900 < $1100

Step 2. Find out how much the Kangs are willing to spend on credit card bills by multiplying $3300 by $\frac{1}{4}$.

$3300 \times \frac{1}{4} = 825
$1050 > $825

Answer: The Kangs are under their spending limit for housing but over their limit for credit card bills. They realize that they will have to reduce their credit card debt before they can buy a new car.

SKILL PRACTICE

Answer the questions based on the sign below. Use your calculator.

1. The regular price for a 3-pound bag of clay is $18.60. How much is the price reduced for the weekend sale? (*Hint:* Find the amount of the discount, not the sale price.)

crafty creations

* * * * * *

THIS WEEKEND ONLY! ALL CRAFT AND ART SUPPLIES $\frac{1}{4}$ OFF

2. Watercolor brushes are regularly $5.20 apiece. What is the sale price for 4 brushes?

3. A set of art markers is regularly $84.95. Cecilia has a $10-off coupon. If she uses the coupon during the sale weekend, how much will she pay for the markers to the nearest cent?

After taxes and other deductions, the Millers' monthly take-home pay is $2000. Use this information and the budget below to answer the questions. Use your calculator when necessary.

4. The amount spent on food is about what fraction of the Miller's monthly take-home pay? *Hint:* You may find this problem easier if you work with decimals.

(1) $\frac{1}{2}$

(2) $\frac{3}{8}$

(3) $\frac{1}{3}$

(4) $\frac{1}{5}$

(5) $\frac{1}{8}$

MILLER FAMILY MONTHLY BUDGET	
Rent	$750
Food	$420
Phone	$50
Utilities	$85
Transportation	$300
Savings	$50
Other	$345

5. Which of the following items total more than $\frac{1}{2}$ of the Miller's monthly take-home pay?

(1) Rent and Utilities

(2) Rent and Transportation

(3) Food and Phone

(4) Food and Transportation

(5) Rent, Utilities, and Savings

Answers and explanations start on page 314.

Working with Time

In the world of work and finance, time is often expressed as a fraction.

Examples: Minutes can be written as a fraction of an hour.
10 minutes are $\frac{10}{60}$ or $\frac{1}{6}$ of an hour.

Hours can be written as a fraction of a day.
18 hours are $\frac{18}{24}$ or $\frac{3}{4}$ of a day.

Months can be written as a fraction of a year.
8 months are $\frac{8}{12}$ or $\frac{2}{3}$ of a year.

> **Did you notice?**
>
> The denominator tells the number of parts in the whole.
>
> 60 minutes = 1 hour
> 24 hours = 1 day
> 12 months = 1 year

You can find the amount of interest Elaine will pay on the loan by multiplying the principal (the amount borrowed) by the interest rate expressed as a decimal by the time in years. On the GED Math Test, the formula for simple interest is written $i = prt$; where p = principal, r = rate, and t = time.

Example: Find the interest amount that Elaine will pay on an $800 loan at 5% simple interest for 9 months.

> The principal (p) is **$800**.
>
> The interest rate (r) of 5% can be written as 0.05.
>
> The time (t) is 9 out of 12 months: $\frac{9}{12} = \frac{3}{4}$ year

Step 1. Express the time as a decimal to work on a calculator. $\frac{3}{4} = 0.75$

Step 2. Multiply. $i = prt = \$800 \times 0.05 \times 0.75 = \$30$

Answer: Elaine will pay **$30** in interest on the loan.

Working with Measurement

You can also express units of measure in different terms using fractions.

Examples: Inches can be written as a fraction of a foot or a yard.
9 inches are $\frac{9}{12}$ or $\frac{3}{4}$ foot.
24 inches are $\frac{24}{36}$ or $\frac{2}{3}$ yard.

Feet can be written as a fraction of a yard or a mile.
1 foot is $\frac{1}{3}$ yard.
528 feet are $\frac{528}{5280}$ or $\frac{1}{10}$ mile.

Ounces can be written as a fraction of a pound.
8 ounces are $\frac{8}{16}$ or $\frac{1}{2}$ pound.

> **Use these equivalencies:**
>
> 12 inches = 1 foot
> 36 inches = 1 yard
> 3 feet = 1 yard
> 5280 feet = 1 mile
> 16 ounces = 1 pound

MATHEMATICS

Example: Roberta is planning a breakfast to raise money for a local youth program. She needs to order pancake mix. Roberta estimates that she will need 2 ounces of mix per person. How many people can she feed using a 10-pound bag of mix?

Step 1. Express 2 ounces as a fraction of a pound. $\qquad$ 2 ounces $= \frac{2}{16}$ or $\frac{1}{8}$ pound

Step 2. Find how many times $\frac{1}{8}$ pound goes into 10 pounds. $\qquad$ $10 \div \frac{1}{8} = \frac{10}{1} \times \frac{8}{1} = 80$

Answer: A 10-pound bag of pancake mix will feed **80 people.**
Check: If it takes $\frac{1}{8}$ pound to feed one person, 1 pound will feed 8 people.
$10 \times 8 = 80$. The answer makes sense.

SKILL PRACTICE

Solve each problem. Express your answer as a fraction in lowest terms. Use your calculator when necessary.

1. What part of a day is 10 hours?

2. What part of a year is 3 months?

3. Martin borrows $1200 for 6 months at 8% interest. Using 0.08 as the annual interest rate, which of the following expressions could be used to find the amount of simple interest Martin will pay?

   (1) $1200 \times 6 \times 0.08$
   (2) $1200 \times \frac{1}{6} \times 0.08$
   (3) $1200 \times \frac{1}{3} \times 0.08$
   (4) $1200 \times \frac{1}{2} \times 0.08$
   (5) $1200 \times \frac{3}{4} \times 0.08$

4. What part of a foot is 7 inches?

5. A package weighs 12 ounces. What is the weight of the package expressed as a fraction of a pound? Give both fraction and decimal equivalents.

6. Which of the following fractions is closest to 1000 feet expressed as a fraction of a mile?

   (1) $\frac{1}{10}$
   (2) $\frac{1}{5}$
   (3) $\frac{1}{4}$
   (4) $\frac{1}{3}$
   (5) $\frac{1}{2}$

SCIENCE Connection

To conduct an experiment, Jeanette needs $\frac{1}{2}$ ounce of iron filings. She places the filings on a scale, reads the weight, and exclaims, "Close enough."

When is a measurement close enough? Measurements are only as accurate as the tools used in making them. In science, procedures allow for a margin of error, sometimes called an error tolerance. In the experiment above, Jeanette needs $\frac{1}{2}$ ounce of iron filings, but the procedure allows an error tolerance of $\pm\frac{1}{8}$ ounce. The symbol $\pm$ means <u>plus or minus.</u> Add and subtract the error tolerance to find the acceptable range.

$\frac{1}{2} - \frac{1}{8} = \frac{3}{8}$ $\qquad$ $\frac{1}{2} + \frac{1}{8} = \frac{5}{8}$ $\qquad$ Any amount from $\frac{3}{8}$ to $\frac{5}{8}$ ounce is close enough.

An experiment calls for $\frac{3}{4}$ ounce of sodium aluminum sulphate with an error tolerance of $\pm\frac{1}{16}$ ounce. **What range of measurements is acceptable?**

Answers and explanations start on page 314.

MATHEMATICS

PART ONE DIRECTIONS: Choose the <u>one best answer</u> to each of the following problems. Use a calculator wherever necessary.

1. Los Olivos Nurseries has $3\frac{1}{2}$ acres to use for growing salad greens. If they divide this area into 5 plots, what size would each plot be in acres?
   (1) $\frac{3}{10}$
   (2) $\frac{1}{2}$
   (3) $\frac{7}{10}$
   (4) $1\frac{3}{7}$
   (5) $8\frac{1}{2}$

<u>Questions 2 and 3</u> are based on the following sign.

SALE:
EXCEL TX41 TIRES

Orig. $54.00
Saturday Only

$\frac{1}{4}$ OFF!

2. Libby is pricing tires on Saturday. What will one Excel TX41 tire cost her, before tax?
   (1) $13.50
   (2) $16.20
   (3) $40.50
   (4) $51.00
   (5) $72.00

3. The next week, the store offers $\frac{1}{3}$ off the original price of the Excel TX41 if a set of 4 tires is purchased. How much would 4 tires cost at the new sale price?
   (1) $168.00
   (2) $144.00
   (3) $108.00
   (4) $72.00
   (5) Not enough information is given.

4. Which of the following is equal to 58/4 rewritten as a mixed number and reduced to lowest terms?
   (1) $4\frac{1}{2}$
   (2) $14\frac{2}{4}$
   (3) $14\frac{1}{2}$
   (4) $14\frac{5}{4}$
   (5) $57\frac{1}{4}$

<u>Questions 5 through 7</u> are based on the following drawing.

| START |—— 1.7 mi ——|— 1 mi —|—— 2.3 mi ——| FINISH |
| | Terri | Phil | Marco | |

5. Middlebury's public parks sponsored a relay race to raise money for bike stands. The team of Terri, Phil, and Marco ran the race. What fraction of the race did Terri and Marco run?
   (1) $\frac{3}{10}$
   (2) $\frac{4}{10}$
   (3) $\frac{3}{5}$
   (4) $\frac{4}{5}$
   (5) Not enough information is given.

6. What is the distance in miles that Marco ran?
   (1) 4
   (2) $2\frac{3}{10}$
   (3) $1\frac{7}{10}$
   (4) $\frac{7}{10}$
   (5) $\frac{3}{10}$

7. Terri, Phil, and Marco's team took a total of 40 minutes to run the race. What fraction of their finish time was Phil's part of the relay?
   (1) $\frac{1}{10}$
   (2) $\frac{1}{6}$
   (3) $\frac{1}{5}$
   (4) $\frac{4}{5}$
   (5) Not enough information given.

8. What is the correct order of the following fractions, from <u>least to greatest</u>?
   (1) $\frac{1}{10}, \frac{1}{4}, \frac{2}{7}, \frac{3}{10}, \frac{1}{3}$
   (2) $\frac{1}{10}, \frac{1}{4}, \frac{3}{10}, \frac{1}{3}, \frac{2}{7}$
   (3) $\frac{1}{10}, \frac{2}{7}, \frac{1}{4}, \frac{1}{3}, \frac{3}{10}$
   (4) $\frac{1}{10}, \frac{3}{10}, \frac{1}{4}, \frac{2}{7}, \frac{1}{3}$
   (5) $\frac{1}{3}, \frac{3}{10}, \frac{2}{7}, \frac{1}{4}, \frac{1}{10}$

Question 9 is based on the following table.

Week of March 7	Sam's Reading Times
Sunday	10:40–11:10
Tuesday	1:30–2:30
Wednesday	11:45–12:30
Friday	10:20–10:50

9. Tamara's young son, Sam, kept a chart of how long he practiced reading on his own. How many hours did Sam read during the week of March 7?
   (1) $2\frac{1}{4}$
   (2) $2\frac{3}{4}$
   (3) $3\frac{1}{2}$
   (4) $3\frac{3}{4}$
   (5) $4\frac{1}{4}$

10. At the Native American Jewelry Fair, Tiara sold 18 turquoise beads and 23 amber beads. Which expression best shows what fraction the amber beads were of the total beads sold?
    (1) $\frac{23}{18+23}$
    (2) $\frac{18}{18+23}$
    (3) $\frac{(18+23)}{42}$
    (4) $23(23-18)$
    (5) $\frac{18+23}{23}$

Question 11 is based on the drawing.

11. Hiza Community Center ordered 11 sacks of flour for desserts. Each sack holds 20 pounds. If the Center uses about $\frac{2}{3}$ of a sack every week, <u>approximately</u> how long will this order of flour last?
    (1) Between 7 and 8 weeks
    (2) Between 13 and 14 weeks
    (3) Between 15 and 16 weeks
    (4) Between 16 and 17 weeks
    (5) Between 17 and 18 weeks

12. A neighborhood recycling station collects $2\frac{1}{3}$ tons of plastic a month. At this rate, how many tons will the station collect in $2\frac{1}{2}$ years?
    (1) $5\frac{5}{6}$
    (2) 28
    (3) 70
    (4) $170\frac{1}{2}$
    (5) 175

13. It takes Hans 45 minutes to clean the clinic kitchen. After 15 minutes of cleaning, Hans gets called away to clean up a spill. What fraction of the cleaning job had Hans completed before he stopped to take care of the spill?
    (1) $\frac{1}{4}$
    (2) $\frac{1}{3}$
    (3) $\frac{1}{2}$
    (4) $\frac{2}{3}$
    (5) $\frac{3}{4}$

14. What is the lowest common denominator for the expression $\frac{5}{6}+\frac{2}{3}+\frac{2}{9}+\frac{1}{2}$?
    (1) 6
    (2) 9
    (3) 10
    (4) 18
    (5) 324

PART TWO DIRECTIONS: Choose the <u>one best answer</u> to each of the following problems. *You may not use a calculator on these problems.*

15. Assuming there is no waste, how many feet of wood are needed to replace 6 shelves if each shelf is $3\frac{1}{4}$ feet long?
    (1) $9\frac{1}{4}$
    (2) $18\frac{1}{2}$
    (3) $19\frac{1}{4}$
    (4) $19\frac{1}{2}$
    (5) 78

Questions 16 and 17 refer to the following table.

SALON SERVICE	TIME REQUIRED FOR SERVICE
Shampoo	$\frac{1}{4}$ hour
Haircut	$\frac{1}{2}$ hour
Permanent	$1\frac{1}{4}$ hours
Manicure	$\frac{3}{4}$ hour
Pedicure	$\frac{2}{3}$ hour

16. Sunny of Cher's Salon completes one permanent and two haircuts immediately after lunch. In the time remaining in her 3-hour afternoon schedule, which of the following services could Sunny complete?
    (1) a pedicure
    (2) a permanent
    (3) a manicure and a shampoo
    (4) a haircut and a permanent
    (5) two manicures

17. Tracy of Cher's Salon begins work at 11:00 A.M. She does a shampoo, a permanent, and a pedicure, all in a row. At what time does she finish these services?
    (1) 2:10 P.M.
    (2) 1:20 P.M.
    (3) 1:10 P.M.
    (4) 1:00 P.M.
    (5) 12:40 P.M.

18. Mrs. Chen's cake calls for $2\frac{1}{2}$ cups of whipped cream. Of that, $\frac{1}{3}$ cup is saved for the topping. The rest goes in the batter. What expression could represent how much whipped cream is in the batter?
    (1) $2\frac{1}{2} + \frac{1}{3}$
    (2) $\frac{15}{6} - \frac{2}{6}$
    (3) $\frac{15}{6} - \frac{13}{6}$
    (4) $\frac{3}{6} - \frac{2}{6}$
    (5) $\frac{17}{6} - \frac{2}{6}$

19. The village of Batara weaves rugs for sale to tourists. The village artisans can weave 75 rugs a month. If they have already made 45 rugs this month, what fraction of the month's total do they have left to weave?
    (1) $\frac{1}{75}$
    (2) $\frac{1}{7}$
    (3) $\frac{1}{5}$
    (4) $\frac{2}{5}$
    (5) $\frac{3}{5}$

20. Ahmed is cutting up a 42-inch piece of plastic pipe for a scout project. Each scout needs a length of pipe measuring $7\frac{1}{2}$ inches. How many pieces of this size can Ahmed cut from the plastic pipe?
    (1) 5
    (2) 6
    (3) 7
    (4) 8
    (5) 9

21. Nestor told his daughter Carole that he would give her $\frac{1}{4} + \frac{3}{10} + \frac{2}{5} + \frac{1}{50}$ of a dollar if she could tell him the equivalent value of that sum in decimal form. How much should Carole say the sum is worth when converted to dollars?
    (1) $9.70
    (2) $1.97
    (3) $0.97
    (4) $0.92
    (5) $0.09

Answers and explanations start on page 315.

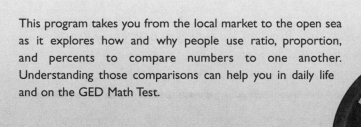

This program takes you from the local market to the open sea as it explores how and why people use ratio, proportion, and percents to compare numbers to one another. Understanding those comparisons can help you in daily life and on the GED Math Test.

Ratio, Proportion, and Percent

OBJECTIVES

1. Use ratios and rates to compare values.

2. Use proportions to solve everyday problems.

3. Use proportion to solve percent problems.

A recipe says a 5-pound roast will serve 12 people, but you only want to make enough for 8 people. Cans of tuna fish are 3 for $1, but you want to buy 5 cans. You know about 3% of your income goes to state taxes, and you need to estimate your state taxes for the year. In each example, there is a relationship between two values: pounds and servings, cans of food and dollars, tax dollars and total income. You can solve each problem using ratio, proportion, or percent.

The ability to work with ratio, proportion, and percent is important to your success on the GED Math Test. You will need to know how to write ratios, use proportion to set up and solve problems, and apply the percent formula. Your work in this program will help you gain other math skills in the areas of measurement, algebra, and geometry.

On the following pages, you will find a brief exercise called *Sneak Preview*. It is designed to introduce you to the topics that will be featured in the video program and the corresponding lesson. After you complete the exercise and check your answers, turn to the vocabulary page. There you will find terms that will help you better understand the video and the lesson that follow. After reviewing page 110, you will be ready to watch Program 32.

For additional practice, visit *LiteracyLink* online at http://www.pbs.org/literacy.

Sneak Preview

This exercise previews some of the concepts from Program 32. After you answer the questions, use the feedback on page 109 to help set your learning goals.

FAMILY LINK: The Burrs are a large family. They save on grocery bills by purchasing many of their food and cleaning items at a discount store called Bargain Central. The family clips coupons and looks for ads in newspapers. The ad below is for a sale on rice, which the Burr family usually buys by the case.

BARGAIN CENTRAL

"We dare you to find it cheaper!"

Long Grain White Rice
BY THE BOX:
$2.09 per 32-oz box

BY THE CASE:
$18.90 per case of 10 boxes

SATURDAY AND SUNDAY ONLY!

Answer these questions based on the advertisement shown above.

1. On Friday Bargain Central sold 28 individual boxes of Long Grain Rice. Because of the sale, they sold only 7 individual boxes on Saturday. What is the ratio of individual boxes sold on Friday to individual boxes sold on Saturday?

   (1) 1:7
   (2) 1:4
   (3) 4:1
   (4) 4:5
   (5) 7:28

2. If the Burrs buy a case of rice on Saturday, which expression represents the cost per box within the case?

(1) $2.09 × 10

(2) $\frac{\$2.09}{10}$

(3) $\frac{\$18.90}{32}$

(4) $\frac{\$18.90}{10}$

(5) $18.90 × 10

3. During the week, the store decides to offer five individual boxes for $9.80. How much would eight boxes cost at that rate?

(1) $6.13

(2) $13.00

(3) $15.68

(4) $78.40

(5) Not enough information is given.

4. To the nearest cent, how much will the 5% sales tax be if the Burrs purchase one case of rice during the sale?

(1) $0.50

(2) $0.80

(3) $0.85

(4) $0.90

(5) $0.95

Feedback

- If you got all of the answers right...   you have a good basic understanding of ratio, proportion, and percent calculations and problem solving.

- If you missed question 1...   you need to work on your understanding of ratios.

- If you missed question 2...   you need to work with solution set-ups and finding unit rates.

- If you missed question 3...   you need to work on solving for an unknown number using ratio and proportion.

- If you missed question 4...   you need to develop your ability to work with percents.

Vocabulary for *Ratio, Proportion, and Percent*

cross products   the results of multiplying the denominator of the first ratio by the numerator of the second ratio and the denominator of the second ratio by the numerator of the first ratio. In a true proportion, cross products are equal. For example, $\frac{3}{6} \bowtie \frac{5}{10}$

part   in a percent problem, a portion of the whole

percent   a method of describing a fractional part of 100

proportion   a mathematical statement that two ratios are equal; for example, $\frac{1}{2} = \frac{6}{12}$

rate (definition 1)   the element in a percent problem that is followed by the % sign; a ratio that compares some number to 100

rate (definition 2)   a special kind of ratio that compares a number to one unit. The word *per* is often used in a rate. For example, 10 miles per hour.

rate of change   the rate of increase or decrease over a period of time between an original amount and a new amount

ratio   a way to compare two numbers or quantities; can be written with the word to, with a colon (:), or as a fraction

simplify   to reduce a ratio to lowest terms; for example, $\frac{3}{6} = \frac{1}{2}$

successive percents   a series of percent calculations in which the answer to each additional percent problem depends upon the previous calculation

unit rate   a special kind of ratio that compares a number to one unit; often uses the word *per*, for example, $2.15 per pound.

whole   the base amount in a percent problem

➡ **NOW WATCH PROGRAM 32:**

The program introduces and defines ratio, proportion, and percent, and shows some real-world applications along with a few classroom math problems. Look for additional problems in the workbook to help you practice for the test.

After you watch the program, work on:

- pages 111–128 in this workbook
- Internet activities at http://www.pbs.org/literacy

MATHEMATICS

Ratio, Proportion, and Percent

On the following pages, you will learn more about the ideas discussed in the video program and have an opportunity to develop and practice your GED math skills.

PROGRAM 32: Ratio, Proportion, and Percent

GED TIPS

When taking the GED Test, you should:

- Write the terms in ratios and proportions in the order they are mentioned in the problem.
- Use your knowledge of equivalent fractions and decimals to save time and check your work.
- Read each problem carefully. Make sure you understand what you are being asked to find before you start any calculations.

Key Points to Think About

In the video program, you explored:

- How people use ratio, proportion, and percent in their daily lives as workers, citizens, and family members.
- How ratios are used to compare quantities and how rates are used to describe special ratios with a denominator of 1.
- Everyday applications of ratio, proportion, and percent, such as those that deal with money, distance, and measurement.

On the GED Math Test:

- You will be expected to know how to solve proportions and percent problems.
- You should know how to set up percent problems using both proportion and the percent formula.
- You will use ratio and proportion frequently to solve problems involving money and measurement.

As you work through the lesson for Program 32:

- Think about the importance of order when setting up ratios in a proportion.
- Make sure you **simplify** all rates and ratios, since all answer choices on the GED Math Test are written in lowest terms.
- Be aware of opportunities to use ratio and proportion to solve problems in your daily life, not just on the GED Math Test.

Working with Ratios

Understanding Ratios

A **ratio** is a way to compare numbers or quantities. A ratio focuses on the size relationship between numbers. The numbers in a ratio can be written with the word *to,* with a colon, or as a fraction. The order of the numbers must match the words in the situation.

$$\frac{\text{number of drivers who didn't stop}}{\text{total number of drivers}} \qquad 12 \text{ to } 48 \qquad 12{:}48 \qquad \frac{12}{48}$$

Ratios make more sense when they are written in lowest terms. Jim could have reported the ratio as 12 to 48, but the reduced ratio of 1 to 4 is easier to picture and understand.

$$\frac{12}{48} = \frac{12 \div 12}{48 \div 12} = \frac{1}{4}$$

To simplify a ratio:
_____

1. Write the ratio as a fraction and reduce it by dividing both terms by the same number.
2. Continue until no number except 1 divides evenly into both terms.
3. *Unlike working with fractions,* do not change a ratio with a larger term on top into a whole number or mixed number.

▶▶ Read this situation carefully before answering.

Example: Cathy coaches a girl's softball team for 11- and 12-year-olds. This year her team won 8 games and lost 2.

What is the ratio of games won to games played?

    (1)   5:4   **(4)**   1:4
    (2)   4:5   **(5)**   1:5
    (3)   4:1

You're right if you chose **(2) 4:5.** The problem asks you to find the ratio of games won to *games played.* To find the number of games played, add the wins and losses. The team played 10 games. The ratio of games won to games played is 8:10, which reduces to 4:5.

On the GED Math Test, if you can't find your answer to a ratio problem among the choices, make sure your answer is written in the correct order and in lowest terms.

Working with Unit Rates

A **unit rate** is a special kind of ratio that compares a quantity to one unit. Unit rates are usually expressed with the word *per*.

Examples: An employee earns $9 per hour. The speed limit is 55 miles per hour.

To find a unit rate:

1. Use the information in the problem to write a ratio in fraction form.
2. Divide the top number by the bottom number. Express the remainder as either a fraction or a decimal.
3. Write the quotient from Step 2 as the top number of the unit rate over 1.

▶▶ Use your knowledge of unit rates to calculate gas mileage.

Example: Since her last fill-up, Lynn has driven 192 miles. When she stops for gas, it takes 12 gallons to fill up her gas tank. How many miles per gallon did she get on her last tank of gasoline?

(1) 12   **(4)** 17

(2) 15   **(5)** 19

(3) 16

You're right if you chose **(3) 16.** Lynn drove 192 miles on 12 gallons of gas. The ratio is $\frac{192}{12}$, which equals a rate of $\frac{16}{1}$. Lynn's car averaged 16 miles per 1 gallon of gasoline.

SKILL PRACTICE

Solve each problem. Reduce ratios to lowest terms. Remember: Do not change a ratio to a whole or mixed number.

1. For a special showing of *The Wizard of Oz*, a movie theater sold 75 tickets to adults and 125 tickets to children. Write the following ratios:

   a. adults to children in the audience
   b. adult tickets sold to total tickets sold

2. Brett took a test on ratios in his math class. Of the 48 items on the test, he missed 4. Write the following ratios:

   a. correct answers to total test items
   b. incorrect answers to total test items
   c. correct to incorrect answers

3. During a 6-hour sale, a bookstore manager counted 246 customers. Of the total customers, 82 spent more than $20.

   a. Write the ratio of total customers to those spending more than $20.
   b. Find the rate of customers per hour.

4. Chris earned $855 for a temporary job. She worked 36 hours the first week and 40 hours the second week. Which expression shows how much she earned per hour?

   (1) $\frac{\$855}{36}$

   (2) $\frac{\$855}{40}$

   (3) $\frac{\$855}{2}$

   (4) $\frac{(36+40)}{\$855}$

   (5) $\frac{\$855}{(36+40)}$

Working with Proportions

FAMILY LINK: Robin approaches a concession stand at the County Fair. A sign advertises: "Hot Dogs—2 for $3". Robin needs to buy 4 hot dogs for her family. Using her knowledge of proportion, she can quickly see that 4 hot dogs will cost $6.

Understanding Proportions

The sign advertises a relationship between a number of hot dogs and a number of dollars. You can write the relationship as a ratio:

2 hot dogs to $3   2:3 $\frac{2}{3}$

As Robin did, you can see that if you double the number of hot dogs, you must double the price. Robin could buy 4 hot dogs for $6. This information can also be written as a ratio.

4 hot dogs to $6   4:6 $\frac{4}{6}$

A **proportion** is a statement that two ratios are equal. For example, $\frac{2}{3} = \frac{4}{6}$. Notice that the order of the items in the ratios is the same. Both compare hot dogs to dollars.

To prove a proportion is true, or correct, compare the **cross products.** Set up the proportion so that the two ratios are separated by an equals sign. Then multiply the numerator of one ratio by the denominator of the other. Multiply the remaining numerator and denominator. If the cross products are equal, the ratios are equal.

$\frac{2}{3} \times \frac{4}{6}$ $\begin{array}{l} 2 \times 6 = 12 \\ 3 \times 4 = 12 \end{array}$ The cross products are equal, so $\frac{2}{3} = \frac{4}{6}$

> **UTAH County Fair**
> Hot Dogs: 2 for $3
> Drinks: $1
> Nachos: $1.50

Solving Proportions in Word Problems

In a proportion problem, one of the terms is unknown. You can solve for the missing term by using your knowledge of cross products.

Follow these steps to find the value of the missing term.

1. Find the cross product for two terms.
2. Divide the cross product by the remaining term.
3. To check, substitute your answer for the missing term and make sure the cross products are equal.

▸▸ Notice how careful labeling of terms can prevent errors.

Example: A company charges $5 to ship 4 pounds of merchandise. What would be the shipping charge on a 10-pound shipment?

Set up the proportion so that the terms are in the same order in each ratio. Write the labels in order as a reminder.

MATHEMATICS

Both ratios compare pounds to dollars.
An *x* is used for the missing term.

$$\frac{\text{pounds}}{\text{dollars}} \qquad \frac{4}{5} = \frac{10}{x}$$

First: Cross multiply.

$5 \times 10 = 50$

Next: Divide the cross product by the remaining term.

$50 \div 4 = 12.5$, or $12.50

Answer: The company will charge **$12.50** for a 10-pound shipment. *Check:* Substitute and cross multiply. The proportion is true.

$$\frac{4}{5} \diagdown \frac{10}{12.50} \qquad \begin{array}{l} 5 \times 10 = 50 \\ 4 \times 12.5 = 50 \end{array}$$

> You could also set up the ratios using dollars over pounds. Try it. The answer is the same.

 A calculator is very useful for solving proportion problems, especially when the numbers are large. Enter the operations one after the other. You don't have to write down and re-enter the first cross product.

Calculator: $\boxed{5} \boxed{\times} \boxed{1} \boxed{0} \boxed{\div} \boxed{4} \boxed{=} \boxed{\qquad 12.5}$

On the GED Math Test, you will sometimes be asked to choose how a proportion problem could be set up. The expression will show both the multiplication and the division step. Remember, the fraction bar means division.

> A correct set-up for the example above is:
>
> $$\frac{5 \times 10}{4}$$

SKILL PRACTICE

Solve each problem.

1. Marti has created a logo for a T-shirt. Her sample design measures 6 inches wide and 10 inches long. If she uses a photocopier to enlarge the design to a 10-inch width, what will its length be to the nearest whole inch?

   (1) 10   (4) 26
   (2) 16   (5) 60
   (3) 17

2. A bread recipe calls for 6 cups of flour and 3 tablespoons of butter. If John makes a smaller batch using only 4 cups of flour, how many tablespoons of butter will he need?

   (1) 2   (4) 5
   (2) 3   (5) 6
   (3) 4

3. Ken earned $218.75 for 25 hours of work. At the same rate, how much would he earn for 40 hours of work?

   (1) $136.72   (4) $350.00
   (2) $258.75   (5) $781.25
   (3) $283.75

4. For every $50 that Max earns, he saves $5. Which expression could be used to find the amount he will save if he earns $300?

   (1) $\dfrac{50 \times 5}{300}$ (4) $\dfrac{300 + 5}{5}$

   (2) $\dfrac{300 \times 50}{5}$ (5) $\dfrac{300 \times 5}{50}$

   (3) $\dfrac{300 \div 5}{50}$

5. Jonisa spent $34.14 for 3 gallons of paint. Which expressions could be used to find the cost of 7 gallons of the same paint?

   (1) $\dfrac{34.14 \times 7}{3}$ (4) $\dfrac{34.14 + 7}{3}$

   (2) $\dfrac{34.14 \times 3}{7}$ (5) $\dfrac{7 \times 3}{34.14}$

   (3) $\dfrac{34.14 \div 3}{7}$

Answers and explanations start on page 315.

Working with Map Scales

A map scale compares distance on a map to actual distance.

A map scale is usually written as a unit rate. On the map below, 1 centimeter = 70 kilometers.

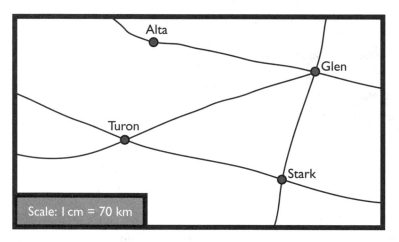

> On the GED Math Test, figures are not always drawn to scale. Use the numbers in the problem to find the answer. Don't just "eyeball" the figure.

If you know the map scale and map distance, you can find actual distance.

▸▸ Use proportion to solve for actual distance in this example.

Example: The distance on the map from Turon to Stark is 4.5 centimeters. Find the actual distance from Turon to Stark.

Set up a proportion: $\dfrac{1 \text{ cm}}{70 \text{ km}} = \dfrac{4.5 \text{ cm}}{x \text{ km}}$

Solve for the missing term:
$$70 \times 4.5 = 315$$
$$315 \div 1 = 315$$

Answer: The actual distance from Turon to Stark is **315 kilometers.**
Check: You know that 4×70 is 280. Your answer is reasonable.

▸▸ Use proportion to solve for map distance in this example.

Example: An airport is going to be built 224 kilometers northeast of Stark. How many centimeters from Stark will it be on the map?

Set up a proportion: $\dfrac{1 \text{ cm}}{70 \text{ km}} = \dfrac{x \text{ cm}}{224 \text{ km}}$

Solve for the missing term: $1 \times 224 \div 70 = 3.2$

Answer: The airport will be **3.2 cm** from Stark on the map.
Check: You know that 3×70 is 210. Your answer makes sense.

MATHEMATICS

Solving Two-Part Proportion Problems

For some word problems, you may have to use information in the problem to calculate one of the terms before you can write a proportion.

Example: David is helping children paint a mural. The pink color used in the mural is made by mixing red and white paint in a 2:7 ratio. If David needs 36 quarts of pink paint, how many quarts of red paint will he use?

David needs to know how much red paint is needed to mix with white to get 36 quarts of pink paint. Set up a proportion using two ratios that compare the amount of red paint to the total amount of paint (pink). Use the ratio you are given to find a total (pink). Add: $2 + 7 = 9$. There are 2 quarts of red paint in 9 quarts of pink. Write the other ratio comparing the unknown amount of red to the total: $\frac{x}{36}$.

Write the proportion and solve: $\frac{2 \text{ red}}{9 \text{ pink}} = \frac{x \text{ red}}{36 \text{ pink}}$ $\qquad \frac{2 \times 36}{9} = 8 \text{ red}$

Answer: David will need **8 quarts** of red paint.

Check: Substitute and find the cross products: $2 \times 36 = 72$ and $9 \times 8 = 72$.

SKILL PRACTICE

Solve each problem.

1. The distance from Kent to Leeds is 175 km. On a map with a scale of 1 cm = 25 km, how many centimeters apart are Kent and Leeds?

2. The scale on a map of Oregon is 1 inch = 36 miles. Ontario and Burns are $5\frac{1}{2}$ inches apart on the map. What is the actual distance between the cities?

3. The ratio of children to adults on a camping trip is 5:2. If there are 56 people on the camping trip, how many are children?

4. Paul makes 1 sale in his shop for every 8 sales he makes over the telephone. If he averages 180 sales per week, how many are made in his shop?

SOCIAL STUDIES Connection

One strategy when solving a proportion problem on the GED test is to use **labels.** Labels will help you to always keep the ratios in the same order.

Example: In North Dakota, there are approximately 10 square miles of water for every 400 square miles of land. If the land area of North Dakota is nearly 69,000 square miles, how many of the state's square miles are water?

Write the labels in the order you want the numbers to appear. Then write the numbers.

$$\frac{\text{water sq mi}}{\text{land sq mi}} = \frac{10}{400} = \frac{x}{69,000}$$

Solve the proportion. **In North Dakota about how many square miles are covered in water?**

Working with Percent

WORKPLACE LINK: Philip works as a records processing clerk. He has applied for a new job as a supervisor. If he gets the job, he will get an 8% raise. He currently makes $22,400 per year. To find how much more he would make in a year, he finds 8% of $22,400. The new job would bring him a raise of $1,792.

Understanding Percent

Like fractions and decimals, percent is another way to express part of a whole. A percent is a ratio that always compares a quantity to 100. The percent sign (%) means "out of 100."

50% of this figure, or 50 out of 100 parts, is shaded. Because you can reduce $\frac{50}{100}$ to $\frac{1}{2}$, you can see that 50% equals $\frac{1}{2}$.

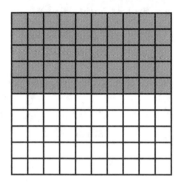

You may find it useful to change percents to fractions or decimals.

To change a percent to a fraction:
1. Write the percent over 100.
2. Reduce to lowest terms.

Example: $25\% = \frac{25}{100} = \frac{1}{4}$

To change a percent to a decimal:
1. Drop the percent sign.
2. Move the decimal point left two places.

Example: $25\% = 0.25$

You can also change fractions or decimals to percents.

To change a fraction to a percent:
1. Write a proportion comparing the fraction to the percent (x) over 100.
2. Solve and add a percent sign.

Example: $\frac{3}{4} = \frac{x}{100}$ $3 \times 100 \div 4 = 75$
Add a percent sign: **75%.**

To change a decimal to a percent:
1. Change the decimal to a fraction.
2. Then use proportion, if necessary, to change the fraction to a percent.

Example: $0.8 = \frac{8}{10}$
$\frac{8}{10} = \frac{x}{100}$ $8 \times 100 \div 10 = 80$
Add a percent sign: **80%.**

Solving Percent Problems

A percent situation has three elements. Note that the rate is always followed by the % sign. A percent problem is actually a proportion. You can use proportion to solve all percent problems.

For example, by plugging the values from the top of the page into the proportion and solving for part, Philip could calculate his raise.

$$\begin{array}{ccc} \text{rate} & \text{whole} & \text{part} \\ \downarrow & \downarrow & \downarrow \end{array}$$
$$8\% \text{ of } \$22{,}400 \text{ is } \$1{,}792$$

$$\frac{\text{part}}{\text{whole}} = \frac{\text{rate}}{100}$$
$$\frac{x}{22{,}400} = \frac{8}{100}$$
$$22{,}400 \times 8 \div 100 = 1{,}792$$

Solving for Part and Rate

The first step in solving a percent problem is to recognize which element is unknown. Once you know the missing element, you can set up the proportion.

Finding the Part

▶▶ Solve for part in this situation about an employee's commission.

Example: Lupe earns a 15% commission on her total sales. Last week she sold $2000 in merchandise. What was her commission?

Whole = $2000 $\frac{\text{part}}{\text{whole}} = \frac{\text{rate}}{100}$ $\frac{x}{2000} = \frac{15}{100}$ $2000 \times 15 \div 100 = 300$
Rate = 15%

Answer: Lupe earned **$300** in commission for the week.
Check: Substitute and find the cross products: $300 \times 100 = 2000 \times 15$.

Finding the Rate

▶▶ Solve for rate (percent) in this situation about family finances.

Example: Jun Bok needs $1500 for a down payment on a car. So far, he has saved $600. What percent of the down payment has he saved?

Whole = $1500 $\frac{\text{part}}{\text{whole}} = \frac{\text{rate}}{100}$ $\frac{600}{1500} = \frac{x}{100}$ $600 \times 100 \div 1500 = 40$
Part = $600   Add a percent sign.

Answer: Jun Bok has saved **40%** of the down payment.
Check: Substitute and find the cross products: $600 \times 100 = 1500 \times 40$.

SKILL PRACTICE

Solve each problem.

1. Find 60% of 420.

2. Find 45% of $700.

3. What is 18% of $490?

4. $400 is what percent of $500?

5. 108 is what percent of 120?

6. What percent is $60 of $80?

7. A preschool has room for 80 children. At present, the school is 80% full. How many children attend the school?

8. Leonard earns $356.00 per week. His employer deducts $106.80 for taxes and insurance. What percent of his earnings are deducted?

9. On Thanksgiving a factory will operate with a skeleton crew. Of the 272 employees, only 25% are scheduled to work. Which expression could be used to find the number of employees who will work on Thanksgiving?

(1) $\frac{272 \times 100}{25}$ (4) $\frac{25 \times 272}{100}$

(2) $\frac{272 + 100}{25}$ (5) $\frac{25 \times 100}{272}$

(3) $\frac{272 \div 4}{100}$

Answers and explanations start on page 315.

The Math Handbook contains a table of decimal, fraction, and percent equivalences on page 336.

COMMUNITY LINK: Marta is writing a letter to the editor of a newspaper about low voter turnout. In her letter, she wants to report how many people voted in the last city election. From the newspaper archives, she finds out that the current mayor received 14,848 votes, or 58% of the votes. Marta calculates that 25,600 people voted in the election.

Solving for the Whole

In a percent problem, the part is a fraction of the whole. The rate is a fraction of 100. The part and the rate represent the same fraction. If you know the part and rate, you can solve for the whole using a proportion.

Part = 14,848
Rate = 58%

$$\frac{part}{whole} = \frac{rate}{100}$$

$$\frac{14,848}{x} = \frac{58}{100}$$

$$14,848 \times 100 \div 58 = 25,600$$

▸▸ Apply your knowledge of percent in this situation about budgeting.

Example: Larry spends $600 or 40% of his yearly transportation budget on car insurance. How much does Larry budget for transportation per year?

$600 is part of Larry's yearly transportation budget. Think of the total yearly transportation budget as 100%. The $600 is equal to 40%. The missing amount is the whole. Write a proportion and solve.

Part = $600
Rate = 40%

$$\frac{part}{whole} = \frac{rate}{100}$$

$$\frac{600}{x} = \frac{40}{100}$$

$$600 \times 100 \div 40 = \$1500$$

Answer: Larry's total transportation budget for the year is **$1500.**
Check: Substitute and find the cross products: $600 \times 100 = 1500 \times 40$.

Using the Percent Formula

There is more than one way to solve percent problems. You have been using proportion. As you gain experience, you may want to use the percent formula.

> Whole × Rate = Part

Example: Find 36% of $250.

The problem gives you the rate and the whole. To find the part, you need to multiply 250 and 36%. First, change the rate to a decimal by dropping the percent symbol and moving the decimal point two places to the left. Then, multiply. This is a good time to use your calculator.

Calculator: [2] [5] [0] [×] [.] [3] [6] [=] [90.]

Answer: 36% of 250 is **90.**

The percent formula can be rewritten to solve for the whole or the rate.

> $$\frac{Part}{Whole} = Rate$$

> $$\frac{Part}{Rate} = Whole$$

Percent: What percent is 75 of 150?

Solve for rate: $\frac{75}{150} = 0.5 = 50\%$

Whole: 4 is 16% of what number?

Solve for whole: $\frac{4}{0.16} = 25$

To solve percent problems, use either proportion or the percent formula. Use the method that seems easier to you.

> Change a decimal to a percent by moving the decimal point two places to the right and adding the % sign.
>
> **Example:** $0.9 = 0.90 = 90\%$

▶▶Be ready to recognize the percent formula in a set-up problem. Remember that division can be shown using the fraction bar.

Example: As a volunteer, Claire called registered voters on election day to remind them to vote. Of the people she called, 40%, or 24 people, said they planned to vote. Which expression can be used to find the number of people Claire called?

(1) 24×40 (4) $\frac{24}{0.4}$

(2) 24×0.4 (5) $\frac{0.4}{24}$

(3) $\frac{24}{40}$

You're right if you chose (4) $\frac{24}{0.4}$. To solve for whole, divide the part by the rate. Change 40% to 0.4 by moving the decimal point two places to the left.

SKILL PRACTICE

For her performance review, Chandra made this list to show how she spends her time in her job as a clerk at the courthouse. Use the list to answer questions 1 through 5.

CLERK'S JOB

Hours	Daily Task	Percent of Time
2	mailing	25%
1.6	counter help	20%
2.8	filing	35%
0.4	meetings	5%
1.2	unassigned	—

1.   Chandra spends 25% of her day, or 2 hours, getting the mail out. How many hours does she work each day? *Hint:* Find the whole.

2.   Based on the answer to item 1, what percent of Chandra's day is spent unassigned?

3.   On Friday Chandra worked 6 hours. If she spent the same percent of time at each task as usual, which expression shows the number of hours she worked at the counter?

(1) 6×0.2 (4) $\frac{0.2}{6}$

(2) $\frac{6}{0.2}$ (5) 6×20

(3) $\frac{6}{20}$

4.   Chandra works 40 hours per week. Last week she spent 16 hours filing. Which expression could be used to find the percent of the time she spent filing last week?

(1) 40×16 (4) 40×0.16

(2) $\frac{40}{16}$ (5) 16×0.4

(3) $\frac{16}{40}$

5.   During the week that property taxes were due, Chandra worked overtime. She spent 55% of her week, or 26.4 hours, behind the counter. Which expression could be used to find how many hours she worked that week?

(1) $\frac{26.4 \times 55}{100}$ (4) $\frac{26.4 + 55}{100}$

(2) $\frac{26.4 \times 100}{55}$ (5) $\frac{55 \times 100}{26.4}$

(3) $\frac{26.4 \div 100}{100}$

Answers and explanations start on page 315.

COMMUNITY LINK: At an antique store, a chest of drawers priced at $1250 had remained unsold for six months. Lamar, the store manager reduced the price by 30% to $875. Still, no one bought it. Lamar reduced the price another 20% to $700, and the chest of drawers was sold. In his sales log, Lamar recorded the final price and noted a price reduction of 44%.

Finding Successive Percents

In the situation above, Lamar discounted the price of the wardrobe twice. This is called finding **successive percents.** The second percent problem depended on the result of the first problem.

The first discount was 30% of the original price of $1250. Lamar subtracted this amount to get a sale price. The second discount was 20% of the sale price. He subtracted this discount to get a new sale price.

30% of $1250 is $375.   The sale price is $1250 − $375 = $875.
20% of $875 is $175.   The new sale price is $875 − $175 = **$700.**
$$\frac{\$700}{\$1250} = 44\%$$

Finding Rate of Change

Rate of change is the change in an amount over time. When an amount goes up, the rate of change is called the rate of increase. When an amount goes down, the rate of change is the rate of decrease.

To find the rate of change:

1. Subtract to find the difference between the final amount and the original amount.
2. Use the percent proportion. The difference is the part. The original amount is the whole.
3. Solve the percent proportion to find the rate of change.

▸▸ Find the rate of decrease in the situation.

Example: Each year a local high school holds a jazz festival to raise money for its music programs. Last year, 480 tickets were sold to the event. This year, only 428 tickets were sold. To the nearest whole percent, find the rate of decrease.

Step 1. Find the difference in the amounts: 480 − 428 = 52 fewer tickets

Step 2. Write and solve a proportion: $\dfrac{52 \text{ fewer tickets}}{480 \text{ tickets}} = \dfrac{x}{100}$

This is a good time to use your calculator.

Calculator: `5` `2` `×` `1` `0` `0` `÷` `4` `8` `0` `=` `10.833333`

Answer: Rounding to the nearest whole percent, **11% fewer tickets** were sold this year than last year. *Check:* You know that 10% of 480 is 48, so 11% makes sense.

For information on how to use the percent key on the Casio *fx*-260, refer to page 338 of the Math Handbook.

MATHEMATICS

⯮ Find the rate of increase in this situation.

Example: At the beginning of the baseball season, Stuart bought an autographed baseball for $40. At the end of the season, he sold the ball for $52. What was the rate of increase in the ball's value?

The difference in the ball's value from the beginning to the end of the season is $12. $52 − $40 = $12. Set up a proportion, using the difference as the part and the original value of the ball as the whole. Solve for the rate.

Part = $12 $\frac{\text{part}}{\text{whole}} = \frac{\text{rate}}{100}$ $\frac{12}{40} = \frac{x}{100}$ $12 \times 100 \div 40 = 30$
Whole = $40   Add a percent sign.

Answer: The percent of increase was **30%**. In other words, the ball was worth 30% more at the end of the season than it was worth at the beginning. *Check:* Substitute and find the cross products. 12×100 and 40×30 equal 1200

SKILL PRACTICE

Solve each problem.

1. Mike repairs VCRs. Last year, he charged $65 per hour for labor. This year, he charges $75 per hour. To the nearest percent, what is the rate of increase in his hourly charge?

2. Linda bought a used car two years ago for $4200. Now she wants to sell it. A car dealer offered $1700 for it. To the nearest percent, what is the rate of decrease in the value of the car?

3. The population of a small town was 49,500 five years ago. The current population is 52,300. To the nearest percent, find the rate of increase in population.

4. During the holiday season, a watch was priced at $82. In January, the price was reduced by 10%. In February, the new price was reduced an additional 25%. What is the current price of the watch, and what is overall rate of decrease in price?

PROBLEM SOLVER Connection

There are several shortcuts to solving percent problems using mental math instead of pencil and paper. You may already use these shortcuts automatically.

Example: Cal sells coins at a local flea market. He spent $430 on a collection of silver coins and then sold the collection for 200% more than he paid. Then Cal paid the manager of the flea market a 5% commission on the sale. What was the selling price of the collection? How much was the commission?

Step 1. Find the selling price. To find 200% of something quickly, just multiply it by 2: $430 × 2 = $860.

Step 2. Find the amount of the commission. To find 5% of something quickly, first find 10% of it by moving the decimal point 1 place to the left. 10% of $860 is 86.0. Then take half of that: $\frac{\$86}{2} = \$43$.

Answer: The collection sold for **$860**. The commission was **$43**.

What shortcut could you use to find 25% of a number? 20% of a number?

MATHEMATICS

PART ONE DIRECTIONS: Choose the one best answer to each of the following problems. Use a calculator wherever necessary.

1. Sebastian spent $38.94 for 3 CDs. Which expression could be used to find the cost of 8 CDs at the same price?

(1) $\frac{38.94+8}{3}$ **(4)** $\frac{3\times8}{38.94}$

(2) $\frac{38.94\times8}{3}$ **(5)** $\frac{38.94\div8}{3}$

(3) $\frac{38.94\times3}{8}$

2. Marla recently got a job selling carpet; she works 8 hours a day, 3 days a week. Marla just made her first sale of $840. She is to receive 6% commission for this sale. What will her commission be?

(1) $600.00   **(4)** $50.40

(2) $504.00   **(5)** $35.00

(3) $100.80

Question 3 is based on the following drawing.

3. A poster is 8 inches wide by 14 inches long. A smaller poster of the same proportions is 6 inches wide. How many inches long is the smaller poster?

(1) 21

(2) $11\frac{1}{2}$

(3) $10\frac{1}{2}$

(4) $10\frac{1}{4}$

(5) 10

4. Cindy is a sculptor who mixes a sculpting compound composed of 60% sand, 25% alumina cement, and 15% plaster. How many ounces of sand will Cindy need of the sculpting compound for 2 sculptures?

(1) 6

(2) 12

(3) 15

(4) 60

(5) Not enough information is given.

Questions 5 and 6 are based on the following map.

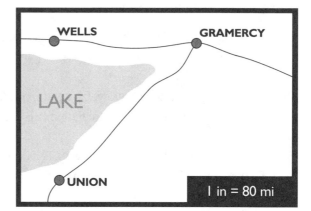

5. On the map the road from Wells to Gramercy is 1.5 inches, and the road from Gramercy to Union is 2 inches. What is the driving distance in miles from Wells to Union?

(1) 3.5

(2) 40

(3) 80

(4) 120

(5) 280

6. The actual distance from a proposed shopping mall to Union is 300 miles. Which expression could be used to find how many inches would represent 300 miles on the map?

(1) $\frac{300\times80}{1}$

(2) $\frac{1+300}{80}$

(3) $\frac{1\times80}{300}$

(4) $\frac{1\times300}{80}$

(5) $\frac{1+80}{300}$

7. Eva makes $12 an hour. Last year, she made 25% less per hour. Which expression could be used to find how many fewer dollars per hour Eva made last year?

(1) $12 ÷ 4

(2) $12 ÷ $\frac{1}{4}$

(3) $12 × $\frac{1}{25}$

(4) 25% × $\frac{1}{4}$

(5) $12 ÷ 25

Questions 8 and 9 are based on the following information.

Mail-Order Linens

SEPTEMBER CATALOG

Twin Bed Quilt $30.00

Full-Size Quilt.........................$40.00

Queen-Size Quilt......................$60.00

King-Size Quilt.........................$80.00

Pillow Sham (All Sizes)...........$15.00

8. From the September catalog, Miko orders a queen-size quilt and two pillow shams. If there is a 5% shipping charge, how much will Miko pay for the order?

(1) $78.75

(2) $90.00

(3) $94.50

(4) $95.00

(5) $99.00

9. In the October catalog, the price for a king-size quilt is marked down 20%. In November, it is reduced another 10%. What is the advertised price in November for a king-size quilt?

(1) $78.40

(2) $68.00

(3) $57.60

(4) $56.00

(5) $50.00

10. At a family reunion, Kay counts 30 of her cousins in a room of 70 relatives. To the nearest whole percent, what percent of relatives in the room are Kay's cousins?

(1) 3%

(2) 23%

(3) 33%

(4) 43%

(5) 57%

11. For one day only, Factory Warehouse, an appliance store, will sell their merchandise for an amount 15% lower than any advertised price from another store. Tami brings in an ad for a microwave priced at $345. How much will the item cost at Factory Warehouse?

(1) $15.00

(2) $51.75

(3) $290.25

(4) $293.25

(5) $330.00

12. Alberto earns $142.60 for 15.5 hours of work. At the same rate, how much would Alberto earn for 40 hours of work?

(1) $368.00

(2) $368.75

(3) $400.00

(4) $468.22

(5) Not enough information is given.

13. Which proportion expression could you write to calculate how many days there are in 390 hours?

(1) $\frac{60}{1} = \frac{390}{x}$

(2) $\frac{1}{24} = \frac{390}{x}$

(3) $\frac{24}{1} = \frac{390}{x}$

(4) $\frac{390 \times 24}{x}$

(5) $\frac{24}{1} = \frac{x}{390}$

PART TWO DIRECTIONS: Choose the <u>one best answer</u> to each of the following problems. *You may not use a calculator on these problems.*

<u>Questions 14 through 16</u> are based on the following information and graph.

A school receives a grant to make improvements to its library. The circle graph shows how the school plans to spend the money.

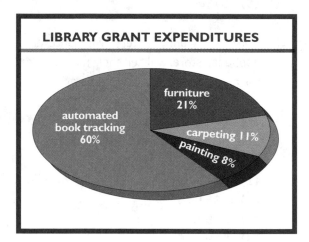

LIBRARY GRANT EXPENDITURES

furniture 21%

automated book tracking 60%

carpeting 11%

painting 8%

14. What percent of the funds will be left after the school paints and carpets the library?
   (1) 3%
   (2) 19%
   (3) 62%
   (4) 81%
   (5) 92%

15. Out of the $15,000 in grant money that the school receives, what amount will be spent on furniture?
   (1) $2,100
   (2) $3,000
   (3) $3,150
   (4) $11,850
   (5) Not enough information is given.

16. What is the ratio of the percent budgeted for painting to the percent budgeted for the automated book tracking system?
   (1) 17:25
   (2) 1:6
   (3) 2:15
   (4) 1:8
   (5) 2:25

17. Los Robles Nursing Home owns a van that gets an average of 24.6 miles per gallon. <u>Approximately</u> how many miles will 5 gallons take the van?
   (1) Between 100 and 115
   (2) Between 115 and 120
   (3) Between 120 and 125
   (4) Between 125 and 130
   (5) Between 130 and 135

18. Last year Chang earned $66 interest on his savings account. The interest rate was 5.5%. How much money was in his account before the interest was added?
   (1) $120
   (2) $1,200
   (3) $6,500
   (4) $9,000
   (5) $12,000

19. Michael sold 55 paperbacks and 33 hardcover books at the neighborhood book fair. What was the ratio of hardcover books sold to <u>all</u> books sold?
   (1) 3:5
   (2) 5:3
   (3) 8:1
   (4) 8:3
   (5) 3:8

<u>Question 20</u> refers to the following information.

CAR STEREO SALE
ONE DAY ONLY
Regular Price: ~~$125.00~~
Sale Price: $68.75

20. What is the rate of decrease from the regular price to the sale price?
   (1) 65%
   (2) 56%
   (3) 54%
   (4) 45%
   (5) 35%

Alternate Math Formats

The questions below are based on the math skills in Programs 31–32. For more information on answering alternate format items, review pages 20–22.

Grid in the answers to questions 21 through 32.

21. The scale on a map is 1 inch = 140 miles. What is the actual distance between two cities that are $3\frac{1}{4}$ inches apart on the map?

22. Brad worked from 8:20 A.M. to 12:20 P.M. Reduced to lowest terms, what fractional part of a 24-hour day did he work?

23. Two gallons of house paint will cover 440 square feet of space. How many gallons will a painter need to buy to cover 2325 square feet of wall space?

24. Caroline bought $4\frac{3}{4}$ yards of fabric to make her daughter a superhero costume. She used $\frac{3}{4}$ of the fabric to make the main body of the costume. How much does she have left to make a cape?

Questions 25 and 26 refer to the chart.

Bonilla Family Monthly Budget	
Housing	$540
Utilities	$85
Transportation	$275
Clothing	$125
Food	$425
Entertainment	$80
Other	$200
Total Budget	**$1730**

25. The Bonillas need to increase their monthly food budget by 5%. How much more money will they budget for food?

26. The Bonillas decide to reduce their transportation expenses by 15% and put the amount into a savings account. What amount do they plan to save each month?

21.

22.

23.

24.

25.

26.

27. Only $\frac{1}{2}$ of the registered voters voted in the last election. Of those who voted, only $\frac{1}{3}$ voted on the referendum. What fraction of the registered voters voted on the referendum?

28. If you want to halve a recipe that calls for $\frac{3}{4}$ teaspoon salt, how much salt should you use?

29. A survey found that $\frac{3}{4}$ of adult students have jobs while going to school. Of those who have jobs, $\frac{3}{5}$ work part-time. What fraction of the adult students who were surveyed work full-time?

30. The sales tax on a VCR selling for $350 is $21. What is the sales tax rate?

Question 31 refers to the following information.

SHAMPOO SALE
Brand A
16 oz
$2.56
Brand B
20 oz
$3.00
Brand C
12 oz
$2.04

31. What is the unit price (price per ounce) for the brand offering the best buy?

32. A recipe calls for $2\frac{1}{2}$ cups of sugar to make 4 dozen cookies. How many cups of sugar would you need to make 10 dozen cookies?

27.

28.

29.

30.

31.

32.

Answers and explanations start on page 317.

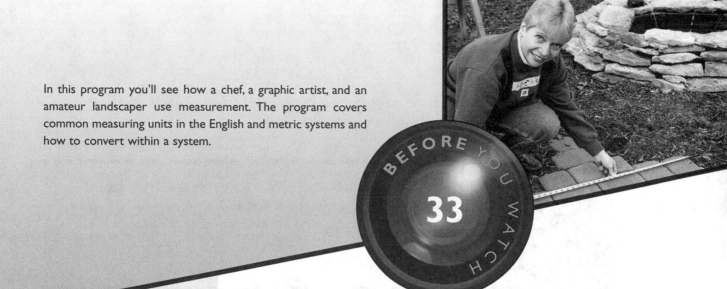

In this program you'll see how a chef, a graphic artist, and an amateur landscaper use measurement. The program covers common measuring units in the English and metric systems and how to convert within a system.

Measurement

OBJECTIVES

1. Estimate and calculate using the English system of measurement.

2. Estimate and calculate using the metric system.

3. Solve for the perimeter and area of regular and irregular shapes.

You have measured the area of your living room in square feet, but carpeting is sold by the square yard. You need to compare two lengths, but one is written in meters and the other in centimeters. These examples call for an understanding of the two measurement systems that are used around the world: the English and the metric systems. With an understanding of the relationships among the units of measure in each system, you can solve these problems.

The ability to work with measurement is important to your success on the GED Math Test. You will need to know how to perform calculations with common units of measure. You may have to convert from one unit of measure to another. You will use formulas for perimeter and area to set up and solve problems. To solve measurement problems, you will also use your understanding of fractions, decimals, ratio and proportion, algebra, and geometry.

On the following pages, you will find a brief exercise called *Sneak Preview*. It is designed to introduce you to the topics that will be featured in the video program and the corresponding lesson. After you complete the exercise and check your answers, turn to the vocabulary page. There you will find terms that will help you better understand the video and the lesson that follow. After reviewing page 132, you will be ready to watch Program 33.

For additional practice, visit *LiteracyLink* **online at http://www.pbs.org/literacy.**

Sneak Preview

This exercise previews some of the concepts from Program 33. After you answer the questions, use the feedback on page 131 to help set your learning goals.

 **WORKPLACE LINK:** Noah runs a small painting business. He specializes in custom finishes and glazes. He was recently hired to paint the main dining room in a local restaurant. The restaurant wants the walls to be light green with a chalky finish. Noah's paint recipe and the dimensions of the dining room are shown below.

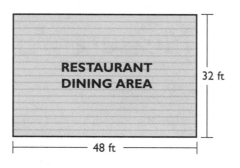

PAINT RECIPE			
Coat	**Ingredients**	**Quantity**	**Coverage**
Gesso Coat	white acrylic gesso	1 liter	15 square meters or 17.5 square yards
Base Coat	white latex flat paint	1 gallon	800 square feet
Glaze Coat	white latex flat paint acrylic glaze emerald green acrylic coloring brilliant green acrylic coloring cobalt green acrylic coloring water	1 pint 1 pint 6 fluid ounces 6 fluid ounces 3 fluid ounces 7 fluid ounces	160 square feet
Protective Coat	clear imported varnish	1.8 liters	200 square feet

Answer these questions based on the information above.

1. Noah has a 5-gallon can of white latex flat paint. How many batches of glaze coat can he make using the 5 gallons? (*Hint:* Use these facts: 2 pints = 1 quart, and 4 quarts = 1 gallon.)

   (1) 10
   (2) 20
   (3) 25
   (4) 40
   (5) 80

MATHEMATICS

2. Noah has four small containers of imported varnish. Each container holds 1200 milliliters of varnish. Noah wants to use the varnish for the protective coat in his paint recipe. If he pours all the varnish together, how many <u>liters</u> of varnish will he have? (*Hint:* There are 1000 milliliters in 1 liter.)

   (1) 0.048
   (2) 0.48
   (3) 4.8
   (4) 48
   (5) 480

3. The restaurant owner asks Noah to install a decorative molding around the edge of the room near the ceiling. Which expression could be used to find the number of feet of molding that Noah will need to do the job?

   (1) $32 + 48$
   (2) $2 \times 32 \times 48$
   (3) $(2 \times 32) + (2 \times 48)$
   (4) $\frac{32 + 48}{2}$
   (5) 32×48

4. To estimate the cost of materials and labor for the job, Noah needs to know the area of each wall. Each wall is 8 feet high. What is the area in square feet of one of the walls that measures 48 feet in length?

   (1) 6
   (2) 56
   (3) 112
   (4) 384
   (5) 640

Feedback

- If you got all of the answers right...   you have a good basic understanding of English and metric measurement systems.

- If you missed question 1...   you need to work on your knowledge of appropriate measuring units and conversions within the English measurement system.

- If you missed question 2...   you need to work on your understanding of the metric system and how to use its units to make calculations and conversions.

- If you missed question 3...   you need to work with methods for finding the perimeter of rectangles.

- If you missed question 4...   you need to work with finding the area of common shapes.

Vocabulary for *Measurement*

area	the measure of the surface of a flat figure
base	a number that appears with an exponent; the base is multiplied by itself the number of times indicated by the exponent; for example, in 3^2, 3 is the base
benchmark	a common object that can help you remember the relative size of a unit of measure
English system	the measurement system most commonly used in the United States
equivalency	a statement that tells the number of one measurement unit that is equal to another measurement unit; for example, 12 inches = 1 foot
exponent	a number written slightly above and to the right of a base number to specify the number of times to multiply the base by itself; for example, in 3^2, 2 is the exponent
length	a measure of distance
metric system	a measurement system based on the powers of ten; used outside the United States and in science and medicine
perimeter	the distance around a flat figure
power	the number of times a base is multiplied; a base is said to be raised to a certain power, which is indicated by an exponent
volume	the amount a three-dimensional object holds
weight	a measure of heaviness

MATHEMATICS

➡ **NOW WATCH PROGRAM 33:**

Think about the kinds of measurements you use for distance, size, weight, and time. Do you use English, metric, or both? Which system do you think is easier to remember and convert?

After you watch the program, work on:

- pages 133–148 in this workbook
- Internet activities at http://www.pbs.org/literacy

Measurement

On the following pages, you will learn more about the ideas discussed in the video program and have an opportunity to develop and practice your GED math skills.

GED TIPS

When taking the GED Test, you should:

- Read measurement problems carefully to find out the measurement unit in which to express your answer.
- Estimate an answer before you begin calculations; then use the estimate to make sure your answer makes sense.
- Use benchmarks to check the reasonableness of your answers.

Key Points to Think About

In the video program, you explored:

- How people use measurement, both the **English** and **metric systems,** in their daily lives as workers, citizens, and family members.
- **Benchmarks** to help you remember the relative size of the measurement units for **length, weight,** and **volume.**
- Everyday problem-solving situations involving measurement, such as those that deal with **perimeter** and **area.**

On the GED Math Test:

- You will be expected to know how to add, subtract, multiply, and divide measurements using both the English and metric systems.
- You will need to know how to convert from one unit to another within the same measurement system.
- You will use formulas to solve problems involving perimeter and area.

As you work through the lesson for Program 33:

- Look for things in your everyday experience that will help you remember the size of different measurement units.
- Memorize the common equivalencies for each measurement system.
- Be aware of the many ways measurement is used in your daily life, not just on the GED Math Test.

The English System of Measurement

COMMUNITY LINK: Brenda parks her car next to the curb. Just ahead of her car is a fire hydrant. Brenda knows she has to leave 15 feet between her car and the hydrant, but the curbs haven't been painted yet, and she isn't sure of the distance. Brenda walks heel to toe to estimate the distance and avoid a parking ticket.

Finding Benchmarks

Measurement systems are used to measure length, weight, and volume (how much something holds). The standard units of measure used in the United States are part of the English system of measurement.

A benchmark is a common object that can be used as a reference for the estimate of a unit of measure. In the situation above, Brenda knows that the length of her foot is nearly equal to a foot, so she uses her foot as a benchmark to estimate the distance to the hydrant. On the GED Math Test, benchmarks can help you decide whether your answer seems reasonable. Memorize the benchmarks from the table below or create your own.

LENGTH	inch foot yard	the width of two fingers the length of your foot the length of your stride
WEIGHT	ounce pound	weight of an envelope weight of a box of powdered sugar
VOLUME	fluid ounce cup gallon	the amount a tablespoon holds a carton of yogurt a large plastic jug of milk

Making Measurement Conversions

In many situations that you encounter in daily life, you need to be able to change a measurement from one unit to another. You will also need this skill to solve problems on the GED Math Test.

To make measurement conversions, you need to know the basic equivalencies shown below.

LENGTH

1 foot (ft) = 12 inches (in)
1 yard (yd) = 3 feet = 36 inches
1 mile (mi) = 5280 feet

TIME

1 minute (min) = 60 seconds (sec)
1 hour (hr) = 60 minutes
1 day = 24 hours
1 week (wk) = 7 days
1 year (yr) = 365 days

VOLUME

1 cup (c) = 8 fluid ounces (fl oz)
1 pint (pt) = 2 cups
1 quart (qt) = 2 pints = 4 cups
1 gallon (gal) = 4 quarts

WEIGHT

1 pound (lb) = 16 ounces (oz)
1 ton = 2000 pounds

> **Volume** defines how much an object holds.
>
> **Weight** defines how heavy an object is.

To change from one unit of measure to another, write a proportion. Make sure both ratios are written with the labels *in the same order.*

▶▶ This problem changes from a larger unit to a smaller one.

Example: Ky is guessing that she will need 1 cup of punch per guest for an open house. A punch concentrate makes 9 quarts. Ky wants to know how many cups are in 9 quarts to figure out how many guests the punch will serve.

Write a proportion using 1 quart = 4 cups. $\frac{1 \text{ qt}}{4 \text{ c}} = \frac{9 \text{ qt}}{x \text{ c}}$

Find the cross product and divide by $9 \times 4 \div 1 = 36$
the remaining term.

Answer: 9 quarts is equal to **36 cups.**
Check: Make sure cross products are equal: $1 \times 36 = 4 \times 9$.

> When you convert *from a larger unit to a smaller one*, the new number will be larger than the starting number.

▶▶ Notice how the remainder is handled in this situation.

Example: How many feet are in 174 inches?

Write a proportion using the fact that $\frac{1 \text{ ft}}{12 \text{ in}} = \frac{x \text{ ft}}{174 \text{ in}}$
1 foot = 12 inches.

Find the cross product and divide by $1 \times 174 \div 12 = 14 \text{ r}6$
the remaining term.

> When you convert *from a smaller unit to a larger one*, the new number will be smaller than the starting number.

Answer: 174 inches is equal to **14 feet 6 inches or $14\frac{1}{2}$ feet.** *Check:* Work backward. Multiply the number of feet by 12 inches and add the remainder. There are 168 inches in 14 feet ($14 \times 12 = 168$). Add the remainder: $168 + 6 = 174$ inches.

SKILL PRACTICE

Solve each problem.

1. Which of these units would most likely be used to express the weight of a deck of cards?

   (1) fluid ounces   (4) pounds
   (2) pints   (5) ounces
   (3) inches

2. How many quarts of oil are in the container below?

   (1) $3\frac{1}{8}$
   (2) 21
   (3) 42
   (4) 84
   (5) 168

   RECYCLED OIL $10\frac{1}{2}$ GALLONS

3. The centerfield fence at a baseball stadium is 415 feet from home plate. What is the distance, rounded to the nearest yard?

   (1) 36   (4) 1,245
   (2) 138   (5) 4,980
   (3) 432

4. Suppose you need to change 10,560 yards to miles.

   a. Would you expect the answer to be greater or less than 10,560? Why?
   b. Describe how you could use the equivalencies on page 134 to find the number of miles in 10,560 yards.

Answers and explanations start on page 317.

Solving Everyday Measurement Problems

Two common measurement situations are finding a total and finding the difference between measurements. You can add or subtract measurements if they are written in the same units. On the GED Math Test, look at the answer choices to find out which measurement unit is best to use.

▶▶ This situation compares amounts of time written in different units.

Example: Jennifer spent 200 minutes working on a special project. Eva contributed $1\frac{3}{4}$ hours to the same project. How much longer did Jennifer work than Eva?

    (1)   25 minutes
    (2)   45 minutes
    (3)   95 minutes
    (4)   105 minutes
    (5)   140 minutes

> Refer to page 336 of the Math Handbook for a table of common measurement equivalencies.

You're right if you chose **(3) 95 minutes.** The quantity $1\frac{3}{4}$ hours is equal to 60 minutes + 45 minutes, or 105 minutes. Subtract: $200 - 105 = 95$ minutes.

In many problems, you will need to multiply or divide a measurement. Usually, the work will be easier if you convert the measurement to one unit. For example, 1 foot 6 inches can be written $1\frac{1}{2}$ feet, 1.5 feet, or 18 inches.

▶▶ A problem may be easier to solve if you express the amount using fractions or decimals.

Example: As a shipping clerk, Omar has to check orders before they leave the warehouse. A customer bought 7 of the same item. According to the shipping invoice, the weight of one item is 1 lb 12 oz. What is the total weight of the shipment?

    (1)   19 lb 6 oz
    (2)   14 lb 4 oz
    (3)   12 lb 8 oz
    (4)   12 lb 4 oz
    (5)   7 lb 12 oz

You're right if you chose **(4) 12 lb 4 oz.**

You need to multiply 1 lb 12 oz by 7. One way to solve the problem is to express the weight in ounces and then multiply. Remember, 16 ounces = 1 pound.

1 lb 12 oz = 16 oz + 12 oz = 28 oz

Multiply by 7: $28 \times 7 = 196$ oz.
Divide by 16 to convert back to pounds: $196 \div 16 = 12$ r4, or 12 lb 4 oz.

If you recognize that 12 ounces is $\frac{12}{16}$ or $\frac{3}{4}$ of a pound, you can solve the problem more quickly using fractions or decimals.

Express the weight in pounds: 1 lb 12 oz = $1\frac{3}{4}$ lb
Multiply by 7: $1\frac{3}{4} \times 7 = \frac{7}{4} \times 7 = \frac{49}{4} = 12\frac{1}{4}$ lb or 12 lb 4 oz.

To use your calculator, change the fraction to a decimal. Use 0.75 for $\frac{3}{4}$.

Calculator: $\boxed{1}\ \boxed{.}\ \boxed{7}\ \boxed{5}\ \boxed{\times}\ \boxed{7}\ \boxed{=}\ \boxed{12.25}$

Remember, 0.25 is equal to $\frac{1}{4}$, so 12.25 = $12\frac{1}{4}$ lb, which equals 12 lb 4 oz.

SKILL PRACTICE

Solve each problem. Remember, you can only add or subtract measurements if they are written using the same unit of measure.

1. Delia is a manicurist. If she spends 20 minutes per client, how many clients can she see in a 5-hour workday? (*Hint:* Find how many times 20 minutes divides into 1 hour.)

2. Eunsook is making treat bags for her child's birthday party. If she puts 6 ounces of candy in each bag, how many bags can she fill from a 3-pound bag of candy?

3. Which is greater: 5 gallons 3 quarts or 100 cups? How do you know?

4. It takes 12 ounces of pancake mix for Andre to feed his children breakfast. How many breakfasts can he make from the box?

    COUNTRY
    pancakes

    NET WEIGHT 3 lb 12 oz

    (1) 2
    (2) 3
    (3) 4
    (4) 5
    (5) 6

CALCULATOR Connection

A calculator is useful when working with measurements, but you need to make sure that you interpret the decimal remainder correctly.

Example: How many feet are in 57 inches? Remember, 1 foot = 12 inches.

Step 1. You can find the answer on your calculator by dividing 57 by 12.

Calculator: $\boxed{5}\ \boxed{7}\ \boxed{\div}\ \boxed{1}\ \boxed{2}\ \boxed{=}\ \boxed{4.75}$

Step 2. What does the decimal part of the display represent? Since 0.75 is equal to the fraction $\frac{3}{4}$, the answer is $4\frac{3}{4}$ feet. You can also express the remainder using inches. Since 1 foot is 12 inches, $\frac{3}{4}$ of a foot is 9 inches. Therefore, 57 inches is equal to 4 feet 9 inches.

Try these on your calculator.

1. How many hours are in 375 minutes? (Remember, 1 hour = 60 minutes.)
2. How many pounds are in 152 ounces? (Remember, 1 pound = 16 ounces.)

Answers and explanations start on page 317.

The Metric System

WORKPLACE LINK: Ben's doctor instructed him to take 50 milligrams of an over-the-counter medication for his allergies. The medicine comes in 12.5-milligram tablets. Ben figures out that he will need to take four tablets per day to get the amount of medication his doctor recommends.

Understanding Metric Units

Our number system is a place-value system based on tens. Each place-value column is ten times greater than the one on its right. The metric system is also based on tens. It was developed by scientists to make it easier to make measurement calculations using our place-value system of numbers.

The metric system uses three basic units of measure. These units can be multiplied or divided by 10, 100, 1000, and so on to make larger or smaller units.

The Basic Metric Units

meter (m) a little more than 1 yard, a long stride
gram (g)   about $\frac{1}{30}$ of an ounce, the weight of a paper clip
liter (L) a little more than a quart, half of a 2-liter bottle of soda pop

---

To form the names for larger and smaller units of measure, we add prefixes to the basic units.

kilo- means 1000   centi- means $\frac{1}{100}$ milli- means $\frac{1}{1000}$

Add the prefixes to the base words to make new units:

- A millimeter (mm) is $\frac{1}{1000}$ of a meter, the width of a pencil point.
- A centimeter (cm) is $\frac{1}{100}$ of a meter, the width of a pencil.
- A milligram (mg) is $\frac{1}{1000}$ of a gram, the weight of a grain of sand.
- A kilogram (kg) is 1000 grams, about the weight of a hardcover book.

Making Metric Conversions

On the GED Math Test, you will be expected to solve problems using the metric system. To answer an item, you may need to change from one metric unit to another. However, you will not be asked to make conversions between the English and metric systems.

To make measurement conversions, you need to know the basic equivalencies shown below.

LENGTH	WEIGHT	VOLUME
1 meter (m) = 1000 millimeters (mm)	1 gram (g) = 1000 milligrams (mg)	1 liter (L) = 1000 milliliters (mL)
1 meter = 100 centimeters (cm)	1 kilogram (kg) = 1000 grams	
1 centimeter = 10 millimeters		
1 kilometer (km) = 1000 meters		

When using the metric system, you can make conversions by multiplying or dividing by 10, 100, or 1000.

▶▶ Study these examples to see how decimals are used in the metric system.

Example: A pencil is 95 millimeters long. What is the length in centimeters?

You know that 1 cm = 10 mm. To change 95 mm to cm, divide by 10. Remember, you can quickly divide by 10 by moving the decimal point one place to the left.

95 mm = 9.5 cm

Answer: The pencil is **9.5 cm** long. *Check:* Centimeters are larger than millimeters, so the number of centimeters will be less. The answer 9.5 cm makes sense.

Example: A banner is 3.9 meters in length. What is its length in centimeters?

You know that 1 m = 100 cm. To change 3.9 m to cm, multiply by 100 by moving the decimal point two places to the right.

3.9 m = 390. cm

Answer: The banner is **390 cm** long. *Check:* Centimeters are much smaller than meters, so the number of centimeters needed should be much more. The answer 390 cm is reasonable.

SKILL PRACTICE

Solve each problem. For questions 1–6, write the metric unit of measure you would use for each item.

1. height of a doorway

2. weight of a bag of flour

3. amount of water in a teaspoon

4. distance from work to home

5. thickness of a piece of cardboard

6. gasoline in a gas tank

7. Write the weights of the packages below in order from least to greatest.

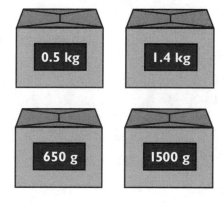

8. A container holds 3.54 liters of lotion. If the lotion is poured into 12 equal smaller bottles, how many milliliters will each smaller bottle hold? (*Hint:* First find the number of milliliters in the container.)

   (1) 2950 mL   (4) 2.95 mL
   (2) 295 mL   (5) 0.295 mL
   (3) 29.5 mL

9. Luis ran four laps on a 750-meter track. How many kilometers did he run? (*Hint:* Find out how many meters he ran in all, then convert to kilometers.)

   (1) 3   (4) 3000
   (2) 30   (5) Not enough
   (3) 300   information
                    is given.

10. A friend claims that 1,000,000 millimeters is equal to 1 kilometer. Do you agree? Prove your answer.

FAMILY LINK: Paul's three children love instant macaroni and cheese. Lately, Paul has been concerned that his children are getting too much fat in their diet. He checks the package and finds that it contains 55.5 grams of fat. He divides by 3 to find that each child is getting 18.5 grams of fat from the product. Paul decides to provide more healthful choices.

Solving Everyday Problems

Many of the products we use at home and at work are sold internationally. Because the metric system is used all over the world, many product labels now contain information in metric units. As time goes by, Americans will need to be comfortable using and understanding the metric system to solve problems.

> Common metric equivalencies can be found on page 336 of the Math Handbook.

One of the most common problem-solving situations is finding a unit rate. In the situation above, Paul knows the amount of fat in the entire dish, and he uses that information to find the amount of fat each child is consuming. He solves for the unit rate, the amount per child.

▶▶ Apply what you know about ratio and proportion in this problem.

Example: Nicola and her family are driving from Montreal to Toronto, a distance of 542 kilometers. They complete the drive in 6.5 hours. To the nearest tenth, how many kilometers per hour did they drive?

(1)	9.8	**(4)**	98.8
(2)	35.2	**(5)**	833.8
(3)	83.4		

You're right if you chose **(3) 83.4.** The ratio of kilometers to hours is 542 to 6.5. You want to find the number of kilometers driven in 1 hour.

Write a proportion and solve: $\frac{542 \text{ km}}{6.5 \text{ hr}} = \frac{x}{1 \text{ hr}}$ 542 × 1 ÷ 6.5 is approximately 83.38, which rounds to 83.4

Because the metric system uses decimals, your calculator can be a useful tool working with metric units.

▶▶ Use a calculator to perform the operations needed to solve this problem.

Example: Mikail has to weld three lengths of pipe to make a single piece. Each of the two welds will destroy approximately 0.5 cm of metal. If the three pieces are 65.8 centimeters, 1.5 meters, and 70.4 centimeters, what is the length of the final piece?

(1)	127.7 cm	**(4)**	276.2 cm
(2)	136.7 cm	**(5)**	285.2 cm
(3)	176.2 cm		

Carefully study the step-by-step instructions on the next page.

MATHEMATICS

To solve the problem, first look at the answer choices. All the choices are written in centimeters. Save time by making sure all your calculations are done in centimeters. Convert 1.5 meters to centimeters by multiplying by 100.

Calculator: $\boxed{1} \boxed{.} \boxed{5} \boxed{\times} \boxed{1} \boxed{0} \boxed{0} \boxed{=} \boxed{ 150.}$

To find the total length of the welded pipe, add the three pieces and subtract the part destroyed by the welding process: $0.5 \times 2 = 1$ cm.

Calculator: $\boxed{6} \boxed{5} \boxed{.} \boxed{8} \boxed{+} \boxed{1} \boxed{5} \boxed{0} \boxed{+} \boxed{7} \boxed{0} \boxed{.} \boxed{4} \boxed{-} \boxed{1} \boxed{=} \boxed{ 285.2}$

Answer: The only choice that shows the correct length of the finished piece is **(5) 285.2 cm.**
Check: Don't forget the importance of estimation. Two of the measurements are close to 70 cm. Double 70 in your head and add 150. The answer must be close to 290. Only choice (5) makes sense.

SKILL PRACTICE

Solve each problem. Use a calculator when needed.

1. A package weighs 1.825 kilograms. Jung Yi will have to pay extra for weight over 1.6 kilograms. How many <u>grams</u> over the weight limit is the package?

2. A board is 1.16 meters long. The board is cut into 4 equal pieces. How many meters long is each piece?

3. Twenty-two grams of juice concentrate make 240 milliliters of cranberry juice. How much juice can you make from 308 grams of concentrate?

4. Which is greater: 505 milligrams or 3 grams? How much greater?

SCIENCE **Connection**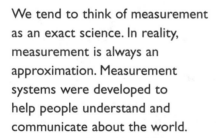

We tend to think of measurement as an exact science. In reality, measurement is always an approximation. Measurement systems were developed to help people understand and communicate about the world.

A year represents the time it takes for the earth to orbit the sun once. We say that 1 year equals 365 days, but the true length of a year is closer to 365.26 days.

Using the more accurate measure, explain why we add an extra day to our calendar every four years, during leap year. *Hint:* We make this adjustment to correct our inexact measurement of the Earth's voyage around the sun.

Answers and explanations start on page 317.

Finding Perimeter and Area

FAMILY LINK: Shandra wants to build a brick path from her patio to her garden. First, she will define the rectangular path with lumber and level the ground. Then she will create a pattern with bricks. To buy the lumber, she needs to measure the perimeter of the rectangle. To buy the bricks, she needs to measure the area, the surface within the rectangle.

Understanding Perimeter and Area

Perimeter is the distance around a flat figure. Perimeter is measured in units of length. Area is the measure of the surface inside a flat figure. Area is measured in square units.

▶▶ Find the perimeter and area of the square pictured below.

Example: A garden is in the shape of a square. Each side of the garden measures 3 meters. Find the perimeter and area.

The perimeter is the distance around the garden. Since the garden has 4 equal sides, and each side measures 3 meters, the perimeter is **12 meters.**

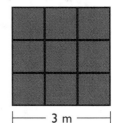

$\vdash$ — 3 m — $\dashv$

$$4 \times 3 = 12 \text{ meters} \quad \text{or} \quad 3 + 3 + 3 + 3 = 12 \text{ meters}$$

The area is measured in square meters. Notice that the garden has been divided into squares, each side 1 meter in length. Count the squares. The area of the garden is **9 square meters.** We can find the area by multiplying the width and the length: $3 \times 3 = 9$ square meters.

Working with Squares and Rectangles

Formulas are useful for finding the perimeter and area of common shapes. Study these formulas.

Rectangles

Perimeter of a rectangle: $P = 2l + 2w$, where P = perimeter, l = length, and w = width
Area of a rectangle: $A = lw$, where A = area, l = length, and w = width

---

See how the formulas are applied to find the area and perimeter of a rectangular brick walkway.

Example: Shandra's rectangular brick walkway is 20 feet long and 2.5 feet wide. Using the formulas above, find the perimeter and area of the walkway.

Perimeter: $P = 2l + 2w$ $= 2(20) + 2(2.5)$ 20(2.5) $= 40 + 5$ square feet $= 45$ feet	**Area:** $A = lw$ $=$ $= 50$

> When variables or numbers and variables are written next to each other, the values are multiplied.
>
> **Example:**
> $2w$ means $2 \times w$.

Answer: The perimeter of the walkway is **45 feet,** and the area is **50 square feet.**

MATHEMATICS

A square is a rectangle with sides that are the same length. Use the formulas below to find the perimeter and area of a square.

Squares

Perimeter of a square: $P = 4s$, where P = perimeter and s = side
Area of a square: $A = s^2$, where A = area and s = side

The formula for the area of a square uses a special number called an **exponent,** or **power.** The variable s stands for the length of the side of the square. This number is called the **base.** The small 2 is the exponent. An exponent tells you how many times to multiply the base by itself. The expression s^2 is read "s *to the second power*" or "s *squared.*" It means "s *multiplied by* s."

▶▶ Study this example to see how exponents are used.

Example: The length of one side of a square patio is 8 feet. Find the perimeter and area of the patio.

Perimeter: $P = 4s$	**Area:** $A = s^2$
$= 4(8)$	$= 8^2$
$= 32$ feet	$= 8 \times 8$
	$= 64$ square feet

> Knowing how to apply a formula can help you find the correct set-up for a problem on the GED Math Test.

Answer: The perimeter of the patio is **32 feet,** and the area is **64 square feet.**

SKILL PRACTICE

Solve each problem.

1. Find the area and perimeter of a square that measures 15 inches per side.

2. The area of a rectangle is 48 square centimeters. Its perimeter is 38 centimeters. Find the length and width of the rectangle. (*Hint:* You'll need to experiment with the numbers. Think of possible dimensions that would give you 48 sq cm. Then check those dimensions to see if they result in the correct perimeter.)

3. Which of the following expressions can be used to find the perimeter of the rectangle shown below?

    (1) $1.5 + 5 + 5$
    (2) $5(1.5 + 1.5)$
    (3) $2(5) + 2(1.5)$
    (4) $1.5(5)$
    (5) $1.5(5 + 5)$

    1.5 m
    5 m

4. Field hockey is played on a rectangular field that is 60 yards wide and 100 yards long. Lacrosse is played on a rectangular field that is 70 yards by 120 yards.

    a. Which sport requires a larger field?
    b. What is the difference in area between the two fields?

5. Martha is sewing a holiday table covering to fit a rectangular table. She plans to add a lace border that will fit around the outside edge of the table covering. If the dimensions of the tablecloth are 105 by 165 centimeters, how many <u>meters</u> of lace will she need to complete the border?

    (1) 2.7   (4) 54
    (2) 5.4   (5) 173.25
    (3) 27

Answers and explanations start on page 318.

Working with Irregular Shapes

Not all shapes are simple squares and rectangles. Some irregular shapes are a combination of several shapes. To find the perimeter of an irregular shape, add the lengths of all the sides. Use logic and common sense to find the lengths of any missing measurements.

▶▶ Use logical thinking to find the lengths of the missing sides.

Example: The diagram shows the swimming pool described at the top of the page. Find the perimeter of the pool.

Before you can add the sides, you need to find the missing lengths. Look at the top edge of the pool. You can see that the top edge is the sum of the width of the swimming lanes and the length of the free play area.
    Add: 23 + 67 = 90 meters

To find the width of the free play area, use logical reasoning. You know that the width plus the side marked 70 m equals the length of the swimming lanes or 100 m. Subtract to find the difference.
    Subtract: 100 − 70 = 30 meters

Now find the perimeter by adding all the sides:
100 + 23 + 70 + 67 + 30 + 90 = 380 meters

Answer: The perimeter of the pool is **380 meters.**

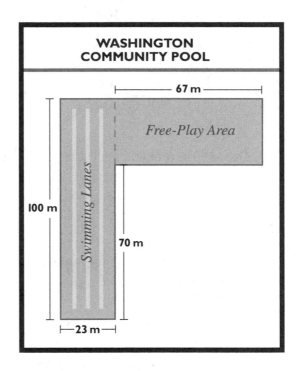

WASHINGTON COMMUNITY POOL

67 m

Free-Play Area

Swimming Lanes

100 m

70 m

23 m

▶▶ Think of the pool as two rectangles to find the area.

Example: Arliss divides the L-shaped pool into two rectangles so that she can use the formula for finding the area of a rectangle.

The rectangle that forms the swimming lanes is 100 m long and 23 m wide. Use the dimensions to find the area of the swimming lanes.

The rectangle that forms the free-play area is 67 m long and 30 m wide. Use the dimensions to find the area of the free-play section.

> Remember that area is expressed in square units.

$A = lw$
$= 100 \times 23$
$= 2300$ square meters

$A = lw$
$= 67 \times 30$
$= 2010$ square meters

MATHEMATICS

Add to find the total area. $2300 + 2010 = 4310$ square meters

Answer: Arliss will tell the city contractor that the area of the pool is **4310 square meters.**

SKILL PRACTICE

A community member has donated a small lot to be used as a parking lot for a public library and recreation center. The figure below shows the dimensions of the lot.

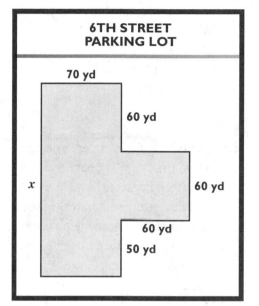

1. Which of the following expressions can be used to find the length of side *x*?

   (1) 50×3 **(4)** $70 + 60$
   (2) $50 + 60^2$ **(5)** $60 + 60 + 50$
   (3) 60^2

2. What is the perimeter of the parking lot in yards?

   (1) 600   **(4)** 430
   (2) 540   **(5)** 300
   (3) 470

3. Find the area of the parking lot in square yards. (*Hint:* The shape is a combination of a square and a rectangle.)

   (1) 16,800   **(4)** 11,900
   (2) 15,500   **(5)** 10,800
   (3) 14,400

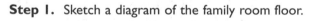

PROBLEM SOLVER Connection

When working with perimeters and areas on the GED test, it makes sense to sketch a diagram. This will help you visualize the measurements you know and solve for the missing measurement.

Example: The Park family is planning to carpet their family room, which measures 18 feet by 24 feet. They will <u>not</u> need to carpet the fireplace hearth, a 3-ft-by-6-ft area centered on one of the 18-foot walls. How many <u>square yards</u> of carpet will they need?

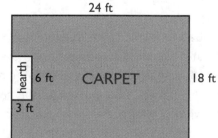

Step 1. Sketch a diagram of the family room floor.

Step 2. Figure the total area of the room ($18 \times 24 = 432$ sq ft) and subtract the floor area covered by the hearth ($3 \times 6 = 18$ sq ft): 432 sq ft − 18 sq ft = 414 sq ft.

Step 3. Convert 414 square feet to square yards. (Remember, 9 sq ft = 1 sq yd.)

How many square yards of carpet do the Parks need?

PART ONE DIRECTIONS: Choose the <u>one best answer</u> to each of the following problems. Use a calculator wherever necessary.

1. Julia taught her son a benchmark for counting: "ONE, one thousand, TWO, one thousand, THREE, one thousand." What is Julia's son most likely measuring?
   (1) inches
   (2) feet
   (3) seconds
   (4) minutes
   (5) hours

2. On Munsen Freeway, emergency call boxes are 0.5 mile apart and are numbered consecutively. To help two stranded vehicles, a patrol officer would have to drive how many miles from Call Box 1 to Call Box 6?
   (1) 2.5
   (2) 3
   (3) 3.5
   (4) 4
   (5) 4.5

3. How many days are in 6216 hours?
   (1) 259
   (2) 269
   (3) 359
   (4) 518
   (5) 528

4. Lauren plans to make lemonade to sell at a school fund-raiser. Each glass holds $1\frac{1}{2}$ cups of lemonade. She estimates that she can sell 200 glasses. To the nearest whole gallon, how many gallons of lemonade should she make?
   (1) 15
   (2) 18
   (3) 19
   (4) 20
   (5) 30

Questions 5 and 6 are based on the following table.

U.S. Mountains	Altitude in Feet
Mount McKinley	20,320
Mount Rainier	14,410
Wheeler Peak	13,161
Borah Peak	12,662
Mount Hood	11,239

5. Which of the locations in the table has an altitude of nearly $2\frac{1}{2}$ miles?
   (1) Mount McKinley
   (2) Mount Rainier
   (3) Wheeler Peak
   (4) Borah Peak
   (5) Mount Hood

6. Which expression could be used to find the difference in miles between the highest and lowest mountains?
   (1) $20,320 - 11,239 - 5,280$
   (2) $(20,320 - 11,239) \times 5,280$
   (3) $20,320 - 11,239 + 5,280$
   (4) $\frac{(20,320 + 11,239)}{5,280}$
   (5) $\frac{(20,320 - 11,239)}{5,280}$

7. A distance of 2.8 kilometers is equal to how many meters?
   (1) 280,000   (4) 280
   (2) 28,000   (5) 28
   (3) 2,800

8. Each serving in a box of breakfast cereal has 280 milligrams of sodium. If there are 14 servings in the box, how many <u>grams</u> of sodium are in the box?
   (1) 0.392
   (2) 3.92
   (3) 39.2
   (4) 392
   (5) Not enough information is given.

MATHEMATICS

Question 9 is based on the following information.

Lamont gave his mother a gift coupon for 10 hours of work. Here is a list of what he has accomplished so far:

polished silverware—1 hr 10 min
repaired Mom's bike—1 hr 40 min
painted tool shed—2 hr 30 min

9. Which expression shows how much time Lamont still owes his mother?
   (1) $600 - 70 - 100 - 150$
   (2) $\dfrac{600}{(70 + 100 + 150)}$
   (3) $10 - 70 - 100 - 150$
   (4) $10 - 1.10 - 1.40 - 2.30$
   (5) $1000 - 110 - 140 - 230$

10. A painting measures 18 inches by 24 inches. How many <u>feet</u> of framing will be needed to frame the painting?
    (1) 3.5
    (2) 5
    (3) 5.5
    (4) 7
    (5) 36

11. In mixing a fruit punch, Garth is to add 4 fluid ounces of syrup to 1 gallon of water. How many cups of syrup will he need to add to a $2\frac{1}{2}$-gallon punchbowl of water?
    (1) $\frac{1}{4}$
    (2) $\frac{1}{2}$
    (3) 1
    (4) $1\frac{1}{4}$
    (5) $1\frac{1}{2}$

12. Using a meter stick, Kyle measures the length of a laundry room. The room's length measures 3 meters, 42 centimeters, and 5 millimeters. Which of the following numbers expresses the length of the room in meters?
    (1) 3.47
    (2) 3.425
    (3) 3.4205
    (4) 3.0425
    (5) 0.3425

Questions 13 through 15 are based on the following information.

Portable Puppy Runs are collapsible enclosures for puppies. Two popular models are shown below.

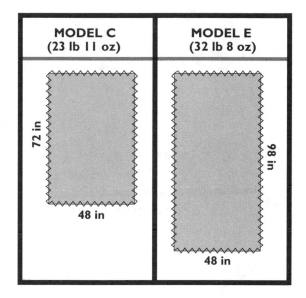

| MODEL C (23 lb 11 oz) | MODEL E (32 lb 8 oz) |

13. Both puppy runs have the same width, but they differ in length. How much longer is Model E than Model C?
    (1) 2 ft 8 in
    (2) 2 ft 4 in
    (3) 2 ft 2 in
    (4) 1 ft 2 in
    (5) Not enough information is given.

14. If George's puppy, Biffy, runs around the entire perimeter of Model E once, <u>approximately</u> how many yards has Biffy traveled?
    (1) 26
    (2) 24
    (3) 12
    (4) 8
    (5) 4

15. How much less does the smaller run weigh than the larger run?
    (1) 8 lb 13 oz
    (2) 8 lb 15 oz
    (3) 9 lb 3 oz
    (4) 9 lb 13 oz
    (5) 11 lb 13 oz

16. Annika needs $4\frac{5}{8}$ yards of material to make a dress. How many dresses can she make from a bolt of fabric containing 50 yards?

(1) 10
(2) 11
(3) 12
(4) 13
(5) 14

17. Rex has 7 hours to weed three gardens. If each one will take about the same amount of time, how much time should he expect to spend at each garden?

(1) 1 hr 20 min
(2) 2 hr 10 min
(3) 2 hr 20 min
(4) $2\frac{1}{2}$ hr
(5) $2\frac{2}{3}$ hr

18. Tamara can run 3 kilometers in 8 minutes. At that rate, how many meters can she run in 1 minute?

(1) $\frac{3}{8}$
(2) 8
(3) 24
(4) 240
(5) 375

19. Ted's seminar, "How to Tie Knots," uses 8-inch lengths of string. How many 8-inch lengths can Tom cut from 5 yards of string?

(1) 180
(2) 90
(3) 23
(4) 22
(5) Not enough information is given.

Questions 20 and 21 are based on the following diagram.

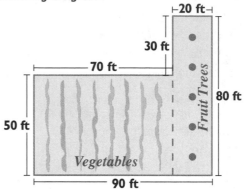

20. A neighborhood association decides to plant a community garden on a vacant lot. If they build a fence around the entire garden, how many feet of fencing will they need?

(1) 310   **(4)** 510
(2) 340   **(5)** 720
(3) 450

21. The neighbors plan to fertilize the vegetable garden. Each bag of fertilizer covers 800 square feet. How many bags of fertilizer will they need to buy to fertilize only the vegetable portion of the garden?

(1) 9   **(4)** 5
(2) 7   **(5)** 3
(3) 6

22. If the TV screen is flat, which expression would best describe the screen's area in square inches?

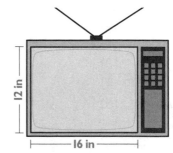

(1) 16×12

(2) $16 + 16 + 12 + 12$

(3) $16 + 12$

(4) $\frac{16 + 12}{2}$

(5) $\frac{16(12)}{2}$

Answers and explanations start on page 318.

MATHEMATICS

A ship captain might use one to figure out where he is at sea. A contractor might use several to determine how much concrete he needs for a job. In this program you'll see how formulas help in a variety of practical situations and review some commonly used formulas.

Formulas

OBJECTIVES

1. Solve formulas using substitution.

2. Use the rules of algebra to rewrite formulas to solve for any variable.

3. Apply common geometry formulas in problem-solving situations.

To carpet or tile a floor, you have to know how much surface there is to be covered. How do you find the surface area of a floor? You could cut a square foot out of cardboard and see how many times it will fit in the space. But instead, you measure the length and width of the room and multiply. You have learned that for a rectangular space, the length times the width equals the surface area of the floor. You are using the formula $A = lw$.

The ability to work with formulas is also important to your success on the GED Math Test. You will need to know how to choose the correct formula for a given situation, apply the formula to set up the problem, and solve the formula by substituting the numbers from the problem. Learning about formulas will also help you develop a strong foundation for your work in algebra and geometry.

On the following pages, you will find a brief exercise called *Sneak Preview.* It is designed to introduce you to the topics that will be featured in the video program and the corresponding lesson. After you complete the exercise and check your answers, turn to the vocabulary page. There you will find terms that will help you better understand the video and the lesson that follow. After reviewing page 152, you will be ready to watch Program 34.

For additional practice, visit *LiteracyLink* online at http://www.pbs.org/literacy.

Sneak Preview

This exercise previews some of the concepts from Program 34. After you answer the questions, use the feedback on page 151 to help set your learning goals.

COMMUNITY LINK: A local recreation center has a small gym that is badly in need of repairs. Some parents from the community decide to form an association to repair the gym and start a youth basketball program. They estimate that it will cost $8000 to repair the gym pictured in the diagram below.

The parents decide that the association will borrow the amount they need and repay it from the money they make from the basketball program. They are considering two financing possibilities: a credit union and a private business owner. The terms of the loans and the formula for finding simple interest are shown below.

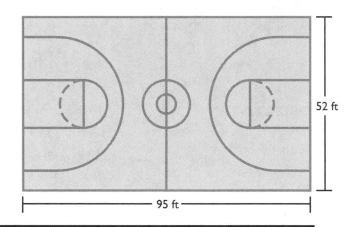

95 ft

52 ft

CITY CREDIT UNION	THOM WASHINGTON
$8000 loan	$8000 loan
9% interest	7% interest
3 years	2 years

simple interest (i) $i = prt$; where p = principal, r = rate, t = time

Answer these questions based on the information given above.

1. Which of these expressions could be used to find the amount of interest the association will pay on the loan from City Credit Union?

  (1) $8000 \times 9 \times 3$
  (2) $8000 \times 0.09 \times 3$
  (3) $8000 \times 9 \div 3$
  (4) $8000 \times 0.09 \div 3$
  (5) $8000 + (8000 \times 0.09 \times 3)$

MATHEMATICS

2. If the association borrows the money from Thom Washington, they will not have to make monthly payments. Instead, the entire amount borrowed plus the amount of interest will be due in two years. What amount would the association owe in two years?

(1) $8007
(2) $8014
(3) $8280
(4) $9120
(5) $9920

3. The parents will need to buy basketball uniforms for the children in the program. A sporting goods store offers to sell them 80 uniforms for $396. Using the cost formula below, which expression could be used to find how much the parents are paying per uniform?

(1) $80 + 396$
(2) 80×396
(3) $\frac{396}{80}$
(4) $\frac{80}{396}$
(5) $396 - 80$

| total cost (c) | $c = nr$; where n = number of units, r = cost per unit |

4. The gym floor needs to be refinished. The cost for refinishing depends on the surface area of the floor. Which of these expressions could be used to find the surface area of the floor? (You may refer to the GED formulas page on page 340.)

(1) $2(95) + 2(52)$
(2) $95 + 95 + 52$
(3) $4(95)$
(4) $4(52)$
(5) $95(52)$

Feedback

- If you got all of the answers right...   you have a good basic understanding of how to identify and use some of the formulas presented on the GED Math Test.

- If you missed question 1...   you need to work on how to solve formulas using substitution.

- If you missed question 2...   you need to work on applying formulas to solve problems with more than one step.

- If you missed question 3...   you need to practice using the rules of algebra to rewrite formulas to solve for any variable.

- If you missed question 4...   you need to study GED Math Test formulas and practice choosing the best formula for a given situation.

Vocabulary for *Formulas*

cube	a 3-dimensional figure in which the length, width, and height are all equal and each face is a square
function	a constant relationship between quantities
parallel	lines on the same flat surface that never meet or intersect
parallelogram	a closed figure with four straight sides; each pair of opposite sides is parallel
rectangular container	a three-dimensional object in which all angles are right angles (square corners)
right angle	a square corner; an angle having a measure of 90 degrees
simple interest	a percentage of an amount of money borrowed or invested that is paid for the use of the money
substitution	a method of solving a formula in which the variables are replaced with values and the indicated operations are completed
triangle	a closed figure with three straight sides
volume	the measure of how much a solid object holds; capacity

➡ **NOW WATCH PROGRAM 34:**

On the GED Math Test, basic formulas will be provided. The concepts and terms introduced in this program—from pi to finding the area of combined shapes—will help you understand how to use formulas on the test.

After you watch the program, work on:

- pages 153–168 in this workbook
- Internet activities at http://www.pbs.org/literacy

MATHEMATICS

152

Formulas

On the following pages, you will learn more about the ideas discussed in the video program and have an opportunity to develop and practice your GED math skills.

Key Points to Think About

In the video program, you explored:

- How people use formulas to solve problems in their daily lives as workers, citizens, and family members.
- How to choose the correct formula for a situation and apply it to find an answer.
- How to apply common geometry formulas to solve for perimeter, area, and volume.

On the GED Math Test:

- You will be expected to read a problem situation and decide whether a formula is needed to solve the problem.
- You will need to choose the correct formula for the situation and solve it by **substitution.**
- You should also be able to use your knowledge of formulas to recognize the correct way to set up an expression to solve a problem.

As you work through the lesson for Program 34:

- Think about the relationship between the variables and the operations in each formula. (Refer to page 57 to review the order of operations.)
- Always follow the order of operations to evaluate formulas.
- Be aware of the mathematical situations you encounter in your daily life that could be solved using formulas.

Using Formulas to Solve Problems

WORKPLACE LINK: In the payroll department, Tanya uses a computer spreadsheet to track workers' earnings. Each week she enters the total number of hours each employee worked. The computer multiplies the hours by the hourly wage and shows the result under *Total Earnings*. The computer uses the formula Total Earnings = Hours × Hourly Wage.

Understanding Formulas

Formulas help us understand the relationship between two or more quantities. In mathematics, this relationship is called a **function.** For example, we can say that distance is a function of rate and time. In other words, how far you drive depends on how fast and how long you drive.

Functions are often expressed as formulas. Formulas make the relationship between the numbers easy to remember and apply. Formulas are written using variables. A variable is a letter or symbol that represents a number.

Three common formulas from the GED Math Test are:

simple interest (*i*)	$i = prt$; where p = principal, r = rate, t = time
distance (*d*)	$d = rt$; where r = rate, t = time
total cost (*c*)	$c = nr$; where n = number of units, r = cost per unit

Solving by Substitution

To use a formula, substitute numbers for the variables and apply the order of operations. Note: one way to show multiplication is to write variables next to each other as in the above formulas.

▶▶ See how substitution is used to solve for simple interest.

Example: Tomas borrowed $1500 from his uncle to help pay for his education. He promised to pay back the money plus 4% interest in 2 years. How much will Tomas pay his uncle when the loan is due?

Simple interest is paid to the person or company making the loan to pay for the use of the money. Tomas will back the $1500 plus the simple interest he owes. Simple interest is based on a certain length of time expressed in *years.*

To solve the problem, use the interest formula. $i = prt$
Think: principal (p) = $1500, rate of interest ($r$) = 4% = 0.04, $i = \$1500 \times 0.04 \times 2$
and time (t) = 2. Substitute numbers for variables and solve. $i = \$120$
Tomas will owe $120 in interest.

Now find the amount he will pay back to his uncle. $\$1500 + \$120 = \$1620$

Answer: The interest plus the principal is **$1620.** *Hint:* Always read interest problems carefully to find out whether you need to find just the interest or the total to be paid back (interest plus principal).

MATHEMATICS

▸▸ Use substitution to solve for distance in this situation.

Example: Krystin can run 7 miles per hour. At that rate, how far can she run in 30 minutes?

(1)	2.1 miles	**(4)**	15 miles
(2)	3.5 miles	**(5)**	21 miles
(3)	14 miles		

> Refer to the GED formulas page on page 340.

You're right if you chose **(2) 3.5 miles.** Remember, 30 minutes is equal to $\frac{1}{2}$ or 0.5 hour. Since the rate is expressed in miles per hour, you must also express the time in hours.

$$d = rt$$
$$d = 7 \times 0.5$$
$$d = 3.5 \text{ miles}$$

Hint: On the GED Math Test, eliminate answer choices that aren't reasonable. If Krystin can run 7 miles in 1 hour, she can't run more than 7 in less than 1 hour. You can eliminate Choices (3), (4), and (5) using your common sense.

▸▸ Use substitution to find the total cost of a purchase.

Example: Jamal finds pre-viewed videotapes in a bargain bin for $4.95 each. How much will 8 tapes cost?

Substitute and solve:

$$c = nr$$
$$c = 8 \times \$4.95$$
$$c = \$39.60$$

SKILL PRACTICE

Choose the correct formula. Then solve by substitution.

1. Ashley Rose coaches a city league basketball team. She plans to take her players out for pizza after the final game. An individual pizza with salad and drink sells for $4.99. How much will Ashley Rose pay for 9 meals, not including tax and tip?

2. During a winter storm, Tyrone averages 20 miles per hour in his delivery truck. After 45 minutes of driving, how far has he traveled? (*Hint:* Express time in hours. 45 minutes = 45/60 hour. Reduce to work with a simpler fraction.)

3. Denzel wants to buy a used van for $7800. He plans to borrow the money from the credit union at 8% interest. To estimate the amount of interest he will pay, he uses the simple-interest formula. How much will he pay in interest if he borrows the money for 48 months? (*Hint:* Write time (*t*) in years.)

4. A small solar-powered aircraft flew 5.4 hours. If the aircraft averaged 30 miles per hour, how many miles did it travel?

5. Computer Warehouse offers the two payment plans shown below. Monique wants to buy a computer system that sells for $1499.

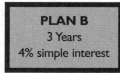

PLAN A	**PLAN B**
5 Years	3 Years
3% simple interest	4% simple interest

  a. Under which plan will Monique pay the least amount of interest?

  b. If Monique chooses Plan A, how much will she pay in all for the computer system?

6. Find the total cost of 50 computer diskettes at $0.23 per diskette.

7. Compare the formulas for distance and total cost. How are they similar?

FAMILY LINK: Ginger's daughter is making a poster for a contest. The rules of the contest state that the finished poster cannot be larger than 432 square inches. Ginger's daughter has a piece of poster board that is 22 inches wide and 24 inches long. Using the formula $A = lw$, Ginger is able to help her daughter understand that her poster will be too big.

Using the GED Formulas Page

When you take the GED Math Test, you will be given a page of formulas. The items in the test do not tell you to use a formula. Instead, you need to decide when a formula will be helpful. Many of the formulas on the GED formulas page (see page 340) are about finding the perimeter, area, and volume of basic shapes.

> **Review these definitions:**
>
> - **perimeter**—measures the distance around the edge of a flat figure
> - **area**—measures the surface of a flat figure
> - **volume**—measures how much a solid object holds

The GED Math Test items will be about the following shapes. You will learn more about the properties of these shapes in Program 35.

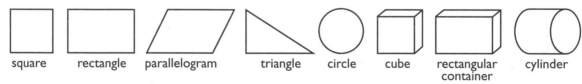

square   rectangle   parallelogram   triangle   circle   cube   rectangular container   cylinder

Now study this portion of the formulas page from the GED Math Test. Notice how the page is organized. The formulas are given in the right column along with the meaning of each variable. As you read, you may see some unfamiliar terms and symbols. Don't worry about it right now. Just focus on the kinds of information you can expect to find on the formulas page.

AREA (A) of a:

square	$A = s^2$; where s = side
rectangle	$A = lw$; where l = length, w = width
parallelogram	$A = bh$; where b = base, h = height
triangle	$A = \frac{1}{2}bh$; where b = base, h = height
circle	$A = \pi r^2$; where π = 3.14, r = radius

PERIMETER (P) of a:

square	$P = 4s$; where s = side
rectangle	$P = 2l + 2w$; where l = length, w = width
triangle	$P = a + b + c$; where $a, b,$ and c are the sides
circumference (C) of a circle	$C = \pi d$; where π = 3.14, d = diameter

VOLUME (V) of a:

cube	$V = s^3$; where s = side
rectangular container	$V = lwh$; where l = length, w = width, and h = height
cylinder	$V = \pi r^2 h$; where π = 3.14, r = radius, and h = height

MATHEMATICS

You will need to be able to apply the right formula at the right time to do well on the GED Math Test. Always read each item carefully. If a geometric figure is described, you may be able to use a formula to solve the problem. Decide whether you need to solve for perimeter, area, or volume. Then select the correct formula.

SKILL PRACTICE

Answer each item using the formulas on page 156.

1. Which measurements do you need to find the area of a triangle?

   (1) side and length   **(4)** side and base
   (2) height and width   **(5)** base and height
   (3) length and width

2. Noah wants to plant a vegetable garden in the rectangular space behind his garage. Which formula can be used to find out how many square feet of ground the garden covers?

   (1) $A = s^2$ **(4)** $P = 2l + 2w$
   (2) $A = lw$ **(5)** $P = 4s$
   (3) $A = \frac{1}{2}bh$

3. A cardboard box is 2 feet wide, 2.5 feet long, and 1 foot in height. Which formula can be used to find how much the box will hold?

   (1) $A = lw$ **(4)** $V = lwh$
   (2) $V = \pi r^2 h$ **(5)** $P = 2l + 2w$
   (3) $P = 4s$

4. A square fish pond measures 3 meters on one side. Which formula can be used to find the distance around the pond?

   (1) $P = 4s$ **(4)** $A = s^2$
   (2) $P = a + b + c$ **(5)** $V = s^3$
   (3) $A = bh$

TECHNOLOGY Connection

A **computer spreadsheet** uses formulas. A formula can be assigned to a cell to perform a specific calculation. A cell is a box within a spreadsheet. Each cell is named using row and column headings, such as the shaded cell D2.

The spreadsheet below can be used to figure out the cost of a catalog order. In cell D2, we write the formula =B2*C2. (The = sign tells the computer the entry is a formula. The symbol * means multiplication.) The computer will automatically multiply the number of model kits by the price per kit and show the answer $15.80 in cell D2. ($2 \times 7.90 = 15.80$)

	A	B	C	D
1	Item	Quantity	Price Per Item	Cost
2	Model Kits	2	$7.90	$15.80
3	Paint Sets	4	$3.75	
4				
5				

1. What formula could you write in cell D3 to find the cost of the paint sets?
2. What formula could you write in cell D4 to find the subtotal of D2 and D3?
   Use + for addition.

Answers and explanations start on page 319.

Solving for Other Variables

COMMUNITY LINK: Wushi is organizing a community literacy program. He plans to limit the program to 150 people. Because funding is limited, he plans to charge participants a small fee. Wushi needs $900 to run the program. Using the cost formula, he can find the amount to charge each person by dividing $900 by the number of participants.

Applying the Rules of Algebra

A formula is designed to help us solve for a certain quantity. For instance, an area formula helps you solve for area. At times, however, we may already know the area and all but one of the measurements of the figure. Instead of solving for area, we need to solve for a missing measurement. Using the rules of algebra, we can solve for any variable in the formula.

A formula is an equation. The two sides of the formula are connected by an equals sign. To solve for a variable, we must isolate that variable on one side of the equation. The variable must stand alone.

We need to change the way the formula is written without upsetting the balance of the equation. To do that, we must always do the same thing to both sides of the equation.

▶▶ Learn how to solve for rate using the distance formula.

Example: Emmanuel drove 289 miles to Reno, Nevada, in 4 hours 15 minutes. What was his average rate of speed?

Use the distance formula. Substitute the known values. The distance (d) = 289 miles. The time (t) = 4.25 hours. Remember, 15 minutes is 1/4 or 0.25 hour. Solve for the rate.

$$d = rt$$
$$289 = r \cdot 4.25$$

The rate (r) is multiplied by 4.25. To isolate r, perform the inverse (opposite) operation. Divide both sides of the equation by 4.25.

$$\frac{289}{4.25} = \frac{r \cdot 4.25}{4.25}$$
$$68 = r$$

Why does this work?
$4.25 \div 4.25 = 1$ and $r \cdot 1 = r$

Answer: 289 ÷ 4.25 = **68 miles per hour**
Check: Put the answer in the original formula: 289 = 68 • 4.25. Since 289 = 289, the equation is balanced, and the answer is correct.

Some formulas are more complicated because they involve more than one operation. Remember, your goal is to isolate the variable. Usually it is best to do the inverse of addition and subtraction steps first and the multiplication and division steps second.

▶▶ See how the formula for finding the perimeter of a rectangle is used to solve for length.

Example: Evelyn knows the perimeter of a room is 104 feet. The width of the room is 16 feet. She wants to find the length without measuring.

Step 1. Use the formula for finding the perimeter of a rectangle. Substitute the known values. The perimeter (P) is 104 feet. The width (w) is 16 feet. Multiply 16 by 2 to simplify the equation.

$P = 2l + 2w$
$104 = 2l + 2(16)$
$104 = 2l + 32$

Step 2. We need to isolate length (l). Since 32 is added, perform the inverse operation. Subtract 32 from both sides.

$104 - 32 = 2l + 32 - 32$
$72 = 2l$

Step 3. The variable l is multiplied by 2. Perform the inverse operation. Divide both sides of the equation by 2.

$\frac{72}{2} = \frac{2l}{2}$

Answer: The length of the room is **36 feet.**
Check: Put the answer in the original formula and make sure the sides are equal.

$36 = l$
$104 = 2(36) + 2(16)$
$104 = 72 + 32$
$104 = 104$

Apply these steps to solve a formula for a missing variable.

1. Substitute the known values.
2. Isolate the unknown variable using inverse operations.
3. Make sure you do exactly the same thing to both sides of the equation.
4. Check your answer using the original formula.

SKILL PRACTICE

Solve the problems by finding the missing variables. See page 340 for a complete listing of the formulas used on the GED Math Test.

1. Kendra earned $198 in simple interest on a 3-year investment. If she invested $1650, what rate of interest did she earn?

2. A side of a square measures 12 inches. A rectangle has the same area as the square. If the width of the rectangle is 8 inches, what is its length?

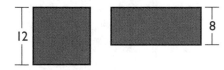

3. It took Colin $3\frac{1}{4}$ hours to drive a tractor 52 miles up a steep canyon road. What was Colin's average speed in miles per hour?

   (1) 13
   (2) 16
   (3) $17\frac{1}{2}$
   (4) 39
   (5) Not enough information is given.

4. Sharon recently ordered software for her school's computer lab. Sharon paid $339.75 for 5 CD-packs. What was the cost of one CD-pack?

5. The perimeter of a rectangular parking lot is 1270 feet. If the lot is 230 feet wide, what is its length?

6. Brad needs to drive from Fresno to San Bernardino, a distance of about 275 miles. If he averages 60 miles per hour, about how long will it take him to make the drive? State your answer to the nearest half hour.

7. Hallie uses 6 feet of metal framing material to go around a painting done on a square canvas. How many <u>inches</u> in length is one side of the painting?

   (1) 1.5   (4) 30
   (2) 9   (5) 36
   (3) 18

Answers and explanations start on page 319.

FAMILY LINK: Troy is helping his son Silas with a school project. Silas has to figure out how many feet per second he can run. Together, they mark off 50 feet on the sidewalk. Then Troy times his son with a stopwatch. Silas runs the distance in 9 seconds. Troy and Silas use the formula $d = rt$ to solve for rate. Silas runs about 5.6 feet per second.

Using Formulas to Solve Set-Up Problems

Approximately 1 in 5 of the items on the GED Math Test will be set-up problems. The answer choices for a set-up problem show possible mathematical expressions that could be used to solve the problem. Your job is to choose the correct expression.

Formulas can be helpful in finding the correct expression. Use these steps:

1. Read the problem carefully to choose the correct formula.
2. Use the rules of algebra to rewrite the formula so that the unknown variable is isolated on one side of the equation.
3. Substitute the values you know for the variables in the expression.
4. Compare your set-up with the answer choices.

▶▶ Apply the simple-interest formula to solve this set-up problem.

---

simple interest (i) $i = prt$; where p = principal, r = rate, t = time

---

Example: Deshawn borrowed money to buy a computer. He financed the computer at 8% simple interest for 4 years. His final invoice tells him that the total interest paid was $592, but Deshawn has forgotten the original cost of the computer. Which of the following expressions could Deshawn use to find the cost of the computer?

> Remember, one way to indicate multiplication is to write numbers next to each other.
>
> One way to indicate division is with the fraction bar.

(1) $\dfrac{592(4)}{0.08}$

(2) $592(4)(0.08)$

(3) $\dfrac{592}{0.08(4)}$

(4) $\dfrac{0.08(4)}{592}$

(5) $\dfrac{592(0.08)}{4}$

Here's how to solve the problem. Begin with the formula for finding simple interest.

$$i = prt$$

The goal is to isolate the principal (p) on one side of the equation. Since r and t are multiplied by p in the original formula, use the inverse operation. Divide both sides by rt.

$$\frac{i}{rt} = p$$

Substitute the known values.

$$\frac{592}{0.08(4)} = p$$

Answer: The correct set-up is **choice (3).**

The formula for finding mean is helpful for remembering what operations are needed to find an average.

mean $= \dfrac{x_1 + x_2 + ... + x_n}{n}$; where the x's are the values for which a mean is desired, and n = number of values in the series

The formula is a reminder to add the numbers you want to average and then divide by the number of values.

Example: Andy needs to find the average of four test scores: 96, 92, 84, and 86. He can use this expression:

$$\dfrac{96 + 92 + 84 + 86}{4}$$

SKILL PRACTICE

Write or choose the correct set-up for each problem. See page 340 for a complete listing of the formulas used on the GED Math Test.

1. Franklin's gas bills for three months were $51.05, $42.50, and $68.62. Write an expression that can be used to find the average bill for the three-month period.

2. Deidre bought 12.6 gallons of gasoline for $17.26. Write an expression that can be used to find the amount she paid per gallon.

3. Write an expression that can be used to find how long it will take L'Tanya to drive 340 miles if she averages 55 miles per hour.

4. A rectangular stained-glass window has an area of 480 sq in. The window has a 24-inch length. Which expression could be used to find its width?

   (1) $\dfrac{480 - 24}{2}$ **(4)** $\dfrac{480}{24}$

   (2) $480 - 2(24)$ **(5)** $480 \cdot 24$

   (3) $\dfrac{24}{480}$

SOCIAL STUDIES Connection

In studying the environment, averages are generally more useful than exact data. For example, knowing the average, or typical, amount of rainfall for Seattle, Washington, may be more helpful than knowing exactly how much it rained. The average monthly temperatures (°F) for two cities are shown on the graphs.

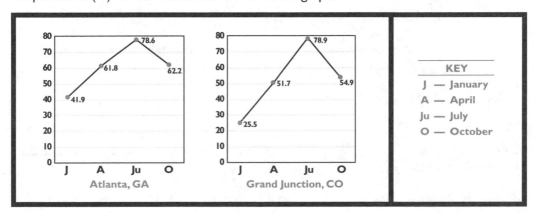

KEY

J — January
A — April
Ju — July
O — October

Atlanta, GA

Grand Junction, CO

For which city is the average monthly temperature higher in January?

Using Geometry Formulas

WORKPLACE LINK: Hayden is installing flooring in a construction project. He needs to find the area of a room with an unusual shape. From the blueprints, Hayden can see that the room can be divided into two triangles. After measuring the base and height of the sections, Hayden uses a formula to solve for the area of the triangles.

Finding Perimeter and Area

To find the perimeter of any figure, you add the lengths of all the outer edges or sides. The perimeter formulas you have learned so far are shortcuts for adding the lengths.

Look at the formula for finding the perimeter (P) of a triangle.

triangle	$P = a + b + c$; where $a, b,$ and c are the sides

A triangle has three sides. The formula tells you to add the sides to find the perimeter.

A flat figure has two dimensions—length and width. To find the area of squares or rectangles, you multiply length by width. Let's apply the same principle to finding the area of triangles and parallelograms.

The figure to the right is a parallelogram. In many ways, a parallelogram is like a rectangle. It has 4 sides and the opposite sides are **parallel** and equal in length. There is one major difference: The angles are not **right angles.** In other words, a parallelogram does not have square corners.

Study the formula for finding the area (A) of a parallelogram.

parallelogram	$A = bh$; where $b=$ base, $h=$ height

The base of the parallelogram is the measure of the longer side. The height is the measure of an imaginary line that is at a right angle to the base. Multiply the base by the height to find the area.

Example: Find the area of the parallelogram to the right.

$$A = bh$$
$$= 6(3)$$
$$= 18 \text{ square centimeters}$$

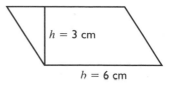

$h = 3$ cm

$h = 6$ cm

Compare the area formulas for rectangles and parallelograms. Both involve the multiplication of two measurements. Study the next example to further understand the relationship.

Imagine that you make a cut along the height of the parallelogram and tape the piece to the other end. You now have a rectangle. The base of the parallelogram (6 cm) becomes the length of the rectangle, and the height (3 cm) becomes the width. The area is still 6 × 3 = 18 square centimeters.

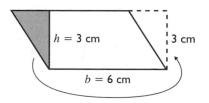

Triangles are also related to rectangles and parallelograms. How does the area formula for a triangle, given below, differ from the area formula for a parallelogram?

> **triangle** $A = \frac{1}{2}bh$; where b = base, h = height

The formula multiplies the product of the base and height by $\frac{1}{2}$. In other words, a triangle is one half of a parallelogram or a rectangle with the same measures for base and height.

▶▶ See how the triangle area formula is applied in this situation.

Example: Julissa wants to plant a lemon tree if she has at least 12 square feet in the triangular area formed by the deck and walkway. Find the area of the space.

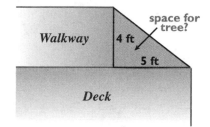

$$A = bh$$
$$= \frac{1}{2}(5)(4) = \frac{1}{2}(20) = 10 \text{ square feet}$$

Answer: The area of the triangular space is **10 square feet,** not enough space to plant the tree.

SKILL PRACTICE

Brent has drawn a plan to landscape space outside an office building. The plan is marked in feet. Use Brent's plan to answer items 1–4.

1. Brent plans to cover the surface of the path with wood chips. What is the area of the path in square feet? (*Hint:* The height of the triangle is also the height of the parallelogram.)

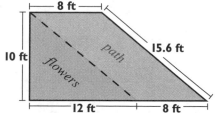

2. To buy soil for flower planting, Brent needs to know the area of the flower garden portion. What is the area of the flower garden in square feet?

3. Brent plans to put a low fence around the flower garden to discourage people from taking a shortcut through the flowers. How many feet of fencing will he need to go around the garden?

4. The building manager suggests that Brent widen the path from 8 feet to 12 feet. This change will not affect the size of the flower garden. Find the total area of the flower garden and the wider path.

Answers and explanations start on page 320.

FAMILY LINK: Belinda is thinking about replacing her old furnace with a new central heating system. The furnace company has a chart showing the estimated costs associated with the new furnace based on the cubic feet in the home. To find the most economical way of heating her home, Belinda has to find the total volume of her house.

Finding Volume

Volume is the measure of how much space there is within a three-dimensional object (one with length, width, and height). Volume can be used to find out how much a container holds.

Volume is measured in cubic units. A **cube** is a solid figure in which all sides are equal. The box to the right represents 1 cubic inch. Each side is 1 inch in length.

Now imagine a larger box that is 4 inches by 2 inches by 3 inches. To find the volume of the box, we need to find out how many cubic inches will fit inside. Look closely. The box in the diagram can be subdivided into 24 smaller cubes.

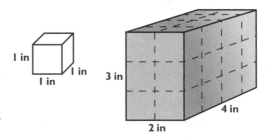

Using geometric language, a box is a **rectangular container.** A rectangular container is a three-dimensional object in which all angles are right angles or square corners. When all the sides of a rectangular container are equal, we call the figure a **cube.**

Study this formula for finding the volume of a rectangular container.

rectangular container	$V = lwh$; where l = length, w = width, h = height

▶▶ Apply the formula to find the volume of a room.

Example: Maurice plans to install a new air-conditioning system in his store. He will need to know the volume of the store in cubic feet. The store measures 50 feet long, 24 feet wide, and 10 feet high. Find the volume of the store.

Substitute the values into the formula and solve.

$$V = lwh$$
$$= 50 \cdot 24 \cdot 10$$
$$= 12,000 \text{ cubic feet}$$

Answer: The store contains **12,000 cubic feet** of space. *Check:* When you are multiplying, numbers increase quickly. Make sure your answer makes sense. Estimation is the best way to check your work. *Think:* $50 \times 20 = 1,000$ and $1,000 \times 10 = 10,000$. The answer 12,000 cubic units seems reasonable.

The formula for finding the volume of a cube looks different, but you are still multiplying the length, width, and height. Study the formula.

cube	$V = s^3$; where s = side

MATHEMATICS

▸▸Solve for volume in this problem about a storage container.

Example: Stow-It Storage offers new storage solutions for busy customers. Customers fill a cube-shaped storage unit measuring 6 feet per side. The company then picks up the unit and stores it in a warehouse. What is the volume of the storage unit?

Substitute the values into the formula and solve.

$$V = s^3$$
$$= 6 \cdot 6 \cdot 6$$
$$= 216 \text{ cubic feet}$$

> Remember, the exponent tells you how many times the number is used as a factor.

Answer: The volume of the storage unit is **216 cubic feet.**

Check: You know 6 × 6 is 36. Use front-end estimation for the final step: 30 × 6 = 180. The answer 216 cubic feet makes sense.

SKILL PRACTICE

Solve each problem.

1. To reach an underground methane gas well, workers dig a rectangular hole 6 feet wide, 8 feet long, and 9 feet deep. How many cubic feet of dirt do they remove from the hole?

2. The height of a cube is 3.5 centimeters. Find the volume of the cube in cubic centimeters.

3. A storage unit has 243 cubic feet of space. What is the volume of the unit in cubic yards? (*Hint:* First figure out the number of cubic feet in a cubic yard.)

4. What is the volume of the cardboard box in cubic inches?

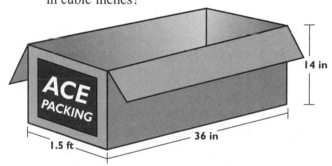

14 in

1.5 ft   36 in

ACE PACKING

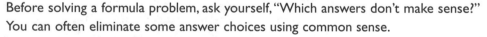

PROBLEM SOLVER Connection

Before solving a formula problem, ask yourself, "Which answers don't make sense?" You can often eliminate some answer choices using common sense.

Example: A train traveled 120 km per hour for $2\frac{3}{4}$ hours. How many miles did it travel?
  (1) 160   **(4)** 330
  (2) 220   **(5)** 360
  (3) 240

Think: The train traveled between 2 and 3 hours. If it averaged 120 km per hour for 2 hours, it would have traveled 240 km. Using common sense, you know that choices (1), (2), and (3) are too low to be correct.

Suppose the train traveled for 3 hours. Multiply 120 by 3. **Which answer choice can you eliminate? Which answer choice must be correct?**

PART ONE DIRECTIONS: Choose the <u>one best answer</u> to each of the following problems. Use a calculator wherever necessary.

Question 1 refers to the following figure.

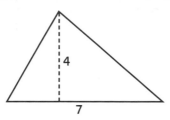

1. Which of the following formulas could be used to find the area of the figure?
   (1) $A = s^2$
   (2) $P = a + b + c$
   (3) $A = lw$
   (4) $A = bh$
   (5) $A = \frac{1}{2}bh$

2. Ned spent $49 to buy masking tape for a job. Each roll of tape cost $3.50. Which expression could be used to find the number of rolls of masking tape that Ned bought?
   (1) $49(3.50)$
   (2) $\frac{3.50}{49}$
   (3) $49 + 3.50$
   (4) $\frac{49}{3.50}$
   (5) $49 - 3.50$

3. The weights of three packages are 12.75, 16, and 3.5 pounds. What is the mean weight in pounds of the packages?
   (1) 1.075
   (2) 10.75
   (3) 12.75
   (4) 14.25
   (5) 107.5

4. Computer diskettes cost $9.36 for a package of 24. At that rate, what is the cost of one diskette?
   (1) $0.22
   (2) $0.39
   (3) $0.44
   (4) $2.24
   (5) $3.90

Questions 5 and 6 are based on the following information.

Nuyen wants to buy a used piano for $725 so her child can start piano lessons. Superior Instruments offers two payment plans.

PLAN A	PLAN B
2.5 Years	4 Years
6% simple interest	4% simple interest

5. Which expression can Nuyen use to compute the amount of simple interest she would pay with Plan B?
   (1) $\$725(0.04)(2.5)$
   (2) $\frac{\$725}{2.5 \times 0.04}$
   (3) $\frac{\$725 \times 4}{0.04}$
   (4) $\$725(0.04)(4)$
   (5) $\frac{\$725(0.04)}{4}$

6. If Nuyen chooses Plan A, how much will she pay in all for the piano?
   (1) $108.75
   (2) $725.00
   (3) $833.75
   (4) $942.50
   (5) $1450.00

Question 7 is based on the following map.

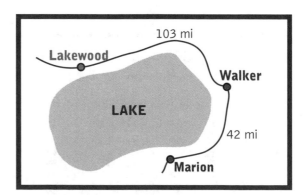

7. Ben drives from Lakewood to Marion in $2\frac{1}{2}$ hours. What is his average speed in miles per hour?
   (1) 45
   (2) 55
   (3) 58
   (4) 60
   (5) 62

MATHEMATICS

8. An art project calls for building a rectangular wood frame to pour plaster into, creating a 10-inch by 14-inch tile. Assuming no waste, how many <u>feet</u> of wood does it take to build the frame?
   (1) 2
   (2) 4
   (3) 4.8
   (4) 48
   (5) 140

9. An Air Tobego plane flew at an average speed of 418 mph. How many miles did it travel in 3.5 hours?
   (1) 1463
   (2) 1290
   (3) 836
   (4) 418
   (5) 119

10. Ariel is training for a community walk-a-thon. She walked 12.4 miles on Monday, 14 miles on Wednesday, 10 miles on Friday, and not as far on Saturday. What was her average, in miles, for the 4 days?
    (1) 9.1
    (2) 12.4
    (3) 36.4
    (4) 40
    (5) Not enough information is given.

11. A plastic cube is used to make snow bricks. It measures 10 cm wide, 10 cm long, and 10 cm deep. Which formula can be used to find how much snow the cube holds?
    (1) $A = s^2$
    (2) $A = lw$
    (3) $V = \pi r^2 h$
    (4) $P = 4s$
    (5) $V = s^3$

Questions 12 and 13 are based on the following information. Refer to the formulas page on page 340 if needed.

The Rosarian family has five children. The ages of the three youngest are 4, 7, and 11; the twins are 14 years old.

12. In years, what is the average age of the Rosarian children?
    (1) 8
    (2) 9
    (3) 10
    (4) 11
    (5) 14

13. In years, what is the median age of the Rosarian children?
    (1) 8
    (2) 9
    (3) 10
    (4) 11
    (5) 14

Question 14 is based on the following drawing.

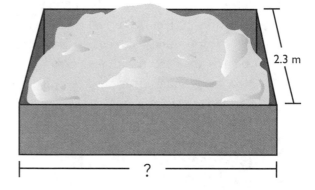

14. The area of Pico Park's rectangular sandbox is 10.35 square meters. One side measures 2.3 m. Which expression represents the length of the other side?
    (1) 10.35(2.3)
    (2) $\frac{10.35}{2.3}$
    (3) $\frac{10.35}{2(2.3)}$
    (4) $\frac{4 \times 2.3}{2}$
    (5) $\frac{2.3}{10.35}$

15. A room measures 12 feet by 16 feet. Which of the following expressions can be used to figure out how many feet of molding to buy for trim around the room's ceiling?

(1) 12(16)

(2) 4(16) + 4(12)

(3) 16 + 12

(4) 2(16) + 2(12)

(5) $\frac{2(12)}{2(16)}$

16. Luisa drove round-trip from Sierra to Clayton in 5 hours. She drove this distance on both Tuesday and Thursday. If Luisa averaged 60 miles per hour, about how many miles is it from Sierra to Clayton?

(1) 60

(2) 120

(3) 150

(4) 300

(5) 600

17. Aaron has a rectangular garden that measures 20 feet by 16 feet. To prevent birds from eating the seeds, he wants to cover the garden with a screen. How many square feet of screen will he need to cover the garden?

(1) 72

(2) 160

(3) 320

(4) 480

(5) 1280

18. A rectangular wooden crate measures 8 feet by 4 feet by 6 feet. Which of the following expressions could you use to find the volume of the crate in cubic feet?

(1) 8(4)(6)

(2) 8 + 4 + 6

(3) 2(8 + 4 + 6)

(4) 2(8) + 2(4) + 2(6)

(5) 8^3

Questions 19 through 21 are based on the following table. Refer to the formulas page on page 340 if needed.

Single-Family Homes Sold in the Belleview Neighborhood			
Street	**Prices of Homes Sold**		
Olive Ave.	$61,900	$62,100	$66,500
Pine St.	$54,500	$57,800	$62,800
Winston	$68,200	$69,300	$71,700
Elm Pl.	$85,200	$89,100	$89,800

19. Based on the information in the table, which street in the Belleview area has the highest mean price among the homes sold?

(1) Olive Avenue

(2) Pine Street

(3) Winston

(4) Elm Place

(5) Not enough information is given.

20. What is the median price of these single-family homes sold in the Belleview neighborhood?

(1) $69,300

(2) $68,300

(3) $67,350

(4) $66,500

(5) $57,800

21. What number would you divide by to find the mean price of all the homes sold in the Belleview neighborhood?

(1) 3

(2) 4

(3) 6

(4) 12

(5) 16

Answers and explanations start on page 320.

MATHEMATICS

In this program you'll see how animators and graphic artists use geometry to affect our perception of a scene or layout. You'll also learn some of the language of geometry and basic properties of angles and triangles.

Geometry

OBJECTIVES

1. Solve problems involving lines and angles.
2. Use proportion and the Pythagorean relationship to solve problems involving triangles.
3. Calculate the circumference and area of circles and the volume of cylinders.

Have you ever flown in an airplane or gone to the top of a skyscraper? As you look at the city below, you can appreciate the vast amount of planning that goes into building a city. Below you lies a geometric arrangement of streets, railway lines, and power lines. These feats of design and construction are made possible through our understanding of geometry.

The ability to work with geometric ideas is important to your success on the GED Math Test. You will need to know how to apply geometric formulas and analyze diagrams of lines, angles, and other basic figures to draw correct conclusions. Your work in this program will reinforce your understanding of other math skills in the areas of ratio and proportion, measurement, and algebra.

On the following pages, you will find a brief exercise called *Sneak Preview*. It is designed to introduce you to the topics that will be featured in the video program and the corresponding lesson. After you complete the exercise and check your answers, turn to the vocabulary page. There you will find terms that will help you better understand the video and the lesson that follow. After reviewing page 172, you will be ready to watch Program 35.

For additional practice, visit *LiteracyLink* online at http://www.pbs.org/literacy.

Sneak Preview

This exercise previews some of the concepts from Program 35. After you answer the questions, use the feedback on page 171 to help set your learning goals.

 **FAMILY LINK:** Pietra and her brother Todd have just converted their family's garage into a guest room. They stripped the walls down to the studs, added insulation, installed two windows, and put up drywall. Then they painted the rectangular room. Now they are ready to install flooring. Pietra's floor plan and Todd's design for a wood tile are shown below.

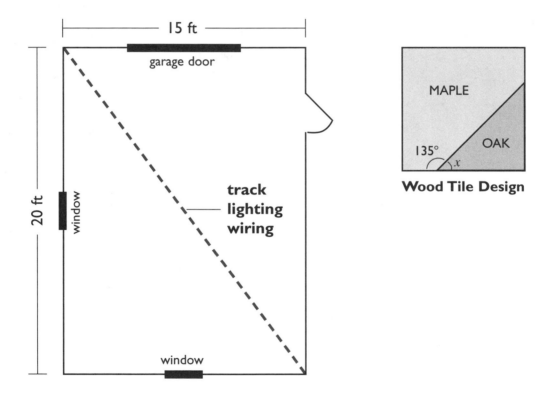

Wood Tile Design

Answer these questions based on the drawings shown.

1. Todd plans to create a wood border for the room using wood tiles of his own design. Todd has already cut the maple pieces for the tiles at the angle shown in the diagram. If the tile forms a perfect square, what is the measure of angle x on the oak piece?

   (1) 35°
   (2) 45°
   (3) 90°
   (4) 180°
   (5) 225°

MATHEMATICS

2. For the track lighting, Todd will run electrical wiring diagonally across the ceiling, from one corner to the other. Todd can find the distance from one corner to the other by solving for which of the following?

   (1) the perimeter of a rectangle
   (2) the area of a rectangle
   (3) the length of the hypotenuse of a right triangle
   (4) the height of a right triangle
   (5) the circumference of a circle

3. To save space, Pietra bought three triangular corner tables that "nest" within each other, each slightly smaller than the one above it. Which statement about these tables is most likely <u>true</u>?

   (1) The 3 tables are different in both shape and size.
   (2) The 3 tables are equal in both in shape and size.
   (3) The 3 tables are the same shape but different in size.
   (4) The 3 tables would form a circle if placed end to end.
   (5) The 3 tables would form a rectangle if placed end to end.

4. Pietra also purchased a round dining table for the room. The formula to compute the area of a circle is $A = \pi r^2$, where π is about 3.14 and r = the circle's radius. About how much area will Pietra's dining table take up, in square feet, if its radius is 2 feet?

   (1) 3.14
   (2) 6.28
   (3) 10.56
   (4) 12.56
   (5) 14.5

Feedback

- If you got all of the answers right...   you have a good understanding of how to apply geometric formulas and analyze geometric figures.

- If you missed question 1...   you need to learn more about line and angle relationships.

- If you missed question 2...   you need to learn more about the properties of triangles.

- If you missed question 3...   you need more work with similar triangles.

- If you missed question 4...   you need practice with the formula for the area of a circle.

ANSWERS FOR SNEAK PREVIEW:
1. Choice (2)   2. Choice (3)   3. Choice (3)   4. Choice (4)

Vocabulary for *Geometry*

circumference	the distance around a circle
complementary angles	two angles whose sum measures 90°
congruent figures	two shapes with identical measures of sides and angles
corresponding angles	angles that are in the same position in the intersections formed when a transversal intersects parallel lines
diameter	the distance across a circle through the center
equilateral triangle	a triangle with three equal sides and angles
hypotenuse	the side opposite the right angle in a right triangle
isosceles triangle	a triangle having two sides with the same length and two angles with the same measure
pi	the ratio of the circumference of a circle to its diameter; rounded to 3.14 on the GED Math Test
radius	the distance from the center of a circle to any point on the circle
right triangle	a triangle having a right angle
similar figures	two shapes with identical angles whose corresponding sides are in proportion
supplementary angles	two angles whose sum measures 180°
transversal	a line that intersects two or more parallel lines
vertex	the endpoint shared by the lines or segments that form an angle
vertical angle	either of two angles with the same measure that lie on opposite sides of two intersecting lines

➡ NOW WATCH PROGRAM 35:

The program introduces a lot of terms. Make note of those that are new to you so you can review them as you study further. Note how learners use the concepts of supplementary and complementary angles to determine the measurements of angles. Understanding these principles will help you on the test.

After you watch the program, work on:

PBS LiteracyLink®

- pages 173–190 in this workbook
- Internet activities at http://www.pbs.org/literacy

AFTER YOU WATCH

35

Geometry

On the following pages, you will learn more about the ideas discussed in the video program and have an opportunity to develop and practice your GED math skills.

GED TIPS

When taking the GED Test, you should:

- Remember that maps, diagrams, and geometric figures may not be drawn to scale. Don't "eyeball" an answer; do the work.

- Make a quick sketch of any figure that is only described and not pictured; then label your sketch.

- Use your calculator, when allowed, to perform difficult or time-consuming calculations.

Key Points to Think About

In the video program, you explored:

- How people use geometric principles and formulas in their daily lives as workers, citizens, and family members.

- How the properties of lines, angles, and other figures are used to draw conclusions and solve problems.

- Everyday applications of geometric ideas, such as those that deal with measurement, construction, and design.

On the GED Math Test:

- You will be expected to know how to solve problems involving lines, angles, triangles, circles, and other simple figures.

- You should know how to apply geometric formulas to set up and solve problems.

- You will use ratio and proportion to analyze similar figures and solve for missing measurements.

As you work through the lesson for Program 35:

- Notice the lines and angles in the objects and structures around you.

- Think about how our measurement systems are linked to our understanding of geometry, and continue to review the common equivalencies in both the metric and English systems of measurement.

- Be aware of opportunities to use geometric ideas to solve problems in your daily life, not just on the GED Math Test.

Working with Lines and Angles

FAMILY LINK: Lance and Carrie are installing a new cabinet in their bathroom. Lance holds the cabinet at the right height, and Carrie marks the spots to drill holes in the wallboard. Before they install the cabinet, they use a yardstick and T square to make sure the holes are parallel with the ceiling and perpendicular to a nearby wall.

Understanding Lines and Angles

Geometry is used to describe the relationship of figures and objects to the space around them. It begins with a single point. A point is an exact location in space. We represent a point with a dot and label it with a letter.

A line is a series of points that continues in both directions. It is named using any two points that lie upon it. A line segment is a section of line between two points. It is named for its endpoints.

An angle is formed when two portions of a line share a common endpoint, or **vertex.** Angles are measured in degrees with an instrument called a protractor. The protractor measures the opening between the lines.

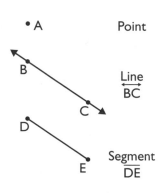

The angle measures 60 degrees, written 60°.

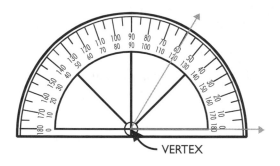

There are three ways to name an angle. You may see any of these methods on the GED Math Test. You can name an angle by its vertex, by three points on the angle (the middle point must be the vertex), or by a number written within the opening of the angle. The angle below could be named ∠K, ∠JKL, or ∠3.

A right angle measures exactly 90° (90 degrees). The corner of a sheet of typing paper is a right angle. Right angles are formed when two lines are perpendicular. In a diagram, a right angle is marked with a square symbol. As you will see, right angles are very useful for solving geometric problems.

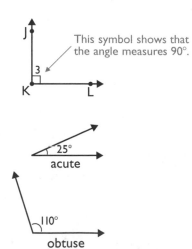

This symbol shows that the angle measures 90°.

25°
acute

110°
obtuse

Supplementary and Complementary Angles

Angles are classified according to their measure. An angle smaller than 90° is an acute angle. An angle larger than 90° is an obtuse angle. A straight angle, which looks no different from a line, measures exactly 180°.

MATHEMATICS

In the diagram below, angles 1 and 2 form a straight angle. When the sum of two angles is 180°, they are called **supplementary angles.** Likewise, angles 3 and 4 form a right angle. When the sum of two angles is 90°, the angles are **complementary angles.**

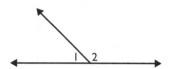

∠1 = 40°   ∠2 = 140°
∠1 + ∠2 = 180°

∠3 = 25°   ∠4 = 65°
∠3 + ∠4 = 90°

▶▶ Look how your knowledge of supplementary angles can be used to solve for an unknown angle measurement.

Example: A map shows that Cole Avenue meets Third Street at a 50° angle. What is the measure of the angle on the opposite side of Cole Avenue?

Third Street is represented by a line, which measures 180°.

Subtract to find the missing angle: 180° − 50° = 130°.

Answer: The opposite angle measures **130°.**
Check: 130° + 50° = 180°

You can use the same method to find a missing complementary angle. If two angles form a right angle, subtract the angle measure you know from 90° to find the missing angle.

SKILL PRACTICE

Solve each problem.

1. Sosia must cut two pieces of tile so that their bases form a straight line. If the first piece is cut at a 60° angle, at what angle must he cut the connecting piece?

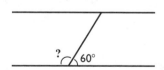

2. Juanita is making a quilt. She wants to cut and join two pieces of cloth to form a square corner. To complete the design, both pieces must have the same angle measure. At what angle should she cut the pieces?

3. What is the supplement of an angle that measures 112°?

In the figure below, AF forms a straight line, and ∠ABD measures 90°. Use the figure to answer questions 4 through 8.

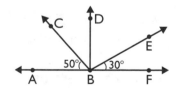

Find the measure of the following angles:

4. ∠ CBD
5. ∠ DBE
6. ∠ CBF
7. ∠ DBF

8. The measure of ∠CBE is 100°. Is this statement true or false? Explain your reasoning.

Working with Vertical Angles

When two lines lie on a flat surface, they are parallel or else they intersect. Parallel lines never meet or intersect. They remain an equal distance apart no matter how far they are extended. The ‖ symbol is used to indicate parallel lines.

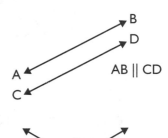

AB ‖ CD

Intersecting lines cross at some point, and when they cross, they form angles. At an intersection, the angles that are opposite each other are called **vertical angles.** Vertical angles are always equal in measure. In the diagram, we are not given the measure of the angles, but we know that ∠1 equals ∠3 and that ∠2 equals ∠4.

Intersecting lines that form right angles are called perpendicular lines. On the GED Math Test, perpendicular lines may be indicated using the symbol ⊥. Always read any markings near a figure or diagram to make sure you have the information you need to solve a problem.

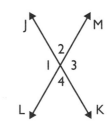

EF ⊥ GH

▸▸ See how the measure of one angle can help you find the measure of another.

Example: In the diagram, the lines JK and LM form vertical angles. The measure of ∠2 is 55°. Find the measure of the remaining angles.

Because ∠2 and ∠1 are supplementary angles, ∠1 = 125°.
   180° − 55° = 125°

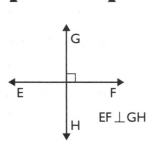

   ∠2 and ∠4 are vertical angles, so ∠4 = 55°.
   ∠1 and ∠3 are vertical angles, so ∠3 = 125°.

Working with Transversals

In this diagram, two parallel lines are intersected by a third line called a **transversal.** The transversal creates four angles at each intersection. Because the transversal crosses both lines at the same angle, we can find special relationships among the angles.

∠1 = 110°

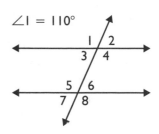

The angles that are in the same position in each intersection are called **corresponding angles.** Corresponding angles have the same measure. Thus, if ∠1 = 110°, then ∠5 = 110°.

We can now use our understanding of vertical angles to find the measure of the remaining angles.

Think: Because ∠1 and ∠2 combine to form a line, their sum must be 180°. Subtract to find the measure of ∠2: 180° − 110° = 70°.

Now find the vertical angle pairs. Angles ∠1 and ∠4 are vertical angles. Since ∠1 measures 110°, so does ∠4. Angles 2 and 3 are vertical, so both measure 70°.

Now look for corresponding angles. Angle 1 corresponds to ∠5, and ∠4 corresponds to ∠8. Angles 1, 4, 5, and 8 measure 110° each. Angle 2 corresponds to ∠6, and ∠3 corresponds to ∠7. Angles 2, 3, 6, and 7 measure 70° each.

SKILL PRACTICE

On this portion of a street map, Main Street and Lincoln Street are parallel. Grant Avenue is perpendicular to Main Street. Use the information from the map to answer items 1–4.

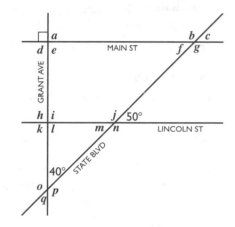

1. List the angles identified with a letter that have a measure of 90°.

2. What is the measure of ∠p?

3. Which angles have the same measure as ∠b?

4. Which of the following is a true statement about the angles shown on the map?

   (1) Angles e and j are supplementary angles.
   (2) Angle q measures 50°.
   (3) Angles g and f are complementary angles.
   (4) Angle f measures 50°.
   (5) Angles h and j have the same measurement.

SCIENCE Connection

The **astrolabe** is believed to be the oldest scientific instrument in the world! It may have been invented as early as 240 B.C., probably in Greece. The astrolabe played a vital role in the history of civilization—it was used until the mid-18th century (when the sextant was invented) to measure the altitude of the sun and other stars. Seamen used the astrolabe to measure time and distance as well.

How many degrees above the horizon is the star in the drawing?

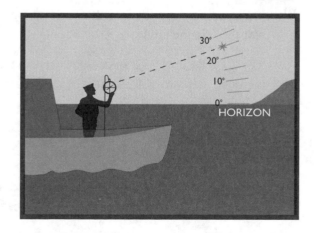

PROGRAM 35: Geometry

FAMILY LINK: Zoila's daughter Wendy is building a bridge out of toothpicks for a school assignment. Wendy has finished the outer framework, but the bridge is unstable. Zoila shows her daughter how right triangles are used in construction to make structures stronger. Together they reinforce the bridge by adding diagonal bracing to form right triangles.

Working with Triangles

Kinds of Triangles

All triangles have three sides and three angles. Triangles are classified by the measures of their sides and angles. All triangles have one thing in common: the sum of the angles in any triangle is 180°.

An **equilateral triangle** has three sides of equal length. Because its angles are also of equal measure, each angle measures 60°. (180° ÷ 3 = 60°)

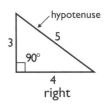

equilateral right

A **right triangle** has one right angle. The longest side of a right triangle is always directly opposite the right angle. This side is called the **hypotenuse.** The remaining sides are called legs.

An **isosceles triangle** has two equal sides. The two angles that are opposite those sides are also equal. A triangle with no equal sides or angles is called a **scalene triangle.**

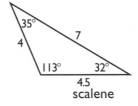

isosceles scalene

▶▶ See how to find a missing angle in a triangle problem.

Example: In triangle RST, or △RST, ∠R measures 75° and ∠S measures 30°. What is the measure of ∠T?

Remember, the sum of the angles in a triangle is 180°. Write an equation using the information from the problem. Solve for the missing angle.

$$75° + 30° + x = 180°$$
$$105° + x = 180°$$
$$x = 75°$$

Answer: ∠T measures 75°. Since two angles in the triangle have the same measure, △RST must be an isosceles triangle.

Check: 75° + 75° + 30° = 180°

> Not all geometry items on the GED Math Test will have a diagram. Making a quick sketch may help you understand the problem.

Similar and Congruent Triangles

Two figures are congruent when their corresponding sides and angles are equal. In other words, **congruent figures** have the same size and shape.

Two figures are similar when their corresponding sides are in proportion to each other. **Similar figures** always have equal corresponding angles. In other words, similar figures have the same shape, but they are not the same size.

▶▶ See how ratio and proportion can be used to solve for a missing length when working with similar triangles.

Example: Chloe wants to find the height of a tree in her front yard. She goes outside at 3:30 P.M. and measures the tree's shadow. At the same time, she measures the shadow of a 6-foot signpost. If the shadow cast by the tree is 15 feet and the shadow cast by the signpost is 3 feet, what is the height of the tree?

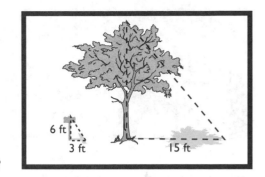

Because the angle of the sun is the same for both objects, there are two similar right triangles. The long leg for each triangle is the height of the object. The short leg is the shadow along the ground.

Because these are similar figures, the ratio of the height to shadow length will be the same. Set up a proportion comparing the two heights to the lengths of the shadows to find the height of the tree.

$$\frac{\text{height}}{\text{shadow}} \qquad \frac{x \text{ ft}}{15 \text{ ft}} = \frac{6 \text{ ft}}{3 \text{ ft}}$$

Solve: $15 \times 6 \div 3 = 30$

Answer: The tree is **30 feet** in height. *Check:* Since the signpost is twice the height of its shadow, the tree should also be twice the height of its shadow. The answer makes sense.

SKILL PRACTICE

Solve each problem.

1. A company logo is in the shape of a right triangle. The artist's drawing of the logo is shown on the left below. If the drawing is reduced to the size on the right, what will the upper edge measure?

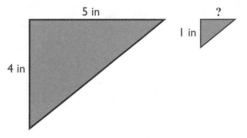

2. In the diagram below, the smaller triangle is in proportion to the larger triangle. Find the length of the side marked *x*.

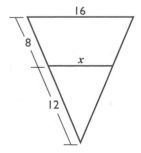

3. Triangles A and B are both right triangles, but are they similar triangles? Explain your thinking.

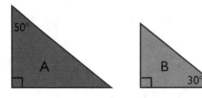

4. △DEF is similar to △ABC, shown below. Without seeing △DEF, which of these statements can you be sure must be true?

(1) △DEF is a right triangle.

(2) The perimeter of △DEF is 20 in.

(3) △DEF is a scalene triangle.

(4) △DEF is an isosceles triangle.

(5) The sides of △DEF are longer than the sides of △ABC.

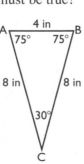

Answers and explanations start on page 321.

WORKPLACE LINK: Craig works for a theater company. He needs to build six 4-by-8-foot platforms that are 3 feet high. For safety, Craig plans to add four diagonal braces to each platform. After noticing that each brace forms the hypotenuse of a right triangle, Craig uses the formula $a^2 + b^2 = c^2$ to find the length of the braces.

Working with Square Roots

To solve problems involving right triangles, you will need to understand **square roots.** Finding a square root is the opposite of squaring a number. The symbol $\sqrt{}$ means square root. The expression $\sqrt{49}$ means the square root of 49.

To solve a square root, think: "What number times itself will equal the number in the bracket?" You know the square root of 49 is 7 because $7^2 = 49$.

You can also use your calculator to find square roots. Enter the number in the bracket and press the square root key. You do not need to press the equals key.

> Refer to page 338 of the Math Handbook for information on square roots and the Casio® *fx*-260.

Calculator: ☐4 ☐9 ☐√ The display reads: ☐ 7.

Understanding the Pythagorean Relationship

Pythagoras was a Greek mathematician who discovered a relationship between the length of the hypotenuse and the legs of a right triangle. This discovery is known as the Pythagorean relationship and is expressed in the following formula.

Pythagorean relationship	$c^2 = a^2 + b^2$; where c = hypotenuse, and a and b are the legs of a right triangle

▶▶ See how the formula is applied in Craig's situation.

Example: The diagram shows the design for the 4-foot end of a theater platform. The top and legs of the platform create right angles. The diagonal brace forms a hypotenuse to one right triangle. What length is needed for the brace?

(1) 4.5 feet   (4) 8 feet
(2) 5 feet   (5) 25 feet
(3) 7 feet

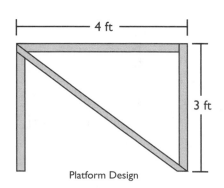

Platform Design

You're right if you chose **(2) 5 feet.** Use the Pythagorean relationship. The legs of the right angle are 3 and 4 feet. Substitute these values in the formula and solve.

To solve $c^2 = 25$, find the square root of both sides of the equation. Ask yourself, "What number times itself is equal to 25?"

$c^2 = a^2 + b^2$
$c^2 = 3^2 + 4^2$
$c^2 = 9 + 16$
$c^2 = 25$
$c = \sqrt{25} = 5$ feet

MATHEMATICS

▶▶ Look how the formula is applied in solving for a leg measure in a right-triangle problem.

Example: One leg of a right triangle measures 5 centimeters. The hypotenuse measures 13 centimeters. Find the length of the remaining leg.

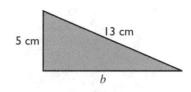

Use the Pythagorean relationship.

$$c^2 = a^2 + b^2$$
$$13^2 = 5^2 + b^2$$
$$169 = 25 + b^2$$

Subtract 25 from both sides to isolate the variable.
$$169 - 25 = 25 - 25 + b^2$$
$$144 = b^2$$

Find the square root of 144.
$$b = \sqrt{144} = 12 \text{ centimeters}$$

Answer: The missing measurement is **12 centimeters.**

Most right triangles do not have three measurements that can be written in whole numbers. Thus, the GED Math Test makes frequent use of a few special ratios. Watch for problems written using a 3:4:5 ratio. Look at the triangle to the right. Do you recognize the ratio? Each of the numbers in the ratio has been doubled.

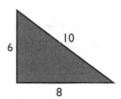

SKILL PRACTICE

Solve each problem.

1. Find the missing side of these right triangles.

	leg a	leg b	hypotenuse
a.	9	12	____
b.	10	____	26
c.	____	24	25

2. The legs of a right triangle each measure 8 inches. Choose the best estimate for the length of the hypotenuse.

   (1) Between 9 and 10 inches
   (2) Between 10 and 11 inches
   (3) Between 11 and 12 inches
   (4) Between 12 and 13 inches
   (5) Between 13 and 14 inches

CALCULATOR Connection

Use your calculator to find the square roots that you have not memorized.

Example: While remodeling his kitchen, Ted needs to cut a piece of dry wall in the shape of a right triangle, to fit into a corner. The shorter sides of this piece measure 8 in and 11 in. What will the longest side measure to the nearest tenth of an inch?

> Refer to page 338 of the Math Handbook for information on squares and the Casio® fx-260.

Step 1. Use the Pythagorean relationship, $8^2 + 11^2 = c^2$.

   Calculator: $\boxed{8}\ \boxed{x^2}\ \boxed{+}\ \boxed{1}\ \boxed{1}\ \boxed{x^2}\ \boxed{=}\ \boxed{\qquad 185.}$

Step 2. Press the square root key ($\boxed{\sqrt{}}$). The display reads $\boxed{\qquad 13.60147}$.

Answer: Round the nearest tenth. The longest side will measure about **13.6 inches.**

Try this one: **The legs of a right triangle measure 5 cm and 9 cm. Find the length of the hypotenuse to the nearest tenth of a centimeter.**

Working with Circles

Understanding Circles

A circle is a flat figure in which every point on the circle is the same distance from its center. Unlike the other shapes we have seen, a circle has no angles or sides, but we can still measure the distance around it and the surface area within it. First, let's go over some definitions of terms.

Using the center, we can make two important measurements:

1. The **radius** is the distance from the center to any point on the circle.
2. The **diameter** is the distance across the circle through the center. The diameter is always twice the length of the radius.

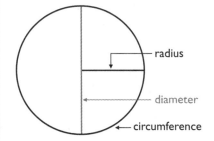

The distance around a circle is called the **circumference.** One way to find the circumference of a circular object is to wrap a string around it and then measure the string.

Using this method, early Greek mathematicians made an important discovery. They observed that the circumference of a circle is always a little larger than three times the circle's diameter. No matter how large or small the circle, the ratio of the circumference to the diameter never changes. This ratio is named **pi** and is represented by the symbol π. Pi is approximately $\frac{22}{7}$ or 3.14 (when rounded to two decimal places). We can use pi to find the approximate circumference and area of any circle.

Finding Circumference

We can use the following formula to solve for the circumference of a circle.

Refer to page 340 for the formulas page provided on the GED Math Test.

circumference (C) $C = \pi d$; where $\pi = 3.14$, $d = $ diameter

▶▶ See how the formula is applied in this situation about making a rug.

Example: Nita makes round rag rugs as a home business. After a rug is completed, Nita sews a binding to protect the edge of the rug. To estimate the cost of the binding material, Nita needs to find the circumference of the rug. What is the approximate distance around a rug with a diameter of 8 feet?

Substitute the diameter from the problem into the formula, using 3.14 for pi. Solve for C.

$$C = \pi d$$
$$\approx 3.14(8)$$
$$\approx 25.12 \text{ feet}$$

MATHEMATICS

Answer: The circumference of the rug is approximately **25.12 feet.** *Check:* You can quickly estimate using 3 for pi. Multiply: $3 \times 8 = 24$. The answer 25.12 makes sense.

Finding Area

When we find the area of a circle, we are attempting to find the number of square units we will need to cover the surface of the circle exactly. Although we cannot fit square units neatly within a circular area, we can use a formula to approximate the area.

area of a circle (A)	$A = \pi r^2$; where $\pi = 3.14$ and r = radius

▶▶ Use the formula to find the area of Nita's rug.

We know the diameter is 8 feet. Divide by 2 to find the radius. $8 \div 2 = 4$ feet

Use the formula. First, square the radius.
Then multiply by 3.14.

$$A = \pi r^2$$
$$\approx 3.14(4^2)$$
$$\approx 3.14(16)$$
$$\approx 50.24 \text{ square feet}$$

Answer: The area of the rug is about **50.24 square feet.**
Check: Multiply using 3 for pi: $3 \times 16 = 48$. The answer 50.24 is reasonable.

When you take the GED Math Test, the formulas for the circumference and the area of a circle will be listed on the formulas page. Make sure you use the correct formula for any given situation.

SKILL PRACTICE

Solve each problem. Use 3.14 for pi.

1. A circular patio has a radius of 5 ft. If it will cost $6 per square foot to pave the patio with brick, how much will the paving cost? (*Hint:* Find the area of the patio, then multiply by the cost per square foot.)

2. LeRoy is building a circular oak table that is 5 feet 6 inches in diameter. He plans to add a metal band on the outside edge of the table. How many feet of banding does he need? (*Hint:* 6 inches = $\frac{1}{2}$ foot)

3. Panteha is making an anniversary cake for her parents. Which would have the greater surface area to write on, a 9-by-13-inch rectangular cake or a 12-inch circular cake?

4. At an aquarium, a circular tide pool is surrounded by a walkway for visitors. The diameter of the pool is 6 meters, and the width of the walkway is 1.5 meters.

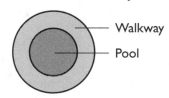

a. What is the circumference of the tide pool?

b. What is the outer circumference of the walkway?

c. What is the area of the walkway to the nearest tenth square meter? (*Hint:* Find the area of the outer circle and subtract the area of the tide pool.)

Finding the Volume of Cylinders

A **cylinder** is a three-dimensional object with circles at each end. The sides of the cylinder are at right angles to the circles. A soup can is an example of a cylinder.

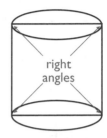

right angles

In life, cylinders are often used as containers for liquids, gases, or dry grains, and seeds. Manufacturers must be able to calculate the space inside a container to know how much it will hold and how much it will weigh when full.

As you recall, volume is the measure of the space inside a three-dimensional object. The formulas for finding volume are built upon our understanding of area. Once we know the area of the base of an object, we can multiply by the height to find the volume.

The base of a cylinder is a circle. Once we know the area of the circle, we can multiply by the height of the cylinder to find the volume.

volume of a cylinder (V)	$V = \pi r^2 h$; where $\pi = 3.14$, r = radius, and h = height

▶▶ See how the formula is applied in this farming situation.

Example: At Lyndon Farms, a new grain bin is in the shape of a cylinder. It measures 20 feet high with a diameter of 18 feet. What is the volume of the bin <u>rounded down</u> to the nearest hundred cubic feet?

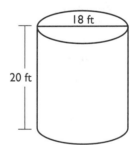

18 ft

20 ft

    (1)   1,100   **(4)** 20,300

    (2)   5,000   **(5)** Not enough

    (3)   5,600   information is given.

Answer: You're right if you chose **(2) 5,000.** Although the problem doesn't give you the radius, you have all the information you need. Remember, the radius is one-half the diameter. Work the problem with a radius of 9 feet.

Substitute the values from the problem into the formula. Use 3.14 for π. Solve for V.

$$V = \pi r^2 h$$

Remember, when you calculate with pi, your answer is only approximate. The volume of the grain bin is about 5,086.8 cubic feet. Rounding down to the nearest hundred, the answer is 5,000 cubic feet.

$$\approx 3.14(9^2)(20)$$
$$\approx 3.14(81)(20)$$
$$\approx 5,086.8 \text{ cubic feet.}$$

Check: After squaring the radius, use front-end estimation: $3 \times 80 \times 20 = 4,800$. Your answer seems reasonable.

MATHEMATICS

▶▶ Use a calculator to solve problems with difficult numbers.

Example: A concrete post is 6 feet long with a 1-foot 3-inch radius. What is the volume of concrete in the post to the nearest cubic foot?

Start by expressing 1 foot 3 inches as a decimal. Three inches is $\frac{3}{12}$, or $\frac{1}{4}$, of a foot. Therefore, 1 foot 3 inches is equal to 1.25 feet.

Substitute the values into the formula.

$$V = \pi r^2 h$$
$$V = 3.14(1.25^2)(6)$$

Use a calculator to do the multiplication.

Calculator: [3][.][1][4][×][1][.][2][5][×][6][=] [29.4375]

Round to the nearest whole number: 29.

Answer: The post contains about **29 cubic feet** of concrete.
Check: Use front-end estimation: $3 \times 1 \times 1 \times 6 = 18$. The answer makes sense.

SKILL PRACTICE

Solve each problem.

1. An oil barrel in the shape of a cylinder has a radius of 24 inches and a height of 4 feet. What is the container's volume in cubic feet?

2. A pipe has an inside diameter of 1 meter and a length of 8 meters. What is its volume in cubic meters?

3. Find the volume in cubic inches of a cylinder with a length of 3 feet and a diameter of 10 inches. (*Hint:* Since the answer must be in cubic inches, change feet to inches.)

4. Yung Mae has built a raised circular flower bed with a diameter of 10 feet and a height of 2 feet. How many whole cubic yards of soil will she need to fill the space? (*Hint:* 1 cubic yard = 27 cubic feet.)

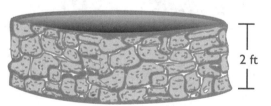

HISTORY Connection

A piece of the pi story...

Pi is a very old number; ancient Egyptian, Hebrew, and Babylonian mathematicians searched for its value. The Greek mathematician Archimedes proved that pi is between $3\frac{10}{71}$ and $3\frac{1}{7}$. In 1706 William Jones first used the symbol π to represent the number 3.141592, because the Greek letter π stands for "perimeter" or "periphery."

Example: Measure and record the circumference of several round objects (jars or lids) using a string and ruler. Measure and record each object's diameter; then divide its circumference by its diameter. Find the average quotient. **What have you discovered?**

PART ONE DIRECTIONS: Choose the <u>one best answer</u> to each of the following problems. Use a calculator wherever necessary. Use 3.14 for π.

1. How many inches is the circumference of a pizza with a diameter of 14 inches?
(1) 14.0
(2) 21.98
(3) 43.96
(4) 153.86
(5) 439.6

<u>Questions 2 and 3</u> are based on the following drawing.

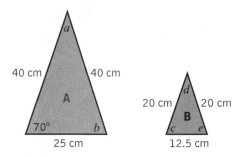

2. Triangles A and B are
(1) similar
(2) congruent
(3) right
(4) equilateral
(5) scalene

3. What is the measure of ∠d?
(1) 20°
(2) 25°
(3) 40°
(4) 50°
(5) 70°

4. A circular patio has a diameter of 12 feet. Which of the following expressions could be used to find the area of the patio in square feet?
(1) 12×6^2
(2) 3.14×12^2
(3) 3.14×12
(4) $3.14 \times 12^2 \times 6$
(5) 3.14×6^2

5. Terry has finished planting a circular rose garden for his neighbor. The circumference of the garden is 50.24 feet. What is the garden's diameter in feet?
(1) 3.14
(2) 8
(3) 16
(4) 24
(5) 25.12

6. What is the volume in cubic centimeters of a cylinder with a diameter of 10 centimeters?
(1) 314
(2) 78.5
(3) 31.4
(4) 15.7
(5) Not enough information is given.

<u>Questions 7 and 8</u> refer to the following figure.

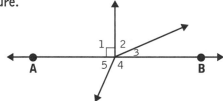

7. Points A and B lie on a straight line. If ∠5 measures 58°, what is the measure of ∠4?
(1) 32°
(2) 35°
(3) 122°
(4) 148°
(5) 302°

8. Angles 2 and 3 are complementary angles. If ∠3 measures 23°, what is the measure of ∠2?
(1) 180°
(2) 157°
(3) 100°
(4) 67°
(5) 23°

MATHEMATICS

9. Jeanine is sewing ribbon around equilateral triangles within the pattern of a baby quilt. One side of each triangle measures 8 inches. Find the perimeter of each triangle in inches.
    (1) 8
    (2) 16
    (3) 24
    (4) 48
    (5) 64

10. Which of these expressions would be used to find the radius of a circle whose area is 50.24?
    (1) $r^2 = \frac{50.24}{3.14}$
    (2) $r = 2 \times \frac{50.24}{3.14}$
    (3) $r^2 = 50.24(3.14)$
    (4) $r = \frac{50.24}{3.14}$
    (5) $r = (50.24)(3.14)(2)$

Question 11 is based on the following map.

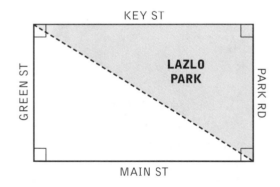

11. Starting at the corner of Park Road and Main Street, Ana's soccer team jogs 9 blocks due north on Park Road and then 12 blocks due west on Key Street. At the corner of Key and Green Streets, they cut straight across the park to where they began. How many blocks is the last leg of their run?
    (1) 6
    (2) 10
    (3) 12
    (4) 15
    (5) 20

12. At 3 P.M. a building casts a shadow 120 meters long. At the same time, a pole, which measures 4 meters in height, casts a shadow of 1.6 meters. If the building and pole are both perpendicular to the ground, what is the height of the building in meters?
    (1) 48
    (2) 140
    (3) 300
    (4) 480
    (5) Not enough information is given.

Question 13 refers to the following figure.

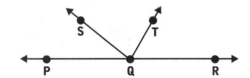

13. Points P, Q, and R lie on a straight line. Which of the following angles is supplementary to ∠TQR?
    (1) ∠SQR
    (2) ∠SQT
    (3) ∠PQS
    (4) ∠PQT
    (5) ∠PQR

14. One leg of a right triangle measures 3 inches. The hypotenuse measures 17 inches. Which equation could be used to find the length of the remaining leg?
    (1) $3^2 + 17^2 = b^2$
    (2) $17^2 = b^2 - 3^2$
    (3) $17^2 - 3^2 = b^2$
    (4) $17^2 = \frac{3^2}{b^2}$
    (5) $b^2 - 17^2 = 3^2$

15. The circumference of a circular granite block in Zuma Beach Plaza is 6.28 meters. What is the area of the surface of granite block in square meters?
    (1) 2.00
    (2) 3.14
    (3) 6.28
    (4) 18.84
    (5) 26.26

PART TWO DIRECTIONS: Choose the <u>one best answer</u> to each of the following problems. *You may not use a calculator on these problems.*

16. What is the <u>approximate</u> circumference of a circle with a radius of 3 inches?
    (1) between 0 and 5 inches
    (2) between 5 and 10 inches
    (3) between 10 and 15 inches
    (4) between 15 and 20 inches
    (5) between 20 and 30 inches

<u>Questions 17 and 18</u> are based on the following figure.

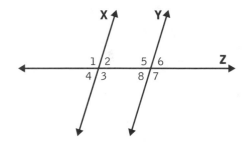

17. Lines X and Y are parallel lines. If the measure of ∠1 is 102°, what is the measure of ∠6?
    (1) 12°
    (2) 51°
    (3) 78°
    (4) 88°
    (5) 102°

18. Which of the following angles has a measure equal to the measure of ∠5?
    (1) ∠2
    (2) ∠3
    (3) ∠4
    (4) ∠6
    (5) ∠8

19. <u>About</u> how many square inches is the area of a circle with a radius of 5 inches?
    (1)   3
    (2) 15
    (3) 25
    (4) 60
    (5) 75

<u>Question 20</u> refers to the following figure.

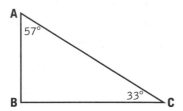

20. What kind of triangle is △ABC?
    (1) equilateral
    (2) isosceles
    (3) right
    (4) scalene
    (5) Not enough information is given.

21. Lines G and H are parallel. Line A is perpendicular to Line G. How many 90° angles are formed by this arrangement?
    (1) 8
    (2) 6
    (3) 4
    (4) 2
    (5) 1

22. △XYZ is a scalene triangle. ∠X measures 36°. Which of the following must be a true statement?
    (1) ∠Y must be a right angle.
    (2) The sum of ∠Y and ∠Z equals 180°.
    (3) ∠X and ∠Y must be complementary angles.
    (4) Angle Z must measure 36°.
    (5) Neither ∠Y nor ∠Z measures 36°.

23. A cylindrical container has an inside radius of 4 inches and a height of 10 inches. <u>Approximately</u> how many cubic inches of juice can it hold?
    (1) 200
    (2) 300
    (3) 400
    (4) 500
    (5) 600

MATHEMATICS

Alternate Math Formats

The questions below are based on the math skills in Programs 33–35.
For more information on answering alternate format items, review pages 20–22.

Grid in the answers to questions 24 through 35.

24. A hiking trail is 2600 meters in length. What is the length of the trail in kilometers?

25. Taraneh needs to cut six 18-inch lengths of wood from a piece of lumber that is 16 feet long. How many feet of lumber will she have left after she makes the cuts? (Disregard any waste.)

Questions 26 and 27 refer to the following diagram.

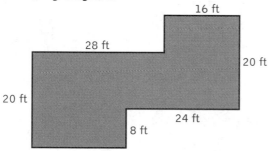

26. Noah is painting and carpeting the rooms shown in the diagram. After painting, he plans to put a wallpaper border along the top of all walls. What is the measure in feet of the perimeter of the rooms?

27. To carpet the rooms, Noah needs to know the area of the rooms. Find the area of the rooms <u>in square feet.</u>

28. Adrianne bought a new sofa for $650. She financed the purchase over 3 years at 8% simple interest. How much will she pay in interest over the length of the loan?

29. To the nearest tenth, what is the area in square centimeters of a circle with a diameter of 8 cm?

Questions 30 and 31 refer to the following diagram.

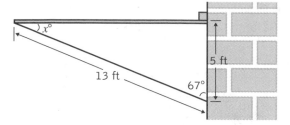

13 ft

$x°$

5 ft

67°

30. A metal pole used to hang banners and advertisements is attached to a brick building to form a right angle. A diagonal brace is placed 5 feet below the pole to give support. What is the length in feet of the pole?

31. The pole, wall, and brace form a triangle. What is the measure of x in degrees?

32. A square tile measures $6\frac{1}{2}$ inches per side. To the nearest tenth, what is the area in square inches of the tile?

Question 33 refers to the following diagram.

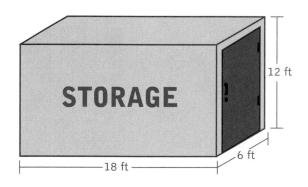

STORAGE

12 ft

6 ft

18 ft

33. The storage compartment is in the shape of a rectangular container. In cubic feet, what is the volume of the storage compartment?

34. Angles 1 and 2 are supplementary angles. If ∠1 measures 85°, what is the measure in degrees of ∠2?

35. A container holds 3.42 liters of cleaning fluid. If the fluid is divided evenly into 3 smaller containers, how many <u>milliliters</u> will each hold?

30.

31.

32.

33.

34.

35.

Answers and explanations start on page 323.

From a calorie table at the doctor's office to a pie chart in the newspaper, the graphics shown in this program present a wide variety of information for practical use. You'll learn what to look for when you read charts and graphs.

Please note that there are two corresponding workbook lessons for Program 36.

Data Analysis, Part One

OBJECTIVES

1. Understand and solve problems with tables, charts, and pictographs.
2. Understand and solve problems with bar and line graphs.
3. Understand and solve problems with circle graphs.

The next time you pass a newsstand, scan the front pages of the newspapers for sale. Many will have tables, charts, and graphs in color with appealing designs. Why? Because tables, charts, and graphs present information visually. At a glance, you can find the main idea. Without complex calculations, you can easily see how the economy is doing, whether crime is on the rise, or whether your favorite team is headed for the championship.

The ability to work with tables, charts, and graphs is important to your success on the GED Math Test. You will need to know how to find the main idea of a graphic and how to search for the facts you need to solve problems and draw conclusions.

Your understanding of percents will help you understand circle graphs. Your work in this program will help you gain other math skills in the areas of problem solving, data analysis, and statistics.

On the following pages, you will find a brief exercise called *Sneak Preview*. It is designed to introduce you to some of the topics that will be featured in the video program and the corresponding lesson. After you complete the exercise and check your answers, turn to the vocabulary page. There you will find terms that will help you better understand the video and the lesson that follow. After reviewing page 194, you will be ready to watch Program 36. Please note that there are two corresponding workbook lessons for Program 36.

For additional practice, visit *LiteracyLink* online at
http://www.pbs.org/literacy.

Sneak Preview

This exercise previews some of the concepts from Program 36. After you answer the questions, use the feedback on page 193 to help set your learning goals.

WORKPLACE LINK: Tracy designs marketing brochures and flyers for King Realty Company. Tracy is given a table showing model house costs. She is asked to design a graph that displays the distribution of costs for a furnished model home in Rosewood Heights. She decides that a **circle graph** (or pie chart) is the best way to graphically represent the data.

DISTRIBUTION OF COSTS FOR FURNISHED MODEL HOMES IN THREE LOCAL COMMUNITIES

Community	Lot	Landscaping	House	Furnishings
Sunnyvale	$25,000	$7,500	$108,500	$16,900
Rosewood Heights	$30,000	$10,000	$116,000	$16,000
Woodland	$35,000	$9,500	$215,000	$22,100

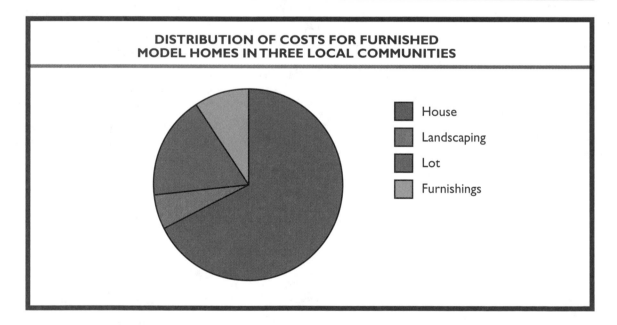

DISTRIBUTION OF COSTS FOR FURNISHED MODEL HOMES IN THREE LOCAL COMMUNITIES

- House
- Landscaping
- Lot
- Furnishings

Answer these questions based on the table and circle graph.

1. One of real estate agents at King Realty needs to find the difference between the cost of the Rosewood Heights lot with landscaping and the Sunnyvale lot with landscaping. Which expression could he use?

    (1) $(30,000 + 25,000) - (10,000 + 7,500)$

    (2) $(30,000 + 10,000) - (25,000 + 7,500)$

    (3) $(35,000 + 9,500) - (25,000 + 7,500)$

    (4) $(30,000 - 10,000) - (25,000 - 7,500)$

    (5) $(35,000 + 9,500) - (30,000 + 10,000)$

MATHEMATICS

2. <u>Approximately</u> how much more are the furnishings for the Woodland model house than the Sunnyvale model house?

  (1) $4,000
  (2) $5,000
  (3) $6,000
  (4) $7,000
  (5) $10,000

3. Each section of the circle graph represents how much is spent on each element of the Rosewood Heights model. For example, $10,000 was spent on landscaping. What is the order of these elements by cost, <u>from least to greatest</u>?

  (1) furnishings, landscaping, lot, house
  (2) house, lot, furnishings, landscaping
  (3) landscaping, house, furnishings, lot
  (4) landscaping, furnishings, lot, house
  (5) landscaping, lot, furnishings, house

4. According to the circle graph, the cost of the Rosewood Heights lot and landscaping is <u>about</u> what fraction of the total cost of the Rosewood Heights model?

  (1) $\frac{1}{4}$
  (2) $\frac{1}{2}$
  (3) $\frac{3}{4}$
  (4) $\frac{6}{7}$
  (5) Not enough information is given.

Feedback

- If you got all of the answers right...
  you have a good basic understanding of how to find and apply information using a table and a circle graph.

- If you missed question 1...
  you need to practice interpreting data in a table and working with set-up solutions.

- If you missed question 2...
  you need to work on interpreting and estimating information in a table.

- If you missed question 3...
  you need to practice reading circle graphs and interpreting the size of the segments that make up the graph.

- If you missed question 4...
  you need to develop your skills of interpreting circle graph data and working with fractions.

ANSWERS FOR SNEAK PREVIEW:
1. Choice (2)   2. Choice (2)   3. Choice (4)   4. Choice (1)

Vocabulary for *Data Analysis, Part One**

bar graph	a graph that uses bars next to a scale to compare quantities
circle graph	a graph that uses sections of a circle to represent parts of a whole; also called a *pie chart*
data	bits of information, often numerical
double-bar graph	a type of bar graph where multiple bars are shown for each date, event, or category; a key is usually needed to interpret the data
horizontal axis	one of two perpendicular lines that define a graph; the line running left and right
key	the information you need to read and interpret a graph; also called a *legend*
line graph	a graph used to display changes in data using points and line segments to represent the data
pictograph	a graph that uses pictures or symbols to represent data
projection	a prediction based on trends in data
stacked-bar graph	a type of bar graph in which each bar is divided into sections; a key is needed to interpret the data
table	a presentation of data organized into columns (up and down) and rows (across)
trend	an observed pattern of change in data
vertical axis	one of two perpendicular lines that define a graph; the line running up and down

*Additional vocabulary for Program 36 is provided on page 214.

➡ **NOW WATCH PROGRAM 36:**

Remember that knowing how to read charts, graphs, and tables is more important than being able to name the type of graphic, so concentrate on understanding how graphics present information.

After you watch the program, work on:

- pages 195–210 in this workbook
- Internet activities at http://www.pbs.org/literacy

MATHEMATICS

AFTER YOU WATCH

36

Data Analysis, Part One

On the following pages, you will learn more about the ideas discussed in the video program and have an opportunity to develop and practice your GED math skills.

Key Points to Think About

In the video program, you explored:
- How people use tables, charts, and graphs in their daily lives as workers, citizens, and family members to find information and solve problems.
- How titles, labels, and legends are used to help people understand the meaning of graphs.
- Everyday applications of tables, bar graphs, line graphs, and circle graphs.

On the GED Math Test:
- You will be expected to know how to read tables, charts, and graphs to find the information you need to solve problems.
- You should know how to read and interpret scales on the axis lines of bar and line graphs.
- You will use data from graphs to draw conclusions, make comparisons, and identify trends.

As you work through this lesson for Program 36:
- Think about the purpose of each table or graph and its overall meaning.
- Look for patterns and trends in data to help you draw conclusions and make predictions.
- Be aware of the tables, charts, and graphs you see in the world around you. Take the opportunity to read, understand, and use them to solve problems in everyday living, not just on the GED Math Test.

GED TIPS

When taking the GED Test, you should:

- Always read the titles and labels on a graph before you use the numerical information to solve a problem.
- Make sure you understand the question a problem is asking before you begin calculations.
- Focus on the facts you need to solve each problem. Don't be distracted by information you don't need.

Reading Tables, Charts, and Pictographs

FAMILY LINK: Tyler and his wife Alicia are planning a driving trip from Mobile, Alabama, to Buffalo, New York, to visit her parents. Tyler goes on the Internet to find a mileage table. On the table he finds where the columns for Mobile and Buffalo intersect and reads that the cities are about 1160 miles apart. Tyler estimates that they could make the drive in about 20 hours.

Finding Information in Tables and Charts

You see tables and charts all the time in newspapers, magazines, and textbooks. Tables organize information in columns and rows. By finding the place where the columns and rows intersect, you can use tables to find out how much income tax you owe, what time your favorite show is on television, or the information you need to solve problems on the GED Math Test.

▸▸ Look at this portion of a table from a bus schedule.

WEEKDAY EASTBOUND—ROUTE 14 BEVERLY BLVD.

Beverly La Cienega	Beverly Western	Beverly Vermont	1st Street Beaudry	Grand Ave. 7th Street	Grand Ave. Adams Blvd.*
7:10 a	7:24 a	7:29 a	7:40 a	7:46 a	7:56 a
7:30 a	7:44 a	7:49 a	8:00 a	8:06 a	8:16 a
7:50 a	8:04 a	8:09 a	8:20 a	8:26 a	8:36 a
8:10 a	8:24 a	8:29 a	8:40 a	8:46 a	8:56 a
8:30 a	8:44 a	8:49 a	9:00 a	9:06 a	9:16 a

*This column shows arrival times. All other times are departure times.

Example: Krisna has a new job downtown. He estimates that it will take him 10 minutes to walk from the corner of Grand and Adams to his workplace. Krisna will catch the bus at Beverly and Western. If he has to be at work by 9 A.M., what is the latest time he can catch the bus and still be at work on time?

To solve the problem, work backward. Since it will take Krisna 10 minutes to walk from the bus stop to work, he must arrive at Grand Avenue and Adams Boulevard by 8:50 A.M. Look in the last column. The bus arriving at 8:36 A.M. is the last one that will get him there on time.

7:56 a
8:16 a
8:36 a
8:56 a
9:16 a

Now follow that row back to the column for Beverly and Western.

Beverly La Cienega	**Beverly Western**	Beverly Vermont	1st Street Beaudry	Grand Ave. 7th Street	**Grand Ave. Adams Blvd.***
7:50 a	**8:04 a**	8:09 a	8:20 a	8:26 a	**8:36 a**

Answer: The latest time that Krisna can catch the bus at Beverly and Western is **8:04 A.M.** Of course, he could always catch an earlier one to make sure he arrives on time.

MATHEMATICS

Charts combine pictures and information. Geometric figures and arrows can help you understand how, when, and where events took place.

▶▶ Study this chart from the sports page of a newspaper.

Example: In 1998, Mark McGwire hit more home runs than any individual had ever hit in a single season. The chart shows the locations of his 70 home runs. To which location did he hit nearly 20% of his home runs?

Answer: You're right if you said **Center Field**. Find 20% of 70: $70 \times 0.2 = 14$, which is nearest the 13 home runs hit to center field.

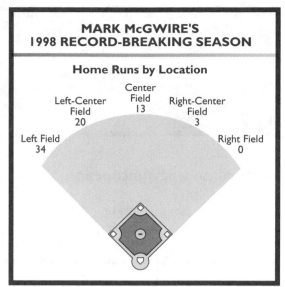

MARK McGWIRE'S 1998 RECORD-BREAKING SEASON

Home Runs by Location

SKILL PRACTICE

Use the information from the table to answer questions 1 through 3 below.

POPULATION OF THE FIVE LARGEST U.S. CITIES

City	1990	1980	1970	1960	1950	1900
New York	7,322,564	7,071,639	7,895,563	7,781,984	7,891,957	3,437,202
Los Angeles	3,485,557	2,968,528	2,811,801	2,479,015	1,970,358	102,479
Chicago	2,783,726	3,005,072	3,369,357	3,550,404	3,620,962	1,698,575
Houston	1,629,902	1,595,138	1,233,535	938,219	596,163	44,633
Philadelphia	1,585,577	1,688,210	1,949,996	2,002,512	1,071,605	1,293,697

Source: Bureau of the Census, U.S. Department of Commerce

1. Write *True* or *False* for each of the following statements.

   a. In 1960 the population of Chicago was greater than that of Los Angeles.
   b. The population of Houston tripled in size between 1950 and 1960.
   c. The population of Philadelphia has increased continually since 1900.
   d. The population of New York decreased from 1970 to 1980.

2. Which city's population increased by the greatest number from 1900 to 1990?

3. In 1990 the population of New York was about ____ times the population of Houston.

   (1) $2\frac{1}{2}$ (4) 4
   (2) 3   (5) $4\frac{1}{2}$
   (3) $3\frac{1}{2}$

Use the chart below to answer items 4 and 5.

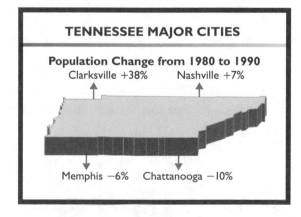

TENNESSEE MAJOR CITIES

Population Change from 1980 to 1990
Clarksville +38%   Nashville +7%
Memphis −6%   Chattanooga −10%

4. Which city experienced the smallest change in population?

5. Using the chart, is there a way to know which city has the greatest population now? Explain.

Answers and explanations start on page 323.

Understanding Pictographs

A **pictograph** uses pictures or symbols to represent quantities. A key shows the value of each symbol. In the pictograph below, the key shows that each symbol is equal to 10 gallons of water.

AVERAGE WATER USAGE BY ACTIVITY

Activity Typical Usage Rate	Daily Usage per Person
Toilet 5 gal/flush	💧 💧 (
Shower 5 gal/min	💧 💧 💧 (
Tub Bath 30 gal/bath	💧 💧 💧
Dishwasher 15 gal/load	💧 (
Clothes Washer 50 gal/load	💧 💧 💧 💧 💧

KEY
💧 = 10 Gallons

As with any table or graph, always read the labels carefully. According to the title, this graph shows the average amount of water used per person in certain activities. Each activity is given a label and a usage rate. The usage rate helps us understand how the water usage was measured.

▸▸ See how a pictograph is used in this situation to compare numbers.

Example: Nina decides to time her shower that evening to find out how much water she is using. From start to finish, her shower takes 9 minutes. Using the rate of 5 gallons per minute from the graph, Nina used 45 gallons of water for her shower. How does her usage compare to the amount shown on the graph?

First, find the average water usage per shower from the graph. There are $3\frac{1}{2}$ (or 3.5) symbols, each worth 10 gallons. (Note that $\frac{1}{2}$ symbol can also be written as 0.5.)

Multiply: $3.5 \times 10 = 35$ gallons. According to the graph, the average shower uses 35 gallons of water.

Find the difference: $45 - 35 = 10$ gallons.

> Since one symbol = 10 gallons, $\frac{1}{2}$ symbol = 5 gallons.

Answer: Nina used **10 gallons more** than the average shown on the pictograph. Nina could save water and money by taking quicker showers.

Use the pictograph below to answer items 1 to 3.

PROFESSIONAL SPORTS — AVERAGE SALARIES — 1997

Football

Basketball $\frac{1}{2}$

Baseball $\frac{1}{4}$

Hockey $\frac{1}{2}$

KEY
= $250,000

Solve each problem.

1. What was the approximate average salary of a professional hockey player in 1997?

2. Based on the average salaries in 1997, about how much more did a basketball player earn than a football player?

   (1) $1,125,000
   (2) $1,132,500
   (3) $1,500,000
   (4) $1,875,000
   (5) $2,625,000

3. Write *True* or *False* for each of the following statements.

   a. The average 1997 football salary was more than one million dollars.

   b. The average 1997 baseball salary was nearly three times greater than the average football salary.

   c. The average 1997 basketball salary was more than twice the average hockey salary.

   d. There was a less than $250,000 difference between the 1997 average baseball salary and hockey salary.

PROBLEM SOLVER Connection

On the GED Math Test, you will sometimes be asked to answer two or more questions based on one paragraph or one graphic. These **item sets** share the same set of information.

To avoid errors when solving item sets, keep in mind these questions:

1. Did I read the direction line to see which test items are based on the graphic or paragraph?
2. Did I read the title, key, and labels on the graphic *before* solving any problems?
3. Did I work the problems one at a time, first determining what is asked in each question?
4. Did I consider "What information do I need to solve this question?" (*Note:* You may not need all the information provided to solve any or all of an item set.)
5. Did I solve the problem with the appropriate facts and operations?

Turn to page 197. How many item sets do you see? Which questions are part of the first item set?

PROGRAM 36: Data Analysis, Part One

Understanding Bar and Line Graphs

WORKPLACE LINK: Rondell works at AC Electronics. Recently, he suggested to his manager that the store could benefit from knowing which areas of the city their customers come from. He suggested asking customers for their zip codes during the store's weekend sale. Rondell volunteered to make a bar graph of the results for his manager's use.

Reading a Bar Graph

A **bar graph** uses bars to represent numerical information. To read the bars, you need to understand how to read the axis lines. A bar graph has two axis lines. One axis presents labels for the bars; the other axis shows a numerical scale. Always read the title and labels before you begin interpreting a graph.

▶▶ Look at the graph that Rondell made for AC Electronics.

The **vertical axis** labels the bars with the customers' zip codes. The **horizontal axis** shows a scale labeled *Number of Customers*. To read the graph, find where the end of a bar falls on the scale.

Example: Approximately how many customers came from the 19137 area?

Find the bar labeled 19137. Imagine a line from the end of the bar to the scale. Read the scale carefully.

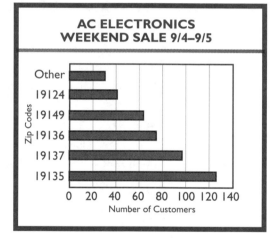

Answer: Since the end of the bar is near 100, the bar represents **about 95 customers.**

Reading Double-Bar and Stacked-Bar Graphs

Other kinds of bars can be used to make more detailed comparisons. In this **double-bar graph,** there are two bars for each event. The bars show the proceeds for the same event for two different years. Use the key to read the graph.

▶▶ Use the double-bar graph to see changes in performance.

Example: Which event showed a decrease in proceeds from Year 1 to Year 2?

    (1)   Food Booths   (4)   Games
    (2)   Auction   (5)   None of the above
    (3)   Rides

Answer: (2) Auction. The auction raised more than $6000 in Year 1, but only about $4500 in Year 2. The proceeds for every other event increased in Year 2.

The bars in a **stacked-bar graph** are divided into more than one part. The portions of the bar are different patterns or colors. Read the key to find out what each portion of each bar represents.

This graph was made by a video rental store. It shows the number of rentals on a certain day, organized by category. The bars are divided into two parts, representing male and female customers.

▶▶ See how a stacked-bar graph is used to make comparisons.

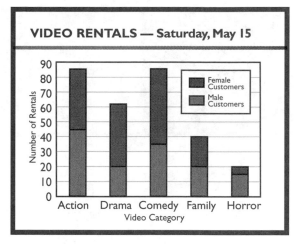

Example: Video World gathers information about its customers' preferences in order to make purchasing decisions. Based on the graph, were more action videos rented by men or women?

The purple, upper portion of each bar represents the number of videos rented by women; the blue, lower portion represents those rented by men. You need to compare the purple and blue portions of the bar for action videos.

The easiest way to do this is to perform a simple calculation. Find the number representing the whole bar and subtract the number representing the lower bar (in this case, the portion representing male customers). The difference is the number representing the female customers.

Whole Bar − Lower Portion = Upper Portion
85   −   45   =   40

Answer: Since the lower, shaded portion of the bar represents male customers, the graph shows that **more action videos were rented by men than women.**

SKILL PRACTICE

Answer the questions using the graphs on pages 200 and 201.

Use the graph titled *AC Electronics*.

1. About how many customers came from the 19136 and 19149 zip code areas combined?

2. Which zip code area had about twice the number of customers as the 19124 zip code?

Use the graph titled *Police Expo Proceeds*.

3. About how much more did the food booths earn than the rides in Year 2?

4. Which event showed the greatest increase in proceeds from Year 1 to Year 2?

Use the graph titled *Video Rentals*.

5. Which category of video was chosen equally by male and female customers?

6. Which of these statements is true?

   (1) Women rented about 40 family videos.
   (2) More than twice as many comedy videos were rented as drama videos.
   (3) Women accounted for most of the horror video rentals.
   (4) The ratio of drama to family videos was about 3:2.
   (5) Men rented nearly 90 comedy videos.

Answers and explanations start on page 324.

MATHEMATICS

Reading Line Graphs

Line graphs also use axis lines to display information. Both axis lines can be marked with a scale. Because line graphs are usually used to show changes over time, one of the axis lines will often show a series of dates.

Data are plotted on a line graph by placing a point where the two scales would intersect. Once all points are plotted, they are connected by line segments.

Line graphs are often used to display financial information. This graph shows the net income from Ken's home-based gardening business.

▶▶ Read the line graph to find necessary information.

Example: Ken is analyzing the performance of his company over the last six years. In what year did Ken's business earn the greatest amount of net income? What was the approximate net income for that year?

Always read the labels on the graph carefully to understand how the scales are constructed. The horizontal scale at the bottom shows years. The vertical scale on the left shows thousands of dollars. For instance, the number 10 on the scale represents $10,000.

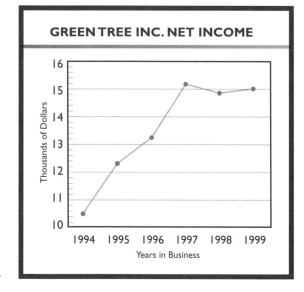

GREEN TREE INC. NET INCOME

Find the highest point on the graph. Follow the point down to the scale at the bottom. The highest point is above the year 1997.

Now move from the highest point to the scale on the left. The point is at the first tick mark on the scale between 15 and 16. The point represents 15.2 thousand or $15,200.

Answer: Ken's best year was in **1997,** when his net income was **$15,200.**

Making Predictions

A **trend,** or pattern of change, can help you make a projection. A **projection** is a prediction of how the data will change in the future based on the patterns of change in the past and the present.

▶▶ See how a projection is made using the data from GreenTree Inc.

Example: When Ken started his business in 1994, he had only a few customers. In 1997, his business had grown so much that he hired an assistant. Now he wants to know whether he should consider hiring another employee in the next couple of years.

Answer: Probably not. The graph shows two trends—a sharp increase in business from 1994 to 1997 and a leveling off from 1997 to 1999. Ken's business will probably hold steady over the next couple of years. It is unlikely to match the amount of increase seen in the earlier years.

SKILL PRACTICE

The graph below shows the performance of two stocks, ARL and CTR, over a 5-week period. Use the line graph below to answer items 1 to 5.

1. On March 26, what was the approximate cost of one share of CTR stock?

2. Which stock has shown the greatest increase in price over the 5-week period?

3. Guido bought 5 shares of ARL stock on March 5. Approximately how much did he pay for the shares?

4. Based on the current trends, which stock will be worth more per share by the end of April?

5. By about how much money did the price of a share of CTR stock increase from March 19 to March 26?

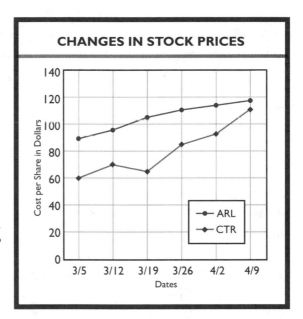

SOCIAL STUDIES Connection

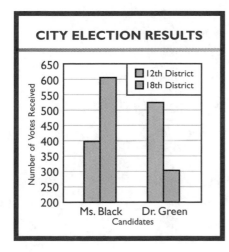

Political opinion polls often use graphics to represent election results. This double-bar graph shows how many votes were received by two candidates in two districts.

Example: Is the following statement true? In the 18th District, Ms. Black received about four times as many votes as Dr. Green.

Answer: The statement is **false.** Read the left-hand scale carefully to see that Ms. Black received **twice** as many votes. *Note:* A graph can appear misleading if the scale doesn't start at 0.

Do you agree with this statement? Why or why not?
Ms. Black received twice as many votes from the 18th District as she did from the 12th District.

Understanding Circle Graphs

COMMUNITY LINK: Sharon is a member of a school's Booster Club, which raises funds to help buy books and computers for the school. She wants to help parents understand the importance of the Booster Club to the school, so she prepares a circle graph showing that the Booster Club is providing nearly one-half of the school's funds for these items.

How Circle Graphs Are Organized

A **circle graph** is used to show how a whole amount is divided into parts. Circle graphs are often used to show how money is spent. The circle in a circle graph represents the whole. In the circle graph below, the circle represents the entire amount of money to be budgeted. The pie-shaped sections represent the percentages budgeted for individual items.

This graph shows how the Miller family budgeted its income. Each section is labeled with the name of an expense and a percent of the family's income.

Compare the sections for savings and taxes. Since 15% is three times more than 5%, the size of the taxes section is three times larger than the section for savings. The sizes of the sections can help you understand the relationship of the sections to each as well as to the total budget.

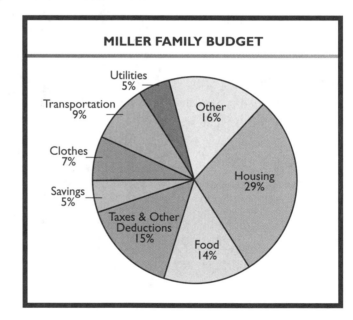

Now add the percents in the sections.

29% + 14% + 15% + 5% + 7% + 9% + 5% + 16% = 100%

The sections add up to 100%, the entire family income.

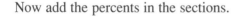 Read the graph to answer this question about the family's budget.

Example: What percent of their income did the Millers budget for food and clothing?

Find the sections for food and clothing on the graph and add:
Food 14% + Clothes 7% = 21%

Answer: The Millers budgeted **21%** of their income on food and clothing.

Circle graphs may also be labeled in cents, with the entire circle representing one whole dollar. Charities often use cents to show their contributors how their dollars are spent.

▶▶Use the value of the whole circle to solve problems.

Example: For every dollar donated to the Booster Club, how many cents are <u>not</u> spent on computers and software?

Subtract the amount spent on computers and software from one dollar.

$1.00 − $0.45 = $0.55

Answer: The Booster Club spends **55 cents of every dollar** on items other than computers and software.

The sections in a circle graph can also be labeled with fractions. When fractions are used, the value of the whole circle is 1. This graph shows the fraction of concert ticket sales sold to each group.

▶▶Compare fractions to solve the problem.

Example: Which group bought the greatest number of concert tickets?

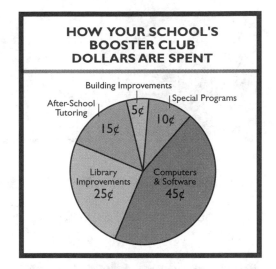

HOW YOUR SCHOOL'S BOOSTER CLUB DOLLARS ARE SPENT

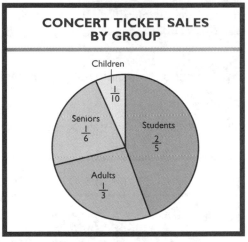

CONCERT TICKET SALES BY GROUP

You can see by the size of the sections that the answer must be either Adults or Students. To find the answer, compare $\frac{1}{3}$ and $\frac{2}{5}$.

$\frac{1}{3} = \frac{5}{15}$ $\qquad$ $\frac{2}{5} = \frac{6}{15}$ $\qquad$ $\frac{2}{5}$ is greater than $\frac{1}{3}$.

Answer: More tickets were sold to **Students** than to any other group.

SKILL PRACTICE

Answer the questions using the graphs on pages 204 and 205.

Use the Miller Family Budget.

1. The amount the Miller family budgeted for housing is about how many times greater than the amount they budgeted to save?

2. The Miller family budgeted $826.50 for housing. Is there any way to know exactly how much the Miller family budgeted for food? Explain your thinking.

3. For which item did the Miller family budget nearly $\frac{1}{10}$ of their income?

Use the Booster Club graph.

4. If a parent donates $50 to the Booster Club, how much of the donation will be spent on library improvements?

Use the graph titled *Concert Ticket Sales by Group.*

5. Adult tickets cost the most at $10. What fraction of the tickets was sold for less than the $10 price?

Solving Problems with Circle Graphs

When you take the GED Math Test, you will be asked to use information from graphs to solve problems. Circle graphs are often used in problems about fractions, ratio, proportion, and percent.

As you have learned, a circle graph represents a whole amount. The sections represent fractional parts of that whole. If you know the amount that the circle represents, you can find the amounts represented by the sections.

▶▶ Apply your understanding of percent in this situation about a restaurant.

Example: A new restaurant asked 300 customers to grade their dining experience. The survey scale and the results are shown in the graph below. How many customers rated the restaurant as "average"?

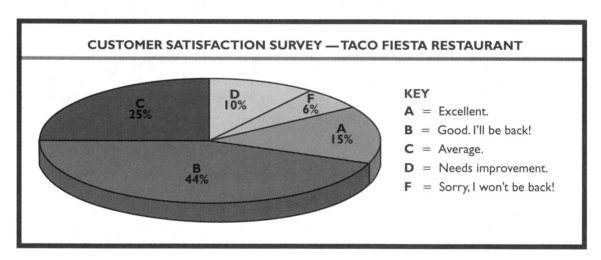

CUSTOMER SATISFACTION SURVEY — TACO FIESTA RESTAURANT

C 25%
D 10%
F 6%
A 15%
B 44%

KEY
A = Excellent.
B = Good. I'll be back!
C = Average.
D = Needs improvement.
F = Sorry, I won't be back!

The question asks for the number of customers, not the percent. First, find the percent. Read the key and the graph. An "average," or C, grade was given by 25% of the customers.

Now find 25% of 300, the number of customers represented by the whole circle.

Using proportion: $\frac{25}{100} = \frac{x}{300}$ $25 \times 300 = 7500$ $7500 \div 100 = 75$

Answer: Of the 300 customers who answered the survey, **75 customers** rated the restaurant as "average."

Check: Solve the problem with a fraction. Since $25\% = \frac{1}{4}$, find $\frac{1}{4}$ of 300, or divide by 4: $300 \div 4 = 75$. The answer is correct.

MATHEMATICS

The Lindon Public Library recently held a book donation drive to expand its nonfiction book section. During the drive, the library received 640 hardcover books. The graph below shows the breakdown of the books by category. Use the graph to answer items 1 to 4.

1. What <u>fraction</u> of the books were about the arts?

2. How many books about sports were donated?

3. How many books were not about either the arts or science?

4. A bookstore heard about the drive and donated an additional 40 books about science. If the library redraws the graph to include the new books, all the percents will change. What percent will be written in the section labeled *Science?*

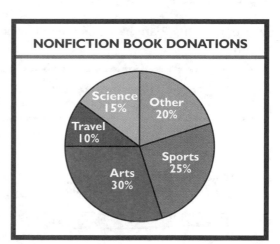

NONFICTION BOOK DONATIONS

Science 15%
Other 20%
Travel 10%
Sports 25%
Arts 30%

TECHNOLOGY Connection

Computer spreadsheets store data that can be used to analyze situations, plan a budget, or make decisions. An amazing variety of charts and graphs can be generated from a spreadsheet.

One-Stop Shopping has three stores, each identified by its location in the city. The stores' sales figures for the four quarters of last year are shown in these three graphs. Each graph contains the same information.

Which one helps you understand the data best? Why?

ONE-STOP SHOPPING SALES

ONE-STOP SHOPPING SALES

ONE-STOP SHOPPING SALES

PART ONE DIRECTIONS: Choose the <u>one best answer</u> to each of the following problems. Use a calculator wherever necessary.

<u>Questions 1 and 2</u> are based on the following graph.

LEGACY MAP COMPANY MAPS SOLD BY REGION

Central States
Northwestern States
Southwestern States
New England States

0   1   2   3   4   5   6
UNITS SOLD IN THOUSANDS

<u>Questions 3 through 5</u> are based on the following graph.

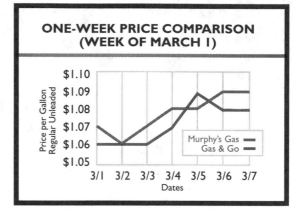

ONE-WEEK PRICE COMPARISON (WEEK OF MARCH 1)

Price per Gallon Regular Unleaded

$1.10
$1.09
$1.08
$1.07
$1.06
$1.05

3/1 3/2 3/3 3/4 3/5 3/6 3/7
Dates

Murphy's Gas
Gas & Go

MATHEMATICS

1. The Legacy Map Company sells road maps of different regions of the United States. Which two regions sold about 5000 units in combined sales?
    (1) Southwestern States and Central States
    (2) New England States and Northwestern States
    (3) Northwestern States and Southwestern States
    (4) Central States and New England States
    (5) Southwestern States and Central States

2. The Legacy Map Company sold twice as many Southwestern States maps this year as it did last year. How many thousands of maps did the company sell last year?
    (1) 10.0
    (2) 7.5
    (3) 2.5
    (4) 0.25
    (5) Not enough information is given.

3. On March 4, what was the difference in price for a gallon of gas between Murphy's Gas and Gas & Go?
    (1) $0.00
    (2) $0.01
    (3) $0.02
    (4) $0.03
    (5) Not enough information is given.

4. Luis bought 15 gallons of gasoline at Gas & Go on March 5. Which expression would you use to figure how much Luis paid for the gas?
    (1) $\frac{\$1.09}{15}$
    (2) $\frac{\$1.07}{15}$
    (3) 15($1.07)
    (4) 15($1.08)
    (5) 15($1.09)

5. If each station had 300 customers on March 7, <u>about</u> how much more money did Gas & Go make in gas purchases than Murphy's Gas?
    (1) $35
    (2) $155
    (3) $200
    (4) $300
    (5) Not enough information is given.

Questions 6 through 8 are based on the following pictograph.

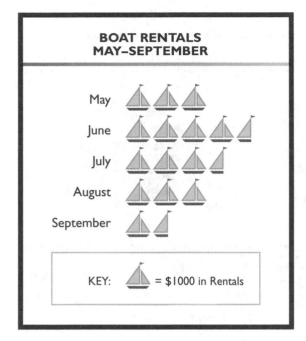

**BOAT RENTALS
MAY–SEPTEMBER**

May

June

July

August

September

KEY: = $1000 in Rentals

Questions 9 through 11 are based on the following graph.

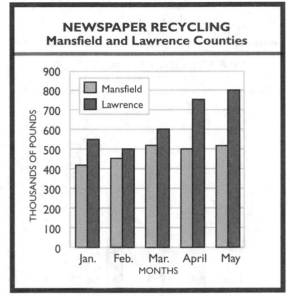

**NEWSPAPER RECYCLING
Mansfield and Lawrence Counties**

6. During the summer months, Stan works at the lake, renting boats. According to the chart Stan made, about how much money did he receive for July rentals?
   (1) $3000
   (2) $3250
   (3) $3500
   (4) $3750
   (5) $4000

7. In which month did Stan receive the most money for his rentals?
   (1) May
   (2) June
   (3) July
   (4) August
   (5) September

8. How much more money did Stan receive in his best month of rentals than in his worst month of rentals?
   (1) $3500
   (2) $3000
   (3) $2500
   (4) $2000
   (5) $1500

9. About how many more pounds of newspaper did Lawrence County recycle in May than in March?
   (1) 200
   (2) 50,000
   (3) 200,000
   (4) 275,000
   (5) 300,000

10. During which month did Mansfield County show a decrease in recycling?
   (1) January
   (2) February
   (3) March
   (4) April
   (5) Not enough information is given.

11. What was the percent of increase in recycling for Lawrence County from March to April?
   (1) 20%
   (2) 25%
   (3) 40%
   (4) 45%
   (5) 50%

PART TWO DIRECTIONS: Choose the one best answer to each of the following problems.
You may not use a calculator on these problems.

Questions 12 and 13 are based on the following stacked bar graph.

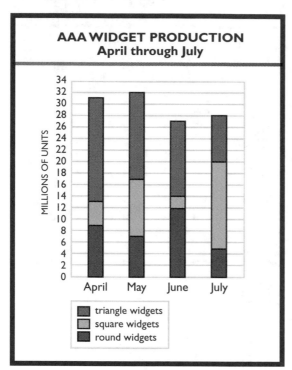

AAA WIDGET PRODUCTION
April through July

MILLIONS OF UNITS

triangle widgets
square widgets
round widgets

Question 15 is based on the following circle graph.

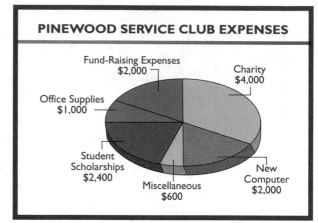

PINEWOOD SERVICE CLUB EXPENSES

Fund-Raising Expenses
$2,000

Charity
$4,000

Office Supplies
$1,000

Student
Scholarships
$2,400

Miscellaneous
$600

New
Computer
$2,000

15. The Pinewood Service Club's total expenses for the year were $12,000. What percent of the total expenses was spent on Office Supplies and Fund-Raising Expenses?

(1) 13% **(4)** 33%
(2) 20% **(5)** 50%
(3) 25%

12. According to the graph, approximately how many round and square widgets combined were produced in May?

(1) 13 million
(2) 14 million
(3) 17 million
(4) 20 million
(5) 32 million

13. How many fewer triangle widgets were produced in July than in April?

(1) 4 million
(2) 5 million
(3) 6 million
(4) 7 million
(5) 10 million

14. What was the total number of square widgets produced during the four-month period shown on the graph?

(1) 28 million
(2) 31 million
(3) 64 million
(4) 112 million
(5) 118 million

Questions 16 and 17 are based on the table.

THE IGLOO HOUSE– Sales for the Week of August 15				
Day	**Smoothies**	**Icies**	**Snowcones**	**Slushies**
Mon.	14	20	18	21
Tues.	7	3	9	14
Wed.	9	9	0	11
Thurs.	21	6	4	6
Fri.	16	20	14	19

16. On which day were more Icies than Slushies sold?

(1) Monday **(4)** Thursday
(2) Tuesday **(5)** Friday
(3) Wednesday

17. Which day had the highest combined sales of Smoothies and Snowcones?

(1) Monday **(4)** Thursday
(2) Tuesday **(5)** Friday
(3) Wednesday

Answers and explanations start on page 324.

Program 36 also looks at different ways to analyze trends in data. Math teachers and the host demonstrate three ways to determine central tendency—mean, median, and mode.

This is the second lesson that accompanies Program 36. You may wish to review the program before starting this lesson.

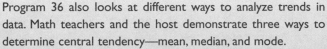

Data Analysis, Part Two

OBJECTIVES

1. Understand how frequency tables, plots, and graphs are used to organize data.
2. Use the normal distribution curve to make predictions.
3. Find common measures of central tendency: mean, median, and mode.

You may have wondered: Do air bags in cars save lives? Can a diet low in fat really reduce your chances for heart disease? What is the best way for you to save money for your retirement? Advances in technology have made more information available to us than ever before. But what do all the numbers mean? How can we use data to draw correct conclusions?

The ability to apply data analysis is important to your success on the GED Math Test. You will need to know how to find the average of a set of data. You will also need to be able to recognize trends in data and make logical predictions. Your ability to read tables, charts, and graphs will help you find the data you need to solve problems. Your work in this program will help you increase your understanding of other math skills in the areas of ratio, proportion, and percent.

On the following pages, you will find a brief exercise called *Sneak Preview*. It is designed to introduce you to some of the topics that are featured in the video program and the corresponding lesson. After you complete the exercise and check your answers, turn to the vocabulary page. There you will find terms that may help you better understand the video and the lesson that follow. After reviewing page 214, you may wish to review Program 36.

For additional practice, visit *LiteracyLink* online at http://www.pbs.org/literacy.

Sneak Preview

This exercise previews some of the concepts from Program 36. After you answer the questions, use the feedback on page 213 to help set your learning goals.

COMMUNITY LINK: The Newman Community Hall is offering several health-care courses. Carter's job is to sell the appropriate manuals to the arriving neighbors who have signed up for the classes. Carter keeps a tally of the books by using a **frequency** table, which shows how many and which kind of each book are sold.

BOOK	HARDCOVER	PAPERBACK
First Aid and You	ℍℍ‖	ℍℍ ℍℍ
A New Look at CPR	‖	ℍℍ ℍℍ ‖
Well-Baby Care	ℍℍ ‖‖‖‖	‖‖‖‖
Aging and Health	‖‖‖‖	ℍℍ ‖‖‖

Answer these questions based on the frequency table shown above.

1. How many paperback copies of *A New Look at CPR* did Carter sell?

   (1)   2
   (2)   7
   (3)   10
   (4)   12
   (5)   14

2. What fraction of the total copies sold of *Aging and Health* were hardcover?

   (1) $\frac{3}{4}$
   (2) $\frac{2}{3}$
   (3) $\frac{1}{2}$
   (4) $\frac{1}{3}$
   (5) $\frac{1}{4}$

MATHEMATICS

3. Based on sales for all four books, what is the mean (average) number of hardcover books sold per title?

   (1) 4.5
   (2) 5
   (3) 5.5
   (4) 8.5
   (5) 22

4. What trend might Carter reasonably predict for the next session of health-care classes?

   (1) The hardcover books will usually sell better than the paperbacks.
   (2) Fewer copies of *Aging and Health* will be sold.
   (3) Hardcover books will never sell well.
   (4) The best-selling book will be *First Aid and You.*
   (5) The number of paperbacks sold will decrease.

5. Which ratio compares the number of *Aging and Health* hardcover books sold to <u>all</u> hardcover books sold?

   (1) 1:12
   (2) 2:11
   (3) 2:9
   (4) 11:2
   (5) 4:17

Feedback

- If you got all of the answers right...   you have a good basic understanding of how data is collected in a frequency table and how to analyze and draw conclusions from that data.

- If you missed question 1...   you need to study how frequency tables are used to organize data.

- If you missed question 2...   you need to work on finding the facts you need to solve a problem and making comparisons.

- If you missed question 3...   you need to work on selecting data and calculating the mean of a set of values.

- If you missed question 4...   you need to practice drawing conclusions based on organized data.

- If you missed question 5...   you need to work with selecting necessary data and ratios.

ANSWERS FOR SNEAK PREVIEW:

1. Choice (4)   2. Choice (4)   3. Choice (3)   4. Choice (4)   5. Choice (2)

Vocabulary for *Data Analysis, Part Two*

cluster	a small group of values that is isolated from other values
convenience sampling	selecting a portion of a population based on its availability
frequency table	a method of organizing data in which tally marks are used to show how often each value occurs
gap	a space between values in a data set
line plot	a method of organizing data in which Xs stand for data values
mean	an approximate value that is typical of the values in a group; the sum of a set of numbers divided by the number of values in the set; also called *average*
median	the middle value in a set of data arranged in order from least to greatest or from greatest to least
mode	the value that occurs most often in a set of data
outlier	a data value that is much greater than or much less than the other values in a set of data
population	the entire group from which a sample is taken
random sampling	selecting a portion of a population so that each member of the population has an equal chance of selection
range	the difference between the greatest and the least values in a set of data
statistics	the science or study of data
systematic sampling	selecting a portion of a population according to a pattern

➡ **NOW WATCH PROGRAM 36:**

Make sure you understand the difference between mean, median, and mode, and how each of these types of central tendency is determined.

After you watch the program, work on:

- pages 215–226 in this workbook
- Internet activities at http://www.pbs.org/literacy

Data Analysis, Part Two

On the following pages, you will learn more about the ideas discussed in the video program and have an opportunity to develop and practice your GED math skills.

GED TIPS

When taking the GED Test, you should:

- Make sure your answer makes sense. Remember that the mean and median represent the center of a set of values.
- Use the workspace in your test booklet to put data values in order before finding the median.
- Use your calculator (when allowed) to find the mean. You will save time for more difficult problems.

Key Points to Think About

In the video program, you explored:

- How people use data analysis in their daily lives as workers, citizens, and family members.
- How mathematicians organize data to see trends and make predictions.
- Everyday applications of the measures of central tendency, including mean, median, and mode.

On the GED Math Test:

- You will be expected to know how to analyze data to recognize trends.
- You should know how to read a variety of tables, charts, and graphs to find the data you need to solve problems.
- You will be expected to find the mean, median, and mode of a set of data.

As you work through this lesson for Program 36:

- Think about the meaning of "average," and how it is applied in different situations.
- Notice the many ways that data can be organized, and make sure that the organization of each table, chart, or graph makes sense to you.
- Be aware of opportunities to use data analysis to solve problems in your daily life, not just on the GED Math Test.

Understanding Data

WORKPLACE LINK: The company that LeeAnn works for plans to offer computer training to its workers. LeeAnn's boss wants her to poll a sample of the company's nearly five hundred workers to see what percent are interested in taking the classes. LeeAnn needs to decide the best way to gather the data.

Collecting Data

Statistics is the science of data. Sometimes called data analysis, statistics is collecting, sorting, analyzing, and interpreting information. Data can be misleading if it is not collected and organized thoroughly and consistently.

Collecting data from an entire group, or **population,** can be very expensive and time-consuming. Most of the time, data is collected by taking a random sample of the population. In a **random sampling,** each member of the population has an equal chance of being chosen. If a random sample is of sufficient size, it represents the entire population fairly.

There are other methods of sampling. In a **systematic sampling,** members of the population are chosen according to a pattern. For example, every tenth article of clothing might be inspected in a garment factory. At times, data is collected from a **convenience sampling.** In other words, the members of the population are chosen because they are readily available. In the situation above, LeeAnn could survey the first 20 workers she sees, but the results might not accurately represent the entire population of workers.

Using Frequency Tables and Line Plots

Once you have the data you need, the next step is to organize it. A fast and easy way to organize data is to create a frequency table. In a **frequency table,** tally marks show how often an item appears in a set of data.

In a **line plot,** an X is used to represent each item of data. The number of X's indicates the frequency of the data. Both frequency tables and line plots are useful for comparing how often items of data occur in a sample.

▶▶ Look at how a frequency table and a line plot can be used to organize data from a survey.

Example: A local television station wants to find out what kind of shows viewers would most like to watch from 6 to 7 P.M. Warren is asked to survey 30 households chosen at random. The results of the survey are shown below.

sitcom	news	game show	children's	drama
sports	news	children's	news	news
news	game show	news	game show	sports
sitcom	game show	sitcom	news	children's
game show	children's	sitcom	sports	news
drama	news	sports	news	sitcom

Warren has organized the data he collected to make a frequency table and a line plot. Both the frequency table and the line plot show the same information.

Results of Television Programming Survey for 6–7 P.M. Time Slot	
Sitcom (Si)	⋕⋕
Sports (Sp)	⦀⦀
News (N)	⋕⋕ ⋕⋕
Game Show (G)	⋕⋕
Children's Show (S)	⦀⦀
Drama (D)	⦀

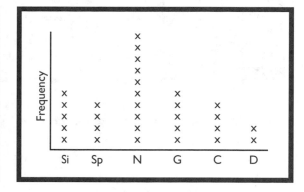

Using the frequency table or line plot, which type of television program was chosen most often? What percent of the households surveyed is this?

Answer: News programming was chosen more often than any other type of programming. In fact, 10 out of 30, or $33\frac{1}{3}\%$, of the households surveyed said that they wanted to see a news show from 6 to 7 P.M.

SKILL PRACTICE

G's Printing offers many services. The frequency table shows the services used by the first 25 customers on April 10. The line plot shows the amount spent by each customer. Use the information to answer items 1 to 5.

Self-Serve Copying	⋕⋕ ⋕⋕ ⦀
Full-Serve Copying	⋕⋕
Color Copying	⋕⋕ ⦀
Printing and Binding	⦀

1. What kind of sampling was used to gather the data displayed in the table and line plot—random, systematic, or convenience?

2. What is the ratio of customers using self-serve copying to those using color copying?

3. What percent of the customers spent $25 or less?

4. How much money do customers requiring full-serve copying usually spend?

   (1) Less than $10
   (2) $10-$25
   (3) $26-$50
   (4) More than $50
   (5) Not enough information is given.

5. Which fraction best expresses the fraction of customers who used color copying?

   (1) $\frac{1}{8}$
   (2) $\frac{1}{6}$
   (3) $\frac{1}{4}$
   (4) $\frac{1}{3}$
   (5) $\frac{1}{2}$

Answers and explanations start on page 325.

FAMILY LINK: Kendra read in the newspaper that her child's school tested above average in reading and math. Based on a test given to all students, the students at her child's school scored 72 in reading and 78 in math. The newspaper lists a great deal of data for each school. Kendra wonders how to interpret the data to find out what the numbers really mean.

The Normal Distribution Curve

Data can help us draw conclusions about the typical characteristics of a population. We may want to know how much the average house costs, how much the average driver spends on car insurance, or how well the average student does in school. The average becomes a measuring stick to which we can compare our own lives.

To find out what is average or typical of a population, statisticians must collect enough data. If a random sample is large enough, data tends to form a curve when it is organized on a line plot. This shape is called the **normal distribution curve.**

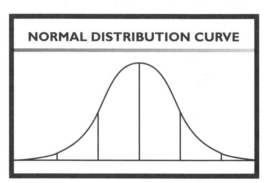

NORMAL DISTRIBUTION CURVE

Suppose you measured the height in inches of 30 nine-year-old children selected at random. A line plot of their heights might look something like this.

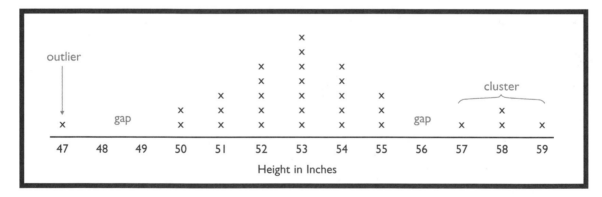

▶▶See how the data set is used to draw conclusions.

Example: Jan's daughter, who is 9 years old, is 56 inches tall. How does her daughter's height compare to that of other 9-year-old children?

Answer: Jan's daughter is **tall for her age.** Based on the graph, the typical height of a 9-year-old child is about 53 inches, the high point on the graph. Only $\frac{2}{15}$ of the children measured were taller than Jan's daughter.

The data values representing a population rarely form a perfect curve. Instead, line plots often have gaps, clusters, and outliers.

- A **gap** is a space between values. There are two gaps in this data set: one between 47 and 50 inches and another at 56 inches.

- A **cluster** is a small group of values isolated from the other values. There is a cluster of data from 57 to 59 inches.

- An **outlier** is a value that is much greater than or much less than the other values in the set of data. The isolated value at 47 inches is an outlier.

Another important statistical measure is the range. **Range** is the difference between the least and the greatest values in a set of data. To find the range of the data set on page 218, subtract 47 from 59. The range is 12 inches, or 1 foot.

SKILL PRACTICE

Use the line plot to answer questions 1 through 4.

1. Which donation amount was received most often?

2. Which value could be considered an outlier?

3. What is the range of the donation amounts?

4. What percent of the donations were more than $40?

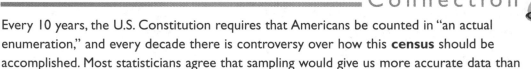

ANIMAL HOSPITAL DONATIONS

```
        x
        x   x
    x   x   x
    x   x   x           x
    x   x   x           x
    x   x   x   x   x                   x
   $10 $20 $30 $40 $50 $60 $70 $80
```

SOCIAL STUDIES Connection

Every 10 years, the U.S. Constitution requires that Americans be counted in "an actual enumeration," and every decade there is controversy over how this **census** should be accomplished. Most statisticians agree that sampling would give us more accurate data than trying to actually count every person.

Whatever method is used, there will be error. Suppose a method has a ±5% margin of error. This means that the results may be over or under by as much as 5%.

Example: The population for a city is stated as 498,000. Afterward, it is discovered that the population was undercounted by as much as 5%. The actual population may be as high as what number?

Step 1. Find 5% of 498,000 by setting up a proportion: $\frac{5}{100} = \frac{x}{498,000}$.
Solve: $5 \times 498,000 \div 100 = 24,900$.

Step 2. The estimate may be off by as much as 24,900.
Add to find the upper limit of the range: $498,000 + 24,900 = 522,900$.

Answer: The actual population may have been as high as **522,900**.

Lakewood City is found to have a population of 125,300. Later, it is determined that the population was overcounted by as much as 3%. **The actual population of Lakewood City may be as low as what number?**

Mean, Median, and Mode

FAMILY LINK: Mike is worried about his math grade. His test scores for this semester are 94, 78, 82, 85, and 42. Mike needs a score between 80 and 90 to get a B, and he is afraid that his low score on the last test will pull his grade down. Mike then remembers that the teacher bases the grade on the median of the test scores, not the mean. He should still get a B.

Finding the Mean

Data is used to gain understanding about a population. As you have seen, in a normal distribution curve, there is a greater number of values grouped in the center section of the curve. Studying the center of a set of data can help us make predictions and draw conclusions about a population.

The **mean** is one measure of the center of a set of data. The mean is the arithmetic average of the data. To find the mean, add the data values and divide by the number of values in the set.

The formula for finding mean is given on the GED formulas page.

> **mean** $= \dfrac{x_1 + x_2 + ... + x_n}{n}$;   where the x's are the values for which a mean is desired, and $n =$ number of values in the series

Use the formula to calculate the mean of Mike's test scores.

Example: In the situation at the top of the page, Mike's test scores were 94, 78, 82, 85, and 42. What is the mean of the test scores?

Add the scores: $94 + 78 + 82 + 85 + 42 = 381$

Divide by 5, the number of test scores: $\frac{381}{5} = 76.2$

Answer: The mean of the test scores is **76.2.** If Mike's teacher were basing his grade on the mean, he would get a C. Fortunately for Mike, the teacher is using the median.

You can think of the mean as the balancing point for a set of data. The fulcrum must be placed at 76.2 on the scale to keep the two sides balanced.

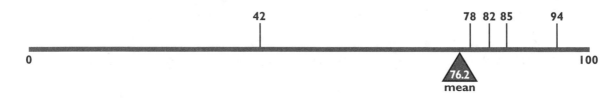

MATHEMATICS

Finding Median and Mode

The median is another measure of central tendency. The **median** is the middle value in a set of data arranged in order from least to greatest or from greatest to least. Half the values will be above the median and half will be below it.

▶▶ Take another look at Mike's test scores.

Example: Find the median of Mike's test scores.
Arrange the scores in order and find the middle value.   42   78   **82**   85   94
                                                                          middle value

Answer: Mike's median score is **82,** or a B.

When a set of data has an even number of values, there will be two values in the middle of the data. To find the median, calculate the mean of the two middle values.

Example: Find the median of these amounts: $34, $28, $47, $22, $14, and $52.
Order the values and find the middle. $52 $47   **$34**   **$28** $22 $14
                                                                          middle values

Average the middle values to find the median. $34 + $28 = $62 $62 ÷ 2 = $31

Answer: The median of the amounts is **$31.**

The **mode** of a set of data is the value that occurs most often. Look at the line plot of data on page 218. The mode of the data is 53 inches—the height that occurred most often. Knowing the mean, median, and mode of a set of data can help you understand the shape and distribution of the data. Note that some sets of data have no mode, while others have more than one mode.

SKILL PRACTICE

Use the information below to answer items 1 to 5.

Max and Anna want to make an offer on a house. Their real estate agent gave the couple a list of the selling prices of similar homes in the area. They plan to use the prices to decide how much money to offer on the home they want.

RECENT SELLING PRICES OF 3-BEDROOM HOMES IN HOPKINS COUNTY				
$75,800	$72,000	$88,000	$72,000	$123,500
$87,600	$94,000	$85,000	$83,200	$90,000

1. Use a calculator to find the mean of the selling prices.

2. What is the median of the selling prices?

3. Which selling price is the mode of the values?

4. Which of the three measures of central tendency is least likely to represent the typical selling price of a 3-bedroom home in Hopkins County? Explain your thinking.

5. If the value $130,000 were added to the list, which measure would change more: the mean or the median? Explain.

Answers and explanations start on page 325.

Everyday Problems in Data Analysis

Understanding the measures of central tendency can help us make important life decisions. For example, averages can help us set goals and plan budgets.

▶▶ See how to find a missing data value when the mean is known.

Example: At the beginning of the year, Taylor made a goal of depositing $120 per month in his saving account. His deposits for the first 4 months are shown below. How much would he need to deposit in the fifth month to average $120 per month for the five-month period?

Month 1: $120   Month 2: $80   Month 3: $140   Month 4: $110

There are several ways to solve the problem.

Work backward.

1. Multiply: $120 × 5 = $600. If Taylor averages $120 per month, he should have $600 after 5 months.

2. Add: $120 + $80 + $140 + $110 = $450. Taylor has already saved $450.

3. Subtract: $600 − $450 = $150. Taylor needs to save $150 to reach his goal.

Make mental adjustments.

Keep in mind that Taylor planned to save $120 each month. Compare the amount he actually saved each month to his goal and adjust the amount for the fifth month.

		Adjusted Amount
1.	Taylor saved $120 in the first month, the correct amount.	$120
2.	Taylor saved $40 less than the goal. Add $40.	$160
3.	Taylor saved $20 more than the goal. Subtract $20.	$140
4.	Taylor saved $10 less than the goal. Add $10.	$150

Answer: $40 − $20 + $10 = $30. Taylor needs to make up $30 in addition to the planned $120. Using either method, he needs to save **$150 in the fifth month.**

▶▶ See how to use an average to project expenses.

Example: Maya is making an annual budget for her family. She wants to estimate her telephone expenses for next year based on the first five bills she received this year. The bills are for the following amounts: $76.03, $48.20, $54.16, $43.39, and $62.57. Using the average of the bills, how much will Maya pay for phone expenses over 12 months?

MATHEMATICS

Find the average monthly telephone bill.

$76.03 + $48.20 + $54.16 + $43.39 + $62.57 = $284.35
$284.35 ÷ 5 = $56.87

Multiply the average by 12 months. $56.87 × 12 = $682.44

Answer: Based on the average for five months, Maya will spend **$682.44** on telephone charges over a 12-month period.

SKILL PRACTICE

Solve each problem.

1. To get out of debt, Reynaldo has made a goal of paying $500 per month on his credit card bills for six months. After five months, he has paid these amounts:
    $550 $400 $600 $525 $450

    How much would he have to pay in the sixth month to average $500 per month?

2. Maggie needs to average 90 points per assignment to get an A in a class. So far, she has the following grades:
    100   84   88   92

    She has one more assignment to complete. How many points does she need to earn on it to average 90 points per assignment?

3. Maria is paid by the week based on the number of hours she works. Her paychecks for the first six pay periods of the year are for the following amounts:
    $288 $320 $256 $280 $288 $332

    Based on the mean of the data, how much will she earn in a year? (*Hint:* 52 weeks = 1 year.)

4. Orson and his family budgeted $120 per week for food. After 12 weeks, they found they had spent $1,620 on food. Are they over or under budget? By how much?

5. Marco set a goal to make 90 sales in a 5-day period. At the end of the time, he had averaged 17 sales per day. Did he make his goal? Explain your thinking.

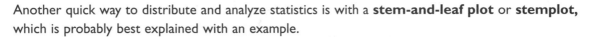

PROBLEM SOLVER Connection

Another quick way to distribute and analyze statistics is with a **stem-and-leaf plot** or **stemplot,** which is probably best explained with an example.

Example: Jerry wants to find the mode and the median of his nine art project scores: 91, 83, 69, 91, 87, 83, 80, 83, 89. He makes a stem-and-leaf plot, ordering the tens-place digits (the stem) from largest to smallest. The ones-place digits (the leaves) are listed from smallest to largest. Jerry records each score, including repeat scores.

```
9 | 1 1
8 | 0 3 3 3 7 9
7 |
6 | 9
```

Step 1. Evaluate the plot. Jerry's plot shows there were two scores in the 90s (both 91), six scores in the 80s (80, 83, 83, 83, 87, 89), no scores in the 70s, and one score in the 60s (69).

Step 2. Find the mode. Look at the leaves in any one line. The most frequent leaf is 3, all with the tens digit of 8. The mode is **83.**

How would you find the median score on this kind of plot? (*Hint:* Arrange the scores in order and find the middle number. Notice that the digits in the right column are arranged from lowest to highest. Use the arrangement to find the middle.)

GED PRACTICE

PART ONE DIRECTIONS: Choose the <u>one best answer</u> to each of the following problems. Use a calculator wherever necessary.

1. Lenny entered a five-game bowling tournament. His scores were 137, 156, 139, 160, and 143. What was Lenny's mean score for this tournament?
   - **(1)** 135
   - **(2)** 138
   - **(3)** 145
   - **(4)** 147
   - **(5)** 155

<u>Questions 2 and 3</u> are based on the following frequency table.

French	ＨＨＩＩＩ
Spanish	ＨＨ
German	ＨＨＩ
Japanese	ＨＨ ＨＨ Ｉ

2. Tina polled her fifth-grade class to see which foreign language each student would most like to learn. Which language was the least favorite?
   - **(1)** French
   - **(2)** Spanish
   - **(3)** German
   - **(4)** Japanese
   - **(5)** Not enough information is given.

3. Which language was chosen by 20% of Tina's students?
   - **(1)** French
   - **(2)** Spanish
   - **(3)** German
   - **(4)** Japanese
   - **(5)** Not enough information is given.

4. Juanita's electric bills for the past four months were $65.23, $49.37, $70.01, and $55.27. What was the median amount of her electric service for those months?
   - **(1)** $59.97
   - **(2)** $60.25
   - **(3)** $70.01
   - **(4)** $120.50
   - **(5)** $239.88

<u>Questions 5 and 6</u> are based on the sign below.

WAITING TIME FOR RIDES

Anchors Away! 23 min
The Whirlygig 41 min
Splash Cove 38 min

5. At FunLand Park, there is a sign that displays the current waiting times for people standing in line at the park's most popular rides. How much time would you wait in line for all three rides?
   - **(1)** 1.42 hours
   - **(2)** 1 hour 2 minutes
   - **(3)** 1 hour 20 minutes
   - **(4)** 1 hour 42 minutes
   - **(5)** 2 hours 42 minutes

6. If the wait for a fourth ride, *Flying Fools,* is 22 minutes, which expression would best indicate the mean waiting time for all four of these rides?
   - **(1)** $\dfrac{23 + 41 + 38 + 22}{15}$
   - **(2)** $\dfrac{23 + 41 + 38 + 22}{60}$
   - **(3)** $\dfrac{38 + 22}{2}$
   - **(4)** $(23 + 41 + 38 + 22) \times 4$
   - **(5)** $\dfrac{23 + 41 + 38 + 22}{4}$

DISTRICT ELECTION RESULTS Total Votes Cast = 30,000	
Candidate	**Percent of Votes Received**
Nicks	24%
Potter	8%
Reyes	35%
Jong	20%
Pace	13%

7. Which of the candidates received nearly 4,000 votes?
- **(1)** Nicks
- **(2)** Potter
- **(3)** Reyes
- **(4)** Jong
- **(5)** Pace

8. What was the average <u>number</u> of votes received by each candidate?
- **(1)** 2,400
- **(2)** 6,000
- **(3)** 10,500
- **(4)** 15,000
- **(5)** 30,000

Question 9 is based on the following information.

Scott is pricing cases of copy paper for his office. After calling six stores, he has gathered the following prices:

$19.69	$17.90	$20.59
$22.15	$18.75	$21.40

9. What is the median price of the figures Scott has gathered?
- **(1)** $18.32
- **(2)** $19.69
- **(3)** $20.08
- **(4)** $20.14
- **(5)** $20.59

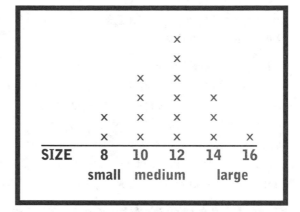

Ming-Yi owns a dress shop. On May 31, she notes on a line plot how many of a certain dress have sold, by size, during that month.

10. To reorder stock, Ming-Yi wants to know which size of this particular dress sold the best. Which measure would be most useful to Ming-Yi for this purpose?
- **(1)** average
- **(2)** mode
- **(3)** median
- **(4)** mean
- **(5)** Not enough information is given.

11. Based only on the line plot of this one month, what conclusion might Ming-Yi reasonably draw about the sales of this dress?
- **(1)** This style of dress is more popular than the store's other styles.
- **(2)** Most of the store's customers wear a size 10.
- **(3)** Size 14 is the most popular.
- **(4)** Medium sizes are more popular than small or large sizes.
- **(5)** Twice as many size 12s sold as sizes 8 and 10 combined.

12. In June Ming-Yi sold 3 times as many of this dress in size 14 as she sold in May. How many did she sell in June?
- **(1)** 1
- **(2)** 3
- **(3)** 6
- **(4)** 9
- **(5)** 12

PART TWO DIRECTIONS: Choose the <u>one best answer</u> to each of the following problems. *You may not use a calculator on these problems.*

<u>Questions 13 through 15</u> are based on the following information.

Jeff works in the office at Freedom Auto Repair. His boss wants him to find the average amount that customers spend on repair bills. To find the information, Jeff decides to keep track of the next 25 repairs the shop makes. He rounds the repair bills to the nearest hundred dollars and prepares the following line plot.

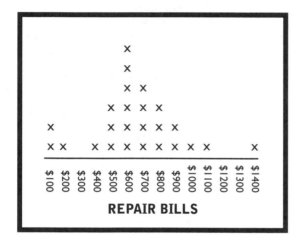

REPAIR BILLS

13. How many gaps are there in the data shown on the line plot?
    (1) 1
    (2) 2
    (3) 3
    (4) 4
    (5) 6

14. Jeff notices an outlier at which of the following amounts?
    (1) $100
    (2) $200
    (3) $600
    (4) $1200
    (5) $1400

15. What is the median amount of the repair bills shown on the line plot?
    (1) $200
    (2) $600
    (3) $656
    (4) $16,400
    (5) Not enough information is given.

<u>Questions 16 through 19</u> are based on the following information.

Janelle and Pat Rosarian have five children. The twins are 14 years old. The other children are 4, 7, and 11 years old.

16. What is the average age of the Rosarian children?
    (1) 8
    (2) 9
    (3) 10
    (4) 11
    (5) 14

17. What is the median age of the Rosarian children?
    (1) 8
    (2) 9
    (3) 10
    (4) 11
    (5) 14

18. Janelle and Pat are aged 38 and 43, respectively. Which expression might you use to determine the mean age for the entire family?
    (1) $7(14+14+4+7+11+38+43)$
    (2) $\frac{50}{5}$
    (3) $\frac{50}{7}$
    (4) $\frac{131}{5} + \frac{(38+43)}{2}$
    (5) $\frac{131}{7}$

19. Pat's age is approximately how many times the age of the middle Rosarian child?
    (1) 10
    (2) 4
    (3) 3
    (4) 2
    (5) Not enough information is given.

Answers and explanations start on page 326.

MATHEMATICS

226

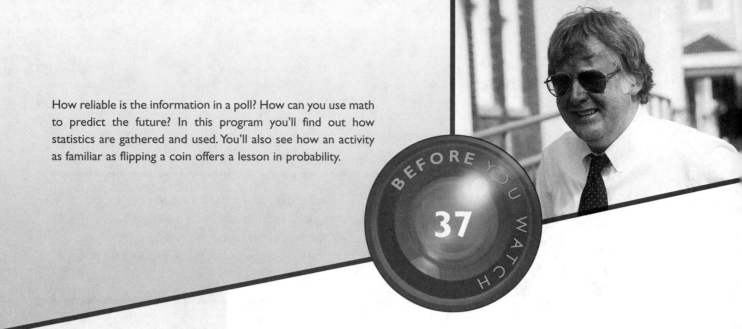

How reliable is the information in a poll? How can you use math to predict the future? In this program you'll find out how statistics are gathered and used. You'll also see how an activity as familiar as flipping a coin offers a lesson in probability.

Statistics and Probability

OBJECTIVES

1. Analyze reported statistics in order to draw conclusions.
2. Understand the meaning of chance; determine experimental and theoretical probability.
3. Solve everyday problems by finding the probability of independent and dependent events.

Each day, we are bombarded with statistics. A news report states that the president's job approval rating is above 60%. A government agency announces that bike helmets can reduce the risk of head injury by 85%. A newspaper article shows that the median housing price in your community is $120,000. Understanding everyday statistics is key to learning more about current events and making important consumer decisions.

The ability to work with statistics and probability is important to your success on the GED Math Test. You will need to know how to analyze a situation to determine the chance of an event happening. Your understanding of fractions and percents will help you make sense of the data. Your work in this lesson will help you gain other math skills in the areas of ratios and data analysis.

On the following pages, you will find a brief exercise called *Sneak Preview*. It is designed to introduce you to the topics that will be featured in the video program and the corresponding lesson. After you complete the exercise and check your answers, turn to the vocabulary page. There you will find terms that will help you better understand the video and the lesson that follow. After reviewing page 230, you will be ready to watch Program 37.

For additional practice, visit *LiteracyLink* **online at**
http://www.pbs.org/literacy.

Sneak Preview

This exercise previews some of the concepts from Program 37. After you answer the questions, use the feedback on page 229 to help set your learning goals.

FAMILY LINK: Sandy wants to make a baseball game using dice. She plans to make game cards like the one shown below. To use the card, Sandy will roll two six-sided dice (one red, one green). Then she will find the dice roll on the chart. For example, a dice roll of Red 3–Green 1 is a strikeout.

SANDY'S BASEBALL GAME CARD

Red-Green	Result	Red-Green	Result	Red-Green	Result
1–1	home run	3–1	strike out	5–1	single
1–2	double	3–2	strike out	5–2	strike out
1–3	double	3–3	home run	5–3	strike out
1–4	double	3–4	single	5–4	strike out
1–5	double	3–5	single	5–5	home run
1–6	triple	3–6	single	5–6	walk
2–1	triple	4–1	single	6–1	walk
2–2	home run	4–2	single	6–2	walk
2–3	strike out	4–3	single	6–3	walk
2–4	strike out	4–4	home run	6–4	walk
2–5	strike out	4–5	single	6–5	walk
2–6	strike out	4–6	single	6–6	home run

Sandy wants her game to be as realistic as possible, so she looks up the statistics for a professional baseball player. Kenny Lofton's statistics for 1998 are shown below.

Answer these questions based on the information.

1. Using Sandy's game card, what is the likelihood of hitting a home run in the dice game?

   (1) $\frac{1}{36}$

   (2) $\frac{1}{18}$

   (3) $\frac{1}{12}$

   (4) $\frac{1}{9}$

   (5) $\frac{1}{6}$

Kenny Lofton—1998

At Bats—600

Singles—120

Doubles—31

Triples—6

Home Runs—12

Walks—87

Strikeouts—80

MATHEMATICS

2. Which of the following is a true statement about the probability of events shown on Sandy's card?

(1) A player is more likely to hit a home run than to strike out.

(2) A player is less likely to hit a double than a triple.

(3) A player is more likely to hit a single than to walk.

(4) A player is more likely to hit a double than a home run.

(5) There is a 50% chance that a player will hit a single.

3. Using Sandy's card, there is a 1 in 4, or 25%, chance of hitting a single. Based on Kenny Lofton's actual statistics, what was his chance of hitting a single in 1998? (*Hint:* Find what percent of his at bats were singles.)

(1) 2%

(2) 5%

(3) 14%

(4) 20%

(5) 50%

4. Sandy rolls the dice 20 times and records the results (shown below).

single	home run	walk	home run	single
walk	double	single	strikeout	strikeout
strike out	home run	strikeout	single	strikeout
strike out	single	strikeout	strikeout	triple

Based on the experiment only, which statement is true?

(1) There is a greater chance of hitting a double than a single.

(2) There is a 25% chance of hitting a single.

(3) There is an equal number of home runs and strikeouts.

(4) There will always be fewer walks than home runs.

(5) There is an 8% chance of striking out.

Feedback

- If you got all of the answers right...   you have a good basic understanding of everyday statistics and drawing conclusions based on those data.

- If you missed question 1...   you need to learn how to express chance as a ratio.

- If you missed question 2...   you need to work on interpreting statistics and on understanding the concepts of probability.

- If you missed question 3...   you need to learn how to express chance as a percent.

- If you missed question 4...   you need practice drawing conclusions based on experimental probability.

PROGRAM 37: Statistics and Probability

ANSWERS FOR SNEAK PREVIEW: 1. Choice (5)   2. Choice (3)   3. Choice (4)   4. Choice (2)

229

Vocabulary for *Statistics and Probability*

chance	the likelihood of an event's occurrence
dependent events	two events in which the outcome of the first event affects the outcome of the second
experimental probability	a method of calculating probability in which chance is based on the results of a number of trials of an experiment
favorable outcome	an event that you want to have happen
independent events	events in which one outcome does not affect the other
margin of error	a percent that shows by how much the results in a statistical study may vary from the actual population; for example, a margin of error of ±3% means that the results may be anywhere from 3% less to 3% greater than the actual population
outcome	the result of a probability experiment
possible outcome	any event that could actually occur
probability	the study of chance
theoretical probability	a method of calculating probability in which chance is based on the ratio of desired outcomes to possible outcomes

---

➡ NOW WATCH PROGRAM 37:

Focus on understanding the basic concepts: what makes a sample reliable, why margin of error is important, and the difference between independent and dependent events.

After you watch the program, work on:

- pages 231–246 in this workbook
- Internet activities at http://www.pbs.org/literacy

Statistics and Probability

On the following pages, you will learn more about the ideas discussed in the video program and have an opportunity to develop and practice your GED math skills.

GED TIPS

When taking the GED Test, you should:

- Write ratios in lowest terms before attempting to find your answer among the answer choices.
- Use your calculator to change ratios written as fractions to decimals. This will help you compare ratios quickly.
- Read each probability situation carefully to make sure you have all the facts you need to solve the problem.

Key Points to Think About

In the video program, you explored:
- How people use statistics and probability in their daily lives as workers, citizens, and family members.
- How ratios and percents are used to express the chance that an event will occur.
- Everyday applications of statistics and probability— making sense of reported statistics and finding the probability of independent and dependent events.

On the GED Math Test:
- You will be expected to know how to find the probability of an independent event.
- You will need to know how to find probability by analyzing the data from an experiment.
- You will use your understanding of statistics and probability to interpret data sets and solve problems involving random events.

As you work through the lesson for Program 37:
- Think about the relationship between ratio and percent and how both can be used to compare a part to a whole.
- Think about the statistics you see and hear in the news. Think about how the items of data were collected and whether the report includes all the information you need or whether the data may be presented in a biased way.
- Be aware of opportunities to use statistics and probability to solve problems in your daily life, not just on the GED Math Test.

Using Statistics to Draw Conclusions

COMMUNITY LINK: Cynthia was surprised to read the results of a newspaper poll that showed 55% of those surveyed were against a local bond to improve public schools. Just yesterday, she heard on the news that the majority of voters were in favor of the measure. Cynthia thought that the newspaper sample of 50 people was too small to be accurate.

Making Sense of Statistics

Some people complain that statistics can be used to prove anything. There may be some truth to this complaint. A set of data only becomes meaningful when it is interpreted. Unfortunately, the same data may lead to different interpretations. How can we protect ourselves from misleading information? By learning more about statistics, we can draw our own conclusions.

▶▶Read this situation about the results of a survey.

Example: A governor proposed an increase in the state's sales tax to pay for disaster relief. The day after the proposal was announced, a newspaper survey reported that 60% of people surveyed were in favor of the proposal. On the same day, a call-in radio show announced that 75% of its callers were against the proposal. How would you account for the difference in findings?

Answer: The newspaper surveyed a population chosen at random, while the radio show did not. The radio show's callers felt strongly enough about the issue to call the station. Their views do not necessarily represent those of the general community. Always find out how data was collected before you accept a survey's findings as true.

Percent of change shows by what percent an amount has increased or decreased over time. Percent of change is often reported in news stories. For example, after passing a state law requiring the use of car seats for children under age 6, infant deaths due to automobile accidents decreased by 5% over a period of two years. This statistic can be used to show that the new law has been effective in helping reduce infant fatalities.

However, percent of change can also be misleading. Watch out for dramatic increases and decreases. They can lead to incorrect conclusions.

▶▶Think about how you would interpret this statistic about safety.

Example: Read this excerpt from an article. Do you think the statistics support the conclusion? What other conclusion could you draw from the statistics?

Do safety helmets work? In 1983 there were only 16,000 skateboarding injuries that needed emergency medical attention. Despite the introduction of safety helmets, the number of skateboarding injuries increased by more than 250% by 1992. Perhaps helmets are causing more accidents than they are preventing.

Answer: While the percent of change is accurate, the conclusion is based on too little information. **There were many more skateboarders in 1992 than in 1983.** When a sport increases in popularity, we expect the number of injuries to rise. The statistics tell us nothing about the use of safety helmets. There is not enough data to conclude that safety helmets don't work.

Because sampling methods can affect results, all surveys and studies have a **margin of error.** The margin of error is usually written as a percent. For example, in a newspaper survey, 67% of the people interviewed approved of the president's handling of the economy. The margin of error for the survey was reported as ±4% (plus or minus 4 percentage points). In other words, the percent for the population may have been as low as 63% or as high as 71%.

The margin of error is often given near the end of an article. It may be in small print below a graph or table. If the margin of error is not given, you should remain somewhat skeptical about the reported statistics. Don't jump to a conclusion before you have all the information.

SKILL PRACTICE

Answer each question.

1. A national report shows a 4% decrease in violent crimes in large cities from one year to the next. For the same time period, a newspaper in a small town reports a change from 2 violent crimes to 3, an increase of 50%. Based on these statistics, which conclusion makes the most sense?

   (1) Annually, there are 46% more violent crimes in small towns than in large towns.

   (2) There will probably be 4 or 5 violent crimes committed in the small town the next year.

   (3) The number of violent crimes in large cities will continue to decrease.

   (4) The number of crimes in the small town is too small to draw a meaningful conclusion.

   (5) Crime prevention methods are more effective in large cities than in small towns.

2. A public library wants to find out why more people from the community do not use the library. A committee develops a written survey asking people to rate the quality of the library's services. The committee plans to give the survey to the next 100 people who enter the library. Do you see any flaws in the committee's plan? If so, what would you do differently?

Questions 3 and 4 refer to the information below.

Each year, 4th-graders are given a standardized test to measure their progress in reading and math. For each school, the scores are averaged and published in the local newspaper. The table below shows the scores for Mountain View Elementary School for three years.

Mountain View Elementary School Fourth-Grade Average Scores		
	Reading	**Math**
1997	84%	76%
1998	83%	81%
1999	82%	86%
Margin of error: ±4%		

3. The teachers at Mountain View were surprised to see that reading scores had declined for the third year in a row. They believed their students were making good progress. Could they be right? Explain your thinking.

4. Does it make sense to conclude that students at Mountain View have improved in mathematics? Explain your thinking.

Understanding the Meaning of Chance

COMMUNITY LINK: Mara is making a game for a school carnival. Players will try to toss balls into a bucket to win a prize ticket. Mara wants about $\frac{1}{3}$ of the players to win the game. To test the game, she invites children from her neighborhood to play it. When the children win nearly 50% of their games, Mara decides that the game is too easy.

Expressing Probability as a Number

Probability is the study of **chance,** or the likelihood that an event will occur. Probability can't tell us what will happen, only what is likely to happen. For example, if you hear on the news that there is a 60% chance of rain tomorrow, you probably won't want to plan a family picnic.

Probability is often expressed as a percent ranging from 0% to 100%. On a sunny, dry day, there is a 0% chance of rain. Conversely, there is a 100% chance of snow during a blizzard.

We also express probability using ratios. When you flip a coin, you can have two possible outcomes: heads or tails. Thus, you have a 1-out-of-2, or 50%, chance of getting heads.

Mathematically, we find probability by comparing the number of **favorable outcomes** to the number of **possible outcomes.** A favorable outcome is an event that you want to have happen. A possible outcome is any event that could actually occur.

$$\text{Probability} = \frac{\text{number of favorable outcomes}}{\text{number of possible outcomes}}$$

▶▶ See how to find the probability of rolling a certain number on one die.

Example: Chaio needs to roll a 5 or higher on a regular 6-sided die. What is the probability that she will get either a 5 or a 6 on her next turn?

A die has six numbers, ranging from 1 to 6. Two of the numbers are favorable outcomes. Find the probability by writing a ratio.

$$\frac{\text{number of favorable outcomes}}{\text{number of possible outcomes}} = \frac{2}{6}$$

Reduce the ratio to lowest terms.

$$\frac{2}{6} = \frac{1}{3}$$

Change the ratio to a percent. Remember, a ratio is a fraction. Divide the numerator by the denominator to change the fraction to a decimal. Then change the decimal to a percent by moving the decimal point two places to the right.

$$1 \div 3 \approx 0.3333 \text{ or } 33\tfrac{1}{3}\%$$

Answer: Chaio has a **1-in-3 or $33\frac{1}{3}$% chance** of winning on her next turn.

Knowing the common fraction-decimal-percent equivalencies will help you solve probability problems in life and on the GED Math Test. You can review them on page 336.

MATHEMATICS

Using Experimental Probability

One way to solve a probability problem is by conducting an experiment. The resulting ratio is called **experimental probability** because it is based on actual data. The ratio compares the number of desired outcomes to the total number of trials.

▶▶ See how experimental probability is used to find chance.

In an ordinary deck of cards, there are four suits:

hearts ♥
diamonds ◆
spades ♠
clubs ♣

Example: Matt decides to conduct an experiment using an ordinary deck of 52 playing cards. If a card is drawn from the deck, what is the chance that the card will be a diamond?

Matt knows that in order for the experiment to be valid, the card must be drawn at random and then replaced in the deck. The deck will be shuffled between trials.

Working with a friend, Matt conducts 20 trials. The results are shown below.

The ratio of diamonds to the total number of trials is $\frac{6}{20}$, which reduces to $\frac{3}{10}$.

Answer: Based on the data, the experimental probability of drawing a card that is a diamond is $\frac{3}{10}$.

SKILL PRACTICE

Use the information below to answer items 1 to 4.

A spinner is divided into five <u>unequal</u> sections. Each section is a different color. The spinner is spun 40 times and the colors are recorded in the table to the right.

1. What is the experimental probability of spinning red?

2. What is the experimental probability of spinning either blue or green?

3. What is the experimental probability of <u>not</u> spinning black?

4. Based on the results of the experiment, make a sketch of the spinner, estimating the size and color of each section.

RESULTS OF 40 SPINS			
green	red	black	blue
blue	black	red	red
black	black	blue	green
red	green	yellow	black
black	black	black	black
red	blue	red	blue
blue	red	black	red
black	black	green	black
yellow	blue	black	blue
black	red	black	red

Using Theoretical Probability

You have seen that experimental probability involves analyzing actual data collected by repeating an experiment for a number of trials. **Theoretical probability** is not based on actual events. Instead, we analyze a situation by finding all the possible outcomes.

▶▶Learn how to use an organized list to find theoretical probability.

Example: In the situation above, Curtis, Frank, and three other employees have applied for a training program. Only two employees will be chosen for the program and these will be selected randomly. What is the probability that both Curtis and Frank will be selected?

One way to solve the problem is to make a list of all the possibilities. Use letters to stand for the five employees: C = Curtis, F = Frank, X = Employee 3, Y = Employee 4, and Z = Employee 5.

Make a list of all the possible combinations of two employees.

CF	FC	XC	YC	ZC
CX	FX	XF	YF	ZF
CY	FY	XY	YX	ZX
CZ	FZ	XZ	YZ	ZY

> **Do you see how the list is organized?**
>
> Each column begins with a different letter, and the second letters are added in alphabetical order, going down the column.

Answer: Of the 20 possible outcomes, 2 include both Curtis and Frank. The ratio $\frac{2}{20}$ reduces to $\frac{1}{10}$, which equals 10%. There is a **1-in-10, or 10%,** chance that both will be chosen for the training program.

▶▶Learn how to find theoretical probability when order matters.

Example: A spinner has four equal sections, numbered 1 through 4. To win a game, Gena has to get a 1 or a 2 on her first spin and either a 2, 3, or 4 on her second spin. What is the theoretical probability of Gena's winning the game?

Make an organized list of the possible combinations of spins. Then count the winning combinations based on the conditions in the problem.

1 – 1	2 – 1	3 – 1	4 – 1
1 – 2	2 – 2	3 – 2	4 – 2
1 – 3	2 – 3	3 – 3	4 – 3
1 – 4	2 – 4	3 – 4	4 – 4

Write a ratio comparing the number of possible wins (6) to the total possible combinations (16). The ratio is $\frac{6}{16}$, which reduces to $\frac{3}{8}$.

MATHEMATICS

Change the ratio $\frac{3}{8}$ to a percent. $3 \div 8 = 0.375 = 37.5\%$ or $37\frac{1}{2}\%$

Answer: Gena's chance of winning the game is **3 out of 8, or $37\frac{1}{2}\%$.**

Of course, you won't need to make a list if you can easily see the number of possible outcomes. Just use the facts of the situation to write a probability ratio and reduce to lowest terms.

▶▶ Find theoretical probability by writing a ratio.

Example: A drawer contains 15 pair of white socks and 5 pair of black socks. If a pair of socks is chosen at random, what is the chance the pair will be white?

You don't need to make a list. Think: There are 20 pair of socks in all and 15 are white. The ratio of white pairs to possible pairs is 15 to 20.

$\frac{15}{20} = \frac{3}{4} = 75\%$

Answer: There is a **75% chance** of choosing a pair of white socks.

SKILL PRACTICE

Solve each problem.

1. Use the organized list of employees on page 236. What is the theoretical probability that <u>neither Curtis nor Frank</u> will be chosen for the training program?

   (1) $\frac{19}{20}$

   (2) $\frac{3}{5}$

   (3) $\frac{3}{10}$

   (4) $\frac{1}{10}$

   (5) Not enough information is given.

2. If you roll two 6-sided dice, each numbered from 1 to 6, what is the theoretical probability that the sum will be greater than 8? (*Hint:* Make an organized list of all possible dice rolls.)

3. Silas bought 3 tickets for a chance to win a cruise to Alaska. If 300 tickets are sold, what is the chance that Silas will win?

SCIENCE Connection

In the field of genetics, scientists study how certain traits are passed from one generation to another. Generally, genes that determine physical traits are found in pairs. During reproduction, each parent provides one gene to create a new pair.

In certain flowers, the gene that produces the red color is represented by R. The gene of a white flower is represented by r. The capital letter represents a dominant gene, meaning that if a flower has the pairing Rr, its color will be red. Only a flower with the pairing rr can be white. Suppose the parent genes are Rr and RR. What are the possible pairings for the offspring? (The subscript numbers below will help you tell which capital R has been used.)

Parent Genes: R_1r R_2R_3

Offspring Possibilities: R_1R_2 R_1R_3 rR_2 rR_3

> **All offspring are red.**

List the possible offspring for parents with the pairings Rr and Rr.

Answers and explanations start on page 327.

Applying Theoretical Probability

FAMILY LINK: Shace is playing a game with her 7-year-old son Bryan. Bryan needs to roll a 10 on two dice to win, but he becomes frustrated when he can't do it. To teach Bryan about chance, Shace helps him make a list of the possible dice rolls. Then they count the rolls that add up to 10. She helps Bryan see that rolling a 10 isn't as easy as he thought it would be.

Finding the Probability of More than One Event

Making an organized list is one way to find the probability of more than one event. You can also use multiplication. To find the probability that two events will occur, multiply the probability that one event will occur by the probability that the other event will occur.

Example: Scott flips a coin twice. What is the probability of his getting heads both times?

You already know that the probability of getting heads on any one coin toss is 1 in 2, or $\frac{1}{2}$. Multiply to the find the probability that both tosses will be heads.

$$\frac{1}{2} \times \frac{1}{2} = \frac{1}{4}$$

Answer: The probability of Scott's getting heads twice is $\frac{1}{4}$, or 25%.

We can check the answer by making a tree diagram.

Using H for heads and T for tails, the diagram shows that the possible results of the first toss are H and T. Then the outcomes are listed for the second toss. Notice that each outcome in the first column has two possible outcomes in the second column.

Of the four possible combined outcomes, only the first shows two heads. The probability of getting heads twice in two coin tosses is $\frac{1}{4}$.

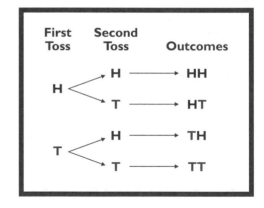

First Toss	Second Toss	Outcomes
H	H	HH
	T	HT
T	H	TH
	T	TT

Independent and Dependent Events

The two coin tosses in the situation above are **independent events,** because the result of the second event does not depend on the result of the first. In other words, the probability of the second coin toss is the same no matter what the outcome of the first coin toss.

Two events are **dependent events** if the probability of the second event is affected by the results of the first event. Recognizing independent and dependent events is key to solving probability problems.

Example: Leah places four white marbles and two black marbles in a bag. She plans to draw out one marble and then a second marble without replacing the first. What is the probability that both marbles will be white?

You can analyze the problem in this way.

For the first drawing, 4 out of 6 marbles are white. The probability that the first outcome is white is $\frac{4}{6}$, which reduces to $\frac{2}{3}$.

Now assume that the first marble is white. For the second drawing, 3 out of the remaining 5 marbles are white. The probability that the second outcome is white is $\frac{3}{5}$.

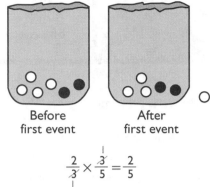

Before
first event

After
first event

$$\frac{2}{\overset{1}{\cancel{3}}} \times \frac{\overset{1}{\cancel{3}}}{5} = \frac{2}{5}$$

Multiply to find the probability of both events: $\frac{2}{3} \times \frac{3}{5} = \frac{2}{5}$.

Answer: The probability of Leah's drawing two white marbles is $\frac{2}{5}$, or 40%.

SKILL PRACTICE

Solve each problem. Express all answers in fraction form.

1. Three coins are tossed at the same time. What is the probability that all three coins will come up tails?

2. Dan and Stan are playing a card game. Of the seven cards Dan has in his hand, five are hearts. If Stan takes two cards from Dan's hand without looking, what is the probability that both cards will be hearts?

Use the spinner below to solve items 3 to 5.

3. What is the chance of spinning a 2?

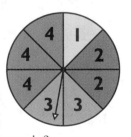

4. Sherry spins the spinner twice. What is the chance that she did <u>not</u> get a 4 on either spin?

5. Alan spins the spinner twice. What is the chance that the sum of the spins is 8?

6. Hasina has 4 bills in her wallet: a $1 bill, a $5 bill, a $10 bill, and a $20 bill. If she draws out two bills at random, what is the chance of her drawing out $30?

7. Of the 12 employees at Olympic Pharmacy, two will be chosen at random to work the night shift. Ana hopes she will not be chosen. The manager writes the employees' names on cards and draws one out without looking. The first name drawn is Grant. What is the chance that Ana's name will be next?

(1) $\frac{1}{2}$ (4) $\frac{1}{23}$

(2) $\frac{1}{11}$ (5) $\frac{1}{132}$

(3) $\frac{1}{12}$

8. Two 6-sided dice are numbered from 1 to 6. If both dice are rolled and the two numbers added, there are 36 possible sums. Which of the following is a true statement? (*Hint:* Make a chart of all possible dice rolls.)

(1) The chance of getting a sum of 2 is $\frac{1}{6}$.

(2) The chance of rolling two 4s is $\frac{1}{12}$.

(3) The chance of rolling two of the same number is $\frac{1}{2}$.

(4) The chance of getting a sum of 6 is $\frac{1}{6}$.

(5) The chance of getting a sum of 11 is $\frac{1}{18}$.

Answers and explanations start on page 327.

Everyday Problems in Probability

Solving a probability problem is as simple as writing a ratio and reducing it. The challenge is to decide which numbers to use in the ratio. On the GED Math Test, you will often be given more information than you need to solve a problem. Before you begin calculations, use your common sense to sift through the information in the problem. Remember, to write a probability ratio, you need to know the number of desirable outcomes and the number of possible outcomes.

▸▸ You may need to add or subtract to find the numbers needed for the probability ratio.

Example: A PTA meeting is attended by 38 parents, 5 teachers, and 7 classroom aides. As each person enters, he or she is given a ticket with a number. At the end of the meeting, the PTA president will draw out a number, and the person with the winning ticket will receive a prize. What is the chance that a teacher or a classroom aide will win the prize?

(1) 50%   (4) 4%
(2) 24%   (5) Not enough information given.
(3) 12%

Answer: You're right if you choose **(2) 24%.** You have all the information you need to compare the total number of teachers and classroom aides to the total number of people with tickets.

There are 5 teachers and 7 classroom aides. Since you are trying to find the chance of a teacher or an aide winning the prize, the first number in the ratio is the total of teachers and aides: $5 + 7 = 12$.

Add to find the total number of people at the meeting: $38 + 5 + 7 = 50$ people with tickets. The probability ratio is $\frac{12}{50}$, which is equal to 24%.

▸▸ Subtract from 100% or 1 to find the chance of an event <u>not</u> happening.

Example: A jar contains 5 red marbles, 10 blue marbles, 3 green marbles, and 2 yellow marbles. If a marble is picked at random, what is the probability that the marble chosen will <u>not</u> be red.

(1) $\frac{3}{4}$ (4) $\frac{1}{4}$
(2) $\frac{2}{3}$ (5) $\frac{1}{5}$
(3) $\frac{1}{3}$

Answer: You're right if you chose **(1) $\frac{3}{4}$.** Five out of 20 marbles in the jar are red. The probabilty of drawing red is $\frac{5}{20}$, which reduces to $\frac{1}{4}$.

Since the number 1 represents a certain probability, the chance that an event will not happen is equal to 1 minus the probability that an event will occur. In this case, $1 - \frac{1}{4} = \frac{3}{4}$, the probability that the marble will not be red.

SKILL PRACTICE

Solve each problem.

1. Three coins are tossed in the air. What is the chance that they will <u>not</u> all come up heads?

2. Ten items in a sale bin are priced:

$1	$1	$2	$2	$2
$2	$3	$3	$4	$4

   One item is chosen at random. What is the probability that the item costs either $1 or $2?

   (1) $\frac{1}{5}$ **(4)** $\frac{1}{2}$

   (2) $\frac{3}{10}$ **(5)** $\frac{3}{5}$

   (3) $\frac{2}{5}$

3. The spinner below is divided into eight equal sections.

   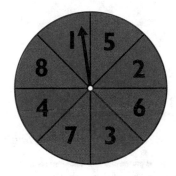

   What is the probability of <u>not</u> spinning an odd number?

TECHNOLOGY Connection

Many companies use contests to boost sales. Usually, the consumer has to find a certain bottlecap or game piece inside the product to win a prize. By law, companies must list the odds of winning a prize on the packaging or container.

Chunky Cookie Contest Rules and Odds

RULES: Winning game pieces are randomly placed inside specially marked packages of Chunky Cookies. If you find a bag of cookies with a specially marked game piece inside, scratch off the cookie chunks on the game piece to find out how much you've won.

Prize	Number of Winning Pieces	Estimated Odds
Grand Prize—$1000	250	1:36,000
First Prize—$500	500	1:18,000
Second Prize—$100	1,000	1:9,000
Third Prize—Case of Cookies	3,000	1:3,000
Fourth Prize—Bag of Cookies	2,250,000	1:4

For example, if you buy a bag of Chunky Cookies, you have a 1-in-4, or 25%, chance of winning fourth prize, another bag of cookies. As you can see, more valuable prizes are more difficult to win.

If you bought 500 bags of cookies, about how many would have a game piece winning fourth prize? About how much harder is it to win $500 than to win $100?

PART ONE DIRECTIONS: Choose the <u>one best answer</u> to each of the following problems. Use a calculator wherever necessary.

MATHEMATICS

1. Carlton's change purse contains a dime, a nickel, and two quarters. What is the probability that the first coin taken from the purse will be the dime?
   (1) $\frac{1}{2}$
   (2) $\frac{1}{3}$
   (3) $\frac{1}{4}$
   (4) $\frac{2}{3}$
   (5) $\frac{3}{4}$

Question 2 refers to the following table.

ANNUAL SALES—STYLE A			
Store	Small	Medium	Large
Best Fit	7	28	45
Clothes Depot	73	10	39
Wearhouse	15	122	90
Fine Fashions	4	21	12

2. Aunt Lu sells hand-knitted sweaters to clothing stores. Which store bought approximately twice as many medium-sized sweaters as the other three stores combined?
   (1) Best Fit
   (2) Clothes Depot
   (3) Wearhouse
   (4) Fine Fashions
   (5) Not enough information is given.

3. A baseball card company manufactured 30,000 card packs. A special autographed collector's card was inserted into 5,000 packs, chosen at random. What is the chance of buying a pack with a collector's card?
   (1) 1 in 5,000
   (2) 1 in 600
   (3) 1 in 60
   (4) 1 in 30
   (5) 1 in 6

4. In a bag of 25 oranges, 3 are starting to rot. What would be the probability of Lee's randomly selecting an orange that is <u>not</u> starting to rot from the bag?
   (1) $\frac{3}{25}$
   (2) $\frac{3}{28}$
   (3) $\frac{22}{25}$
   (4) $\frac{25}{22}$
   (5) $\frac{3}{22}$

5. Waldo bought eight raffle tickets for a chance to ride a steam-engine train through the mountains. Exactly 400 tickets were sold. What is the chance, expressed as a <u>percent</u>, that Waldo holds the winning ticket?
   (1) 1%   **(4)** 5%
   (2) 2%   **(5)** 8%
   (3) 4%

6. A bag holds 20 tokens, identical in shape and size. The tokens are either white or blue. Mike conducts an experiment in which he draws out a token at random, records its color, and replaces it. After 12 trials of the experiment, he has recorded the following data:

   blue   blue   blue   white   blue   blue
   white   blue   blue   blue   white   blue

   Which conclusion could Mike draw from the data about the contents of the bag?
   (1) There are an equal number of blue and white tokens in the bag.
   (2) There are more white than blue tokens.
   (3) All but three of the tokens in the bag are blue.
   (4) There are nine blue tokens in the bag.
   (5) The ratio of blue tokens to white tokens is probably 3:1.

Questions 7 through 9 are based on the following information.

A box contains red (R), white (W), and blue (B) tiles that are identical except for color. Their colors are shown in the table below.

R	R	W	W	B
R	R	W	B	B
R	W	W	B	B
R	W	W	B	B
R	W	W	B	B
R	W	W	B	B
R	W	W	B	B
R	W	W	B	B

7. If a tile is chosen at random from the box, what is the probability that it will be red?
   (1) $\frac{1}{10}$
   (2) $\frac{1}{4}$
   (3) $\frac{1}{3}$
   (4) $\frac{2}{3}$
   (5) Not enough information is given.

8. If one tile is chosen at random from the box, what is the chance that the tile will be either red or white?
   (1) $\frac{1}{3}$
   (2) $\frac{3}{8}$
   (3) $\frac{1}{2}$
   (4) $\frac{3}{5}$
   (5) $\frac{5}{8}$

9. Which of the following changes could be made to the contents of the box so that the chance of randomly selecting a red tile is 50%?
   (1) Add 5 red tiles.
   (2) Remove 5 white tiles and 5 blue tiles.
   (3) Add 10 tiles of each color.
   (4) Add 20 red tiles.
   (5) Remove 5 white tiles and add 5 red tiles.

10. There are 5 green, 3 purple, and 2 red candies in a jar. Marcie chose a purple candy. What is the chance that the next person will randomly pick a red candy?
    (1) $\frac{1}{10}$
    (2) $\frac{1}{9}$
    (3) $\frac{1}{5}$
    (4) $\frac{2}{9}$
    (5) $\frac{1}{2}$

Questions 11 and 12 refer to the following information.

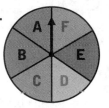

SPIN TO WIN GAME

Each player gets two spins.
Large Prize:
Spin the letter "A" twice.
Small Prize:
Spin any letter twice.

11. Karen plays Spin to Win at a carnival. Which expression shows Karen's probability of winning a large prize?
    (1) 6×6
    (2) $\frac{1}{6} + \frac{1}{6}$
    (3) $\frac{1}{6} \times \frac{1}{6}$
    (4) $\frac{1}{4} + \frac{1}{4}$
    (5) $\frac{1}{3} \times \frac{1}{3}$

12. On her first spin, Karen gets a B. What is her chance of <u>not</u> winning a prize?
    (1) 100%
    (2) $83\frac{1}{3}\%$
    (3) 50%
    (4) $16\frac{2}{3}\%$
    (5) Not enough information is given.

13. A survey lists 1500 registered voters in favor of a new drainage ditch and 700 against. If the margin of error is reported as ±2%, what is the range of the number of voters in favor of the proposition?
    (1) 1470 to 1530
    (2) 1500 to 1530
    (3) 1470 to 1500
    (4) 686 to 714
    (5) 670 to 730

PART TWO DIRECTIONS: Choose the <u>one best answer</u> to each of the following problems. *You may not use a calculator on these problems.*

14. Carla is helping her daughter with a math problem: There are 4 men with 4 hats. The hats are put into a big box. What is the probability that, without looking, each man will pick out his own hat?

    (1) $\frac{1}{256}$

    (2) $\frac{1}{48}$

    (3) $\frac{1}{24}$

    (4) $\frac{1}{4}$

    (5) Not enough information is given.

15. Avion Bird Club monitors bird migration. One day 100 birds fly by the watch station: 65 are ducks and 35 are geese. Which of the following expressions best represents how to calculate the probability that a passing bird is a goose?

    (1) $\frac{35}{65}$

    (2) $\frac{35}{100}$

    (3) $\frac{65}{100}$

    (4) $\frac{(65-35)}{100}$

    (5) $\frac{(35+65)}{100}$

Question 16 is based on the following drawing.

16. A spinner is divided into 12 equal sections and numbered as shown. What is the probability of the pointer stopping on a number less than 5?

    (1) 100%   **(4)** $66\frac{2}{3}$%

    (2) 50%   **(5)** 75%

    (3) $33\frac{1}{3}$%

17. With one roll of a six-sided die, what is the probability that Joel will <u>not</u> roll a three or a six?

    (1) 5 in 6   **(4)** 1 in 3

    (2) 2 in 3   **(5)** 1 in 6

    (3) 1 in 2

Question 18 is based on the following drawing.

18. The Altadena Food Bank sent 15 jars of spaghetti sauce and 20 jars of tomatoes to a shelter. What is the probability that the first jar the cook pulls out of the carton will be a jar of spaghetti sauce?

    (1) $\frac{15}{20}$ **(4)** $\frac{3}{4}$

    (2) $\frac{1}{35}$ **(5)** $\frac{3}{7}$

    (3) $\frac{5}{35}$

19. In a garment plant, 5% of the shirts sewn do not pass inspection and must be sold as seconds. An inspector has 200 shirts to inspect. What is the chance that a shirt chosen at random will <u>not</u> pass inspection?

    (1) 1 in 200   **(4)** 1 in 10

    (2) 1 in 40   **(5)** 1 in 5

    (3) 1 in 20

20. Ian tells Ruth that he will buy her lunch if she draws one of the four aces on the first pick from a deck of 52 cards. What are the chances that Ian will have to buy Ruth lunch?

    (1) 1 in 52   **(4)** 2 in 13

    (2) 3 in 52   **(5)** 12 in 13

    (3) 1 in 13

MATHEMATICS

Alternate Math Formats

The questions below are based on the math skills in Programs 36–37. For more information on answering alternate format items, review pages 20–22.

Grid in the answers to questions 21 through 29.

<u>Questions 21 through 23</u> refer to the following information.

PACKING COMPANY STRETCH WRAP		
Size	Weight per Case	Price per Roll
12 in × 2000 ft	28 lb	$9
12 in × 1500 ft	25 lb	$8
15 in × 1500 ft	35 lb	$11
18 in × 1500 ft	44 lb	$15
18 in × 1000 ft	41 lb	$13

21. A packing company sells stretch wrap by the case. If there are four rolls per case, what will be the cost of two cases of stretch wrap measuring 18 in × 1000 ft?

22. What is the mean price per roll for the sizes shown in the table?

23. What is the median weight of the cases listed in the table?

24. David collects baseball cards from his favorite teams. He has 250 cards of Dodger players, 400 of Yankee players, and 350 of Cardinal players. If he puts all the cards in a box and draws out one at random, what is the probability, expressed as a fraction, that the card will be a Dodger player?

25. The game spinner has eight equal sections. The sections have the following colors: red, blue, red, white, red, blue, red, and white. Written as a fraction, what is the probability of getting either red or white when you spin the spinner?

26. Melanie records the temperature for six days at 1 P.M. The temperatures are 82°, 78°, 83°, 84°, 86°, and 85°. What is the mean temperature for the six-day period?

245

27. Sylvia repairs computers for a living. The amount she charges varies according to the amount of time the repair takes. The graph to the right shows the charges for Sylvia's last five repairs. What amount would Sylvia most likely charge for a 4-hour repair?

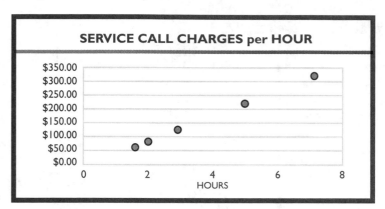

SERVICE CALL CHARGES per HOUR

28. The number of children enrolled in a city youth basketball league has increased steadily for the past five years. The rate of increase is shown on the graph. Predict the enrollment for Year 6.

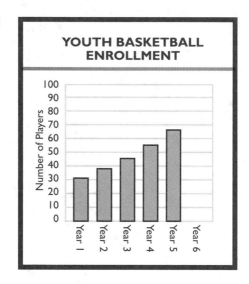

YOUTH BASKETBALL ENROLLMENT

29. Each year, a community organization holds a Spring Festival to raise money for the public library. The event organizers have observed a relationship between the price of a family ticket and the number of family tickets sold. Study the data on the graph. Predict the expected ticket sales if ticket prices are raised to $30 per family.

SPRING FESTIVAL TICKET SALES

MATHEMATICS

Algebra will seem less mysterious if you can relate it to math you're familiar with and if you understand some basic concepts and properties. In this program, math teachers and the host introduce you to equations, inverse operations, properties, and signed numbers.

Introduction to Algebra

OBJECTIVES

1. Perform operations using signed numbers.
2. Simplify, evaluate, and write algebraic expressions.
3. Write and solve equations.

Algebra lets you represent values in equations using symbols such as letters. Why learn algebra? You would probably be surprised at how often you use algebraic thinking to solve problems. For example, suppose a worker earns $10 per hour and works for 40 hours. Using arithmetic, you know that the worker will be paid $400. Using algebra, you know that any hourly employee's pay can be expressed by the number of hours worked and the rate per hour. You could show the relationship using variables: $p = hr$, where p = pay, h = hours worked, and r = hourly rate. Using algebra, we have translated a mathematical idea from words to mathematical language.

The ability to work with algebra is important to your success on the GED Math Test. You will need to know how to write and evaluate mathematical expressions and solve equations. Your understanding of formulas will help you solve problems. Your work in this lesson will help reinforce your understanding of fractions, decimals, and geometry.

On the following pages, you will find a brief exercise called *Sneak Preview*. It is designed to introduce you to the topics that will be featured in the video program and the corresponding lesson. After you complete the exercise and check your answers, turn to the vocabulary page. There you will find terms that will help you better understand the video and the lesson that follow. After reviewing page 250, you will be ready to watch Program 38.

For additional practice, visit *LiteracyLink* online at
http://www.pbs.org/literacy.

Sneak Preview

This exercise previews some of the concepts from Program 38. After you answer the questions, use the feedback on page 249 to help set your learning goals.

 **FAMILY LINK:** Mitch would like to invest in the stock market someday. He decides to follow the stock of Kerzon Industries (KZS), a retail sales company. Each week he has recorded the closing price of the stock at week's end to the nearest whole dollar. Using his computer, he has prepared the following graph to show the changes.

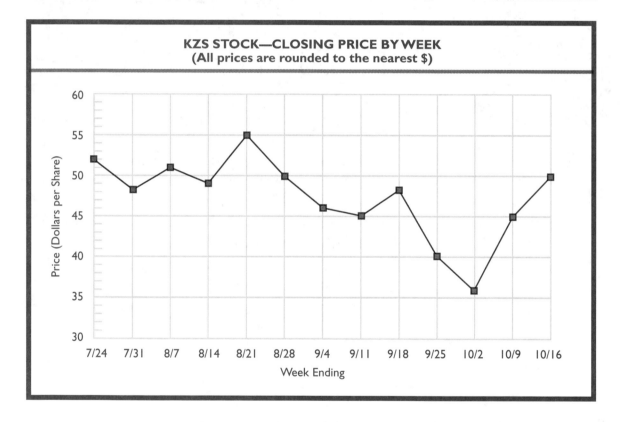

Answer these questions based on the chart shown above.

1. Which of the following expressions could be used to represent the total change in the stock's value from 7/24 to 8/21?

    (1) $(-4) + (-3) + (-2) + (-6)$
    (2) $4 - 3 - 2 - 6$
    (3) $4 + 3 + 2 + 6$
    (4) $(-4) + 3 + (-2) + 6$
    (5) $(-4) + (-2)$

2. Which of the signed numbers shows the change in value of 50 shares from the week ending 8/21 to the week ending 10/2?

(1) −$1800
(2) −$950
(3) −$600
(4) +$19
(5) +$950

3. On 10/16, Mitch would have sold 50 shares of KZS at the price shown on the graph. He would have used that amount to purchase 40 shares of RGL stock. Let x equal the cost per share of the RGL stock. Which of the following equations could be used to find the price per share of the new stock?

(1) $50(\$50) = 40x$
(2) $50(\$50)(40) = x$
(3) $\$50 = \frac{40}{x}$
(4) $50x = 40(\$50)$
(5) $50 + \frac{40}{x} = \$50$

4. On 10/23, the cost of one share of KZS stock went up twice as much as it did from 10/9 to 10/16. What was the cost of one share of KZS stock on 10/23?

(1) $40.00
(2) $45.00
(3) $50.00
(4) $55.00
(5) $60.00

Feedback

- If you got all of the answers right... you have a good basic understanding of signed numbers, algebraic expressions, and equations.

- If you missed question 1... you need to work on using signed numbers to write algebraic expressions.

- If you missed question 2... you need to practice operations using signed numbers.

- If you missed question 3... you need to practice writing equations.

- If you missed question 4... you need to work on using equations to solve problems.

Vocabulary for *Introduction to Algebra*

consecutive numbers	numbers in counting order
equation	a mathematical sentence in which two expressions or numbers are equal
evaluate	to find the value of an expression by substituting values for the variables and carrying out the operations according to the order of operations
exponent	a small number written slightly above and to the right of a base number to specify the number of times to multiply the base by itself
like terms	terms that have identical variables; for example, $5xy$ and $3xy$ are like terms because the variable portions are alike
negative numbers	the set of values less than zero
order of operations	a set of rules that give the sequence for performing the mathematical operations in an expression
positive numbers	the set of values greater than zero
scientific notation	a useful system for writing a very large or a very small number as the product of a number between 1 and 10 and a power of 10
signed numbers	the set of positive and negative numbers
term	in an expression or equation, a single number or a single variable or the product of a number and one or more variables
variable	a letter or symbol used to represent a number

➡ **NOW WATCH PROGRAM 38:**

This program introduces practical skills that will help you on the GED Test—from knowing how to isolate a variable to working with positive and negative numbers. Follow the examples in the program, and look for opportunities to practice these skills in the workbook and online.

PBS
LiteracyLink®

After you watch the program, work on:

- pages 251–268 in this workbook
- Internet activities at http://www.pbs.org/literacy

Introduction to Algebra

On the following pages, you will learn more about the ideas discussed in the video program and have an opportunity to develop and practice your GED math skills.

Key Points to Think About

In the video program, you explored:

- How people use algebra in their daily lives as workers, citizens, and family members.
- How to translate words into algebra to write algebraic expressions and equations.
- Everyday applications of algebra, such as those that deal with money, time, and measurement.

On the GED Math Test:

- You will be expected to know how to write and solve equations.
- You should know how to simplify and evaluate expressions using your knowledge of signed numbers.
- You will also use algebra to choose the best expression to solve a problem.

As you work through the lesson for Program 38:

- Think about how algebra is used to express problem-solving situations in mathematical language.
- Memorize the rules for working with signed numbers and apply them according to the order of operations.
- Be aware of opportunities to use algebra to solve problems in your daily life, not just on the GED Math Test.

PROGRAM 38: Introduction to Algebra

GED TIPS

When taking the GED Test, you should:

- Use the formulas page whenever possible to set up problems involving simple interest, distance, cost, or geometric figures.
- Check your answer by substituting it for the variable in the original equation.
- Consider using "guess and check" to solve difficult problems. In other words, try each answer choice in the problem situation to see which works.

Working with Signed Numbers

COMMUNITY LINK: Farzad is keeping track of the fund-raising efforts for a high school band. She makes a list of checks and cash collected during a fund-raising drive, listing each donation as a positive number. Then she lists the band's expenses as negative numbers. Finally, she combines the numbers from both lists to see how much the band has in its account.

Using a Number Line

Signed numbers are all the positive and negative numbers, as well as 0. **Positive numbers** are greater than zero, and **negative numbers** are less than 0. A positive number may be written without any sign or with a positive sign (+). A negative number must have a negative sign (−). The sign tells you the number's relationship to zero.

On the number line below, the positive numbers are to the right of zero, and the negative numbers are to the left. Zero is neither positive nor negative. The arrows on the ends of the line show that the number line extends to infinity.

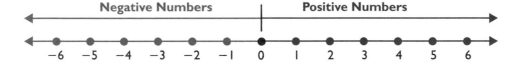

On the GED Math Test, you may be asked to identify points on a number line.

▶▶ Use your knowledge of fractions and decimals when working with a number line.

Example: On the number line below, which point represents $-\frac{11}{4}$?

The improper fraction $-\frac{11}{4}$ is equal to $-2\frac{3}{4}$. If the mixed number were positive, it would be between 2 and 3 on the number line. Since it is negative, the point is between −2 and −3.

Answer: The fraction $-\frac{11}{4}$ is represented by **Point B.**

A number line is also helpful when you need to compare numbers.

Example: Which is greater: −4 or −3?

Look at the number line above. The numbers increase in size as you move to the right. Since −3 is to the right of −4, the number −3 is greater than −4.

Answer: $-3 > -4$

Adding Signed Numbers

The examples below will help you learn how to add signed numbers. Because a negative sign can be easily confused with a subtraction symbol, signed numbers are often written in parentheses.

To add signed numbers, follow these rules:

1. When numbers have the same sign, find the sum and keep the sign.

$(+6) + (+4) = +10$ $(-6) + (-4) = -10$

2. When numbers have different signs, find the difference of the numbers. Then look at the numbers "without" signs, and use the sign from the larger number.

$(+6) + (-4) = +2$ $(-6) + (+4) = -2$

3. To add more than two numbers with different signs, add the positive and negative numbers separately. Then combine the two sums using rule 2.

$(+3) + (-7) + (-5) + (+6) = ?$
Add the positive numbers: $(+3) + (+6) = +9$
Add the negative numbers: $(-7) + (-5) = -12$
Combine: $(+9) + (-12) = -3$
The answer is $-\textbf{3}$.

Subtracting Signed Numbers

Compare these equations: $8 - 5 = 3$ and $8 + (-5) = 3$. The solutions are the same. From these examples, we can conclude that subtracting a number is the same as adding that number with the opposite sign.

To subtract signed numbers, follow these rules:

1. Change the sign of the number being subtracted to the opposite sign.
2. Change the subtraction sign to addition.
3. Follow the rules for adding signed numbers.

▶▶ Study these examples.

$(-6) - (+5) = ?$ $(+8) - (-2) = ?$ $(-5) - (+2) - (-3) = ?$
$(-6) + (-5) = -11$ $(+8) + (+2) = +10$ $(-5) + (-2) + (+3) = ?$
                                                      $(-7) + (+3) = -4$

SKILL PRACTICE

Solve each problem.

1. $8 + (-2) =$
2. $-35 + (-12) =$
3. $-5 - 10 =$
4. $7 + (-15) =$
5. $32 - (-19) =$

6. $-7 + (-4) + 11 =$
7. $24 - (-12) - 6 =$
8. $3 + (-4) - 4 - (-8) =$
9. $3\frac{1}{2} - (-8\frac{1}{4}) =$
10. $1.8 + (-3.5) - (-5) + 0.4 =$

Answers and explanations start on page 328.

PROGRAM 38: Introduction to Algebra

Multiplying and Dividing Signed Numbers

Remember, multiplication can be shown in several ways. 5×3 $5 \cdot 3$ $5(3)$
Each of the examples at right means "5 times 3."

In algebra, division is indicated by writing a fraction. The fraction $\frac{12}{3}$ means $12 \div 3$.
Think of the fraction bar as a way of saying "divided by."

Study these rules for multiplying and dividing signed numbers:

1. When the signs are the same, the answer is positive.
2. When the signs are different, the answer is negative.

▶▶ Look for patterns as you review these examples. Remember, a number without a sign is positive.

Examples: $(3)(5) = 15$ $(-3)(-5) = 15$ $(3)(-5) = -15$ $(-3)(5) = -15$

$\frac{16}{2} = 8$ $\frac{-16}{-2} = 8$ $\frac{-16}{2} = -8$ $\frac{16}{-2} = -8$

What happens when you multiply more than two signed numbers? First, multiply all the numbers, regardless of their signs. Then, count the number of negative factors. If there is an even number of negative factors, the answer is positive. If there is an odd number, the answer is negative.

Examples: $4(-3)(-2)(1) = 24$ $4(-3)(-2)(-1) = -24$

A Review of the Order of Operations

For expressions with more than one operation, always follow the order of operations.

The Order of Operations

1. Perform operations inside parentheses.
2. **Evaluate** exponents.
3. Perform any multiplication and division steps, working from left to right.
4. Perform any addition and subtraction steps, working from left to right.

Use the order of operations to evaluate this expression.

Example: Evaluate the expression $2(3 + 5)^2 - 30$.

$$2(3 + 5)^2 - 30 \ = \ 2(8)^2 - 30 \qquad \text{Perform the operation in parentheses.}$$
$$= \ 2(64) - 30 \qquad \text{Evaluate the exponent.}$$
$$= \ 128 - 30 \qquad \text{Multiply.}$$
$$= \ 98 \qquad \text{Subtract.}$$

MATHEMATICS

Signed Numbers and Calculators

The numbers you enter on a calculator are assumed to be positive. If you want to enter a negative number, first enter the number as you normally would; then press the +/- key. A negative sign will be added to the number in the display.

▶▶ See how a calculator is used to solve this multi-step problem.

Example: $\frac{-153}{9} - (-12) = ?$

Follow the order of operations. Divide first, then subtract.

Calculator: ┃ 1 ┃ 5 ┃ 3 ┃ +/- ┃ ÷ ┃ 9 ┃ = ┃   **–17.**

                ┃ – ┃ 1 ┃ 2 ┃ +/- ┃ = ┃   **–5.**

Answer: The solution is **–5.**

SKILL PRACTICE

Solve each problem. Check your work with a calculator.

1. $(-4)(-8) =$

2. $(9)(-1)(-2) =$

3. $(15)(-4) =$

4. $(-2)(4)(-3)(-1) =$

5. $\frac{-32}{-8} =$

6. $\frac{-125}{5} =$

7. $\frac{6.3}{-2.1} =$

8. $15 - (\frac{-4}{2}) =$

9. $-6(3 - 8) =$

10. $\frac{(8^2 + -20)}{11} =$

PROBLEM SOLVER Connection

Drawing a number line is one strategy to help you solve signed-number problems. When a problem involves many small changes, counting the changes out on a number line may be the quickest method of solving the problem.

Example: On Friday at 1 P.M., the temperature was 6° Fahrenheit. Over the next four hours, it dropped 4°, increased by 2°, and dropped 3°. What was the temperature at 5 P.M.?

Draw a number line with 0 in the center. Put your pencil at +6 and quickly count off the changes in temperature.

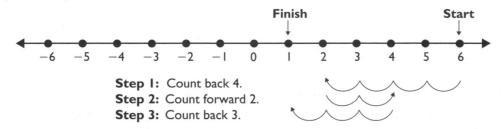

Step 1: Count back 4.
Step 2: Count forward 2.
Step 3: Count back 3.

Answer: Your pencil stops on +1. It was 1° **Fahrenheit** at 5 P.M.

Write an algebraic expression to solve the problem. Which method seems easier?

Working with Expressions

FAMILY LINK: For science homework, Troy's son Peter needs to find the temperature of their home using the Celsius scale. The thermostat shows that the temperature is 72° Fahrenheit. The formula for converting degrees Fahrenheit to degrees Celsius is $\frac{5}{9}$ (°F − 32) They substitute 72 for °F and evaluate the expression. Their home is about 22° Celsius.

Simplifying Algebraic Expressions

Algebra involves the use of variables. A **variable** is a letter or symbol that takes the place of a number. Variables are used in combination with numbers to form expressions. An expression can either have a single **term** or combine several terms. A term is either a single number or variable or the product of a number and one or more variables.

▶▶ Study these examples of algebraic expressions.

Examples: x $-5y$ $2x^2$ $-7xy$
   $4b + 7$ $3(x + y)$ $a + b + c$ $x^2 + 5xy + 6y^2$

To simplify an expression, combine like terms. Like terms have exactly the same variables and exponents.

- The terms $5xy$ and $2xy$ are like terms because both have the combined term xy.
- The terms $3x^2y$ and $3xy^2$ are not like terms because the variables are not raised to the same powers.

▶▶ See how the rules of signed numbers and the order of operations are used to simplify this expression.

Example: Simplify $2x - 5 + 3y + 2 - 2y + 4x$.

Rearrange the terms so that the like terms are next to each other. Be sure to move both the term and the operation symbol in front of it to the new location.

$2x + 4x - 5 + 2 + 3y - 2y$

$6x - 3 + y$
Combine like terms.

> $3y - 2y = y$
>
> It isn't necessary to write 1 before the variable, since $1 \cdot y = y$.

Answer: The simplified expression is **$6x - 3 + y$.**

Working with parentheses is slightly more involved. In the next example, remember that you can subtract by adding the opposite.

Example: Simplify $(-2x + 5) - (-6x - 4)$.

Add the opposite of $(-6x - 4)$.	$(-2x + 5) + (6x + 4)$
Remove the parentheses and rearrange the terms.	$-2x + 6x + 5 + 4$
Combine like terms.	$4x + 9$

Answer: The simplified expression is **$4x + 9$.**

MATHEMATICS

Evaluating Expressions

Evaluating an expression means finding its value. To find the value of an expression, substitute the numbers you are given for the variables. Then use the order of operations to find the value of the expression.

Example: Find the value of $3x + 2y$ if $x = -2$ and $y = 4$.

Substitute the numbers for the variables. $\quad 3x + 2y = 3(-2) + 2(4)$

Multiply. $\qquad\qquad\qquad\qquad\qquad\qquad = -6 + 8$

Add. $\qquad\qquad\qquad\qquad\qquad\qquad\quad = 2$

Answer: The value of the expression is **2.**

If an expression contains parentheses, you may need to change the parentheses to brackets so that you can use parentheses to indicate signed numbers. Do the work within the brackets first, always following the order of operations.

Example: Evaluate $ab + (a^2 - b^2)$ if $a = -3$ and $b = 2$.

Substitute the numbers for the variables. $\quad ab + (a^2 - b^2) = -3(2) + [(-3)^2 - 2^2]$

Do the exponents within the brackets first. $\qquad\qquad\qquad\qquad = -3(2) + [9 - 4]$

Do the subtraction operation in the brackets. $\qquad\qquad\qquad = -3(2) + 5$

Multiply. $\qquad\qquad\qquad\qquad\qquad\qquad\qquad\qquad\quad = -6 + 5$

Add. $\qquad\qquad\qquad\qquad\qquad\qquad\qquad\qquad\quad\;\; = -1$

Answer: The value of the expression is **–1.**

SKILL PRACTICE

Simplify by combining like terms.

1. $3a + b - 4 + 6a - 4b$

2. $5x - 6 + 2x + 3$

3. $6(2x + 7) - 9x$

4. $4m + 3m^2 + 12 - m^2 - 6m$

5. $7b^2 - 8b + 13a^2 - 12b^2 + 5b$

6. $2x - y + 5y - 3x + \frac{4y}{2} + 2(x - 2y)$

Evaluate by substituting given numbers for the appropriate variables.

7. Evaluate $5x + 3y$ if $x = 2$ and $y = 4$.

8. Find the value of $4(a^2 - b^2)$ if $a = 6$ and b = 3.

9. If $x = 2$ and $y = 6$, evaluate $4x - 2y$.

10. If $s = -4$ and $t = -2$, find the value of $2s^2 + 4t^2$.

11. If $m = 6$ and $n = -5$, evaluate $5m - 8n$.

12. Evaluate $4(a - b) + 2(a + b)$ when $a = 10$ and $b = 9$.

13. If $x = 4$, $y = 2$, and $z = -5$, what is the value of $x(2y + z)$.

14. Evaluate $\frac{6mn}{q}$ when $m = -2$, $n = -4$ and $q = 6$.

15. If $x = -3$ and $y = 2$, find the value of $\frac{2x^2 + y}{5x - (-5)}$

16. Evaluate $100(4p + 1.25p + 0.75p)$ when $p = 20$.

Answers and explanations start on page 329.

FAMILY LINK: For a report, Timor's daughter needed to find the distance from Earth to the planet Jupiter. In a reference book, she read that the distance was 3.67×10^8 miles. Timor explained that the number was written using scientific notation. He showed her how to add zeros and move the decimal point to write the number in standard form.

Working with Exponents

In algebraic expressions, we often see numbers or variables raised to a power. In the example below, 6 is the base and 4 is the exponent. The base tells the factor to be multiplied. The exponent tells how many times the base is a factor.

Example: $6^4 = 6 \times 6 \times 6 \times 6 = 1296$

Numbers and variables with exponents are easy to work with if we follow a few simple rules. These rules are called the laws of exponents.

The Laws of Exponents

1. To multiply numbers with the same base, add the exponents: $a^m \times a^n = a^{m+n}$
2. To divide numbers with the same base, subtract the exponents: $a^m \div a^n = a^{m-n}$
3. To raise a number with an exponent to a power, multiply the exponents: $(a^m)^n = a^{m \cdot n}$

You can always solve problems with exponents by writing out all the factors. Study the examples below. Each problem is solved using two different methods. On the GED Math Test, use either method.

EXAMPLES	WRITING OUT FACTORS	USING THE LAWS OF EXPONENTS
Multiply 3^2 by 3^3.	$3^2 \times 3^3 = (3 \times 3)(3 \times 3 \times 3) = 3^5$	$3^2 \times 3^3 = 3^{2+3} = 3^5$
Divide x^6 by x^2.	$\dfrac{x^6}{x^2} = \dfrac{x \cdot x \cdot x \cdot x \cdot x \cdot x}{x \cdot x} = x^4$	$x^6 \div x^2 = x^{6-2} = x^4$
$(2^3)^2 = ?$	$(2 \times 2 \times 2)(2 \times 2 \times 2) = 2^6$	$(2^3)^2 = 2^{3 \cdot 2} = 2^6$

Using Scientific Notation

Scientific notation is useful for writing very large or very small numbers. A number written in scientific notation has two factors. The first factor is between 1 and 10. The second is a power of 10.

To write a number using scientific notation:

- Move the decimal point to the right of the first digit.
- Count how many places you moved the decimal point. Write the number of places as a power of ten. Use a positive exponent if you moved the decimal point to the left. Use a negative exponent if you moved it to the right.

Examples: Write each number in scientific notation.

The distance from the Earth to Jupiter is 367,000,000 miles.	Move the decimal point 8 places to the left, adding zeros as needed.	$367{,}000{,}000 = 3.67 \times 10^8$ mi
The pace of a fast garden snail is 0.005 miles per hour.	Move the decimal point 3 places to the right	$0.005 = 5 \times 10^{-3}$ mph

Scientific calculators express very large or small numbers using scientific notation. Try the following multiplication on your calculator.

Calculator: $2{,}000{,}000 \times 3{,}000{,}000 =$
Your display may read ⎡ 6. 12 ⎤ or ⎡ 6 E 12 ⎤ .
The display means 6×10^{12}.

To change a number from scientific notation to standard form:

- If the exponent is positive, move the decimal point to the right the number of places indicated by the exponent.
- If the exponent is negative, move the decimal point to the left.
- Add zeros as needed.

Examples: Write each number in standard form.

The weight of an elephant in pounds is about 2×10^4.	Move the decimal point 4 places to the right.	$2 \times 10^4 = 20{,}000$ pounds
The weight of an ant in pounds is about 2×10^{-5}.	Move the decimal point 5 places to the left.	$2 \times 10^{-5} = 0.00002$ pound

SKILL PRACTICE

Simplify each expression using the rules of exponents.

1. $4^6 \cdot 4^3$
2. $b^4 \cdot b^7$
3. $10^8 \cdot 10^2$
4. $m^2 \cdot m^3 \cdot m^1$
5. $3^8 \div 3^5$
6. $n^{10} \div n^2$
7. $x^4 \div x^3$
8. $10^8 \div 10^6$
9. $(10^3)^4$
10. $(y^2)^5$
11. $(2^9)^2$
12. $(a^2)^6$

Use your understanding of scientific notation to answer these questions.

13. Which is less: 3.2×10^{-2} or 2.1×10^{-3}?

14. Which is greater: 9.4×10^4 or 3.6×10^5?

15. The area of France is 209,970 square miles. Write the area in scientific notation.

16. The area of the United States is about 3.614×10^6 square miles. Write the number in standard notation.

17. The distance from our Sun to the nearest star is about 2.5×10^{13} miles. Write the distance in standard notation.

18. How many times greater is 4×10^4 than 4×10^3?

19. Scientists measure the energy of moving things using joules. A bumblebee in flight expends about 0.002 joules. Write the number in scientific notation.

Working with Equations

FAMILY LINK: After spending $418 for a car repair, Alvin wonders how much his mechanic charges per hour for labor. The bill for the repair shows $158 for parts plus 4 hours of labor. Using r for the labor rate per hour, he writes the equation $4r + 158 = 418$.

Solving Equations

As you learned in Program 29, an **equation** is a mathematical sentence stating that two expressions or numbers are equal.

Take a close look at this equation: $4r + 158 = 418$.

The equation states that the expression $4r + 158$ is equal to 418. To solve the equation, we need to find the value for r that will make the equation true.

Since an equation is like a balance scale, you can add or subtract the same quantity from both sides of the equation without upsetting the balance. You can also multiply or divide both sides by the same quantity. To isolate the variable, always do the opposite of the operations in the equation.

▶▶ See how inverse operations are used to isolate the variable.

Example: Solve $4r + 158 = 418$.

In the equation, 158 is added to $4r$. Eliminate the addition operation by subtracting 158 from both sides of the equation.	$4r + 158 - \mathbf{158} = 418 - \mathbf{158}$ $4r = 260$
The variable r is multiplied by 4. Eliminate the multiplication operation by dividing both sides of the equation by 4.	$\frac{4r}{4} = \frac{260}{4}$

Answer: The solution is **65**.
Check: Substitute 65 into the original equation.
The value 65 makes the equation true.
The answer is correct.

$$r = 65$$
$$4(65) + 158 = 418$$
$$260 + 158 = 418$$
$$418 = 418$$

▶▶ Learn how to eliminate division in an equation.

Example: Solve $\frac{y}{2} - 15 = -9$.

$$\frac{y}{2} - 15 + \mathbf{15} = -9 + \mathbf{15}$$

Add 15 to both sides.
Multiply both sides by 2.

$$\frac{y}{2} = 6$$
$$\mathbf{2} \cdot \frac{y}{2} = 6 \cdot \mathbf{2}$$

Answer: The solution is **12**.
Check: Substitute 12 into the original equation.
The answer is correct.

$$y = 12$$
$$\frac{12}{2} - 15 = -9$$
$$6 - 15 = -9$$
$$-9 = -9$$

Writing Equations

When using algebra to solve problems, you need to translate problem situations expressed in words to algebraic symbols. Study the table below to see how the four basic operations are indicated in algebra problems.

Operation	Word Phrase	Algebraic Expression
Addition	the sum of b and 3	$b + 3$
	5 more than x	$x + 5$
	y is increased by 2	$y + 2$
Subtraction	x decreased by 10	$x - 10$
	the difference of a and b	$a - b$
	6 less than r	$r - 6$
Multiplication	the product of 2, x, and y	$2xy$
	-4 times x	$-4x$
Division	x divided by y	$\frac{x}{y}$

Remember:
In subtraction and division problems, order matters. Make sure the expression matches the order indicated by the words.

▸▸ See how to translate a word problem to algebraic language and solve.

Example: The sum of 2 times a number and 18 is 30. What is the number?

Write the equation. Let the variable x represent the unknown number. "The sum of 2 times a number and 18" can be written $2x + 18$. The word *is* translates to the equals sign, and the entire expression equals 30.

The equation is written: $2x + 18 = 30$.

Solve the equation. Subtract 18 from both sides.

$$2x + 18 - \mathbf{18} = 30 - \mathbf{18}$$
$$2x = 12$$

Divide both sides by 2.

$$\frac{2x}{2} = \frac{12}{2}$$
$$x = 6$$

Answer: The variable x is equal to **6**.
Check: Substitute 6 for x in the original equation.
The answer is correct.

$$2(6) + 18 = 30$$
$$12 + 18 = 30$$
$$30 = 30$$

SKILL PRACTICE

Solve each equation. Check the solution.

1. $2y - 7 = 1$

2. $\frac{-10}{x} + 14 = 19$

3. $5n - 4 = -9$

4. $-4b + 18 = 2b$

5. $\frac{a}{6} - 5 = 0$

6. $4x + \frac{x}{2} = 36$

7. The sum of three times a number and 6 is 42. Write an equation and solve.

8. Five times a number, decreased by 9 is -14. Write an equation and solve.

9. The quotient of 32 and a number, increased by 5 is 1. Write an equation and solve.

10. Two times a number decreased by 22 is 4. Write an equation and solve.

Algebra Word Problems

Many algebra problems are about number relationships. In most word problems, one number is defined by describing its relationship to another number. One other fact, such as the sum or product of the numbers, is also given. To solve the problem, you need to find a way to express both numbers using the same variable.

▶▶ See how to write an equation about two amounts using one variable.

Example: Together, Victor and Tami Vargas earn $33,280 per year. Tami earns $4,160 more per year than Victor earns. How much do Victor and Tami each earn per year?

You are asked to find two unknown amounts.
Represent the amounts using algebra.

Victor's earnings: x
Tami's earnings: $x + 4,160$

Write an equation showing that the sum of the two amounts is $33,280. Solve the equation.

$$x + x + 4,160 = 33,280$$

- Combine like terms.

$$2x + 4,160 = 33,280$$

- Subtract 4,160 from both sides of the equation.

$$2x + 4,160 - \mathbf{4,160} = 33,280 - \mathbf{4,160}$$
$$2x = 29,120$$

- Divide both sides by 2.

$$\frac{2x}{2} = \frac{29,120}{2}$$
$$x = 14,560$$

Now go back to the beginning, when you first wrote the amounts in algebraic language. Since x represents Victor's earnings, you know that Victor earns $14,560 per year. Tami's earnings are represented by $x + 4,160$. Add: $14,560 + 4,160 = 18,720$. Tami earns $18,720 per year.

Answer: Victor earns **$14,560,** and Tami earns **$18,720.**

Check: Return to the original word problem and see whether these amounts satisfy the conditions of the problem. The sum of the amounts is $33,280, and $18,720 is $4,160 more than $14,560. The answer is correct.

▶▶ Learn how to apply algebraic thinking to problems about age.

Example: Erica is four times as old as Blair. Nicole is three years older than Erica. The sum of their ages is 21. How old is Erica?

The problem concerns three ages. Let x equal Blair's age.
Represent the amounts using the same variable.

Blair's age: x
Erica's age: $4x$
Nicole's age: $4x + 3$

Write an equation showing the sum equal to 21.

$$x + 4x + 4x + 3 = 21$$

MATHEMATICS

Solve the equation. $x + 4x + 4x + 3 = 21$

The variable x is equal to 2, but that doesn't answer the question posed in the problem. The problem asks you to find Erica's age, which is equal to $4x$, or $4(2)$.

$$9x + 3 = 21$$
$$9x = 18$$
$$x = 2$$

> This worked example does not show every step. As you gain experience, you will do many of the steps mentally.

Answer: Erica is **8 years old.**
Check: Blair is 2, Erica is 8, and Nicole is 11. The ages total 21.

▶▶ Learn how to write equations for consecutive number problems.

Example: The sum of three consecutive numbers is 75. Name the numbers.

Consecutive numbers are numbers in counting order. To solve problems of this type, let x equal the first number. The second and third numbers can be expressed as $x + 1$ and $x + 2$.

Write an equation. $x + x + 1 + x + 2 = 75$
Solve.

$$3x + 3 = 75$$
$$3x = 72$$
$$x = 24$$

Answer: The numbers arc **24, 25, and 26.**
Check: The numbers are consecutive, and their sum is 75.

SKILL PRACTICE

For each problem, write an equation and solve. Check your answer.

1. Name two numbers if one number is 3 more than twice another, and their sum is 57.

2. Erin is 8 years less than twice Paula's age. The sum of their ages is 40. How old is Erin?

3. Lyle and Roy do landscaping. They recently earned $840 for a project. If Lyle earned $4 for every $1 earned by Roy, how much of the money went to Lyle?

4. The sum of four consecutive numbers is 626. Find the four numbers.

5. A movie theater sold 5 times as many children's tickets as adult tickets to an afternoon show. If 132 tickets were sold in all, how many were children's tickets?

6. Together, Grace and Carlo spent $51 on a gift. If Grace contributed twice as much money as Carlo, how much did Carlo spend?

7. Fahi's age is $\frac{3}{4}$ of Mia's age. The sum of their ages is 91. How much older is Mia than Fahi?

8. The sum of two consecutive odd numbers is 64. Name the numbers. (*Hint:* Let x represent the first number and $x + 2$ the second number.)

9. One number is 8 more than $\frac{1}{2}$ of another number. The sum of the numbers is 23. What arc the numbers?

10. Adena, Julius, and Tia volunteered to read to children at the public library. Julius worked two hours less than Tia. Adena worked twice as many hours as Julius. Altogether they worked 58 hours. How many hours did Adena work?

    (1) 14   **(4)** 42
    (2) 16   **(5)** 46
    (3) 28

More Algebra Word Problems

Many algebra problems are about the figures that you encounter in geometry. To solve these problems, you will need to combine your understanding of geometry and its formulas with your ability to write and solve equations.

▶▶ Learn how to solve for the dimensions of a rectangle.

Example: In the situation above, Jodi is given the perimeter of a rectangle. She also knows that the length is twice as many meters as the width. Using the formula for finding the perimeter of a rectangle, find the dimensions of the rectangle.

The formula for finding the perimeter of a rectangle is $P = 2l + 2w$, where l = length and w = width. You will be given a page of formulas when you take the GED Math Test. A copy of that page is printed for your study on page 340 of this book.

When an item on the GED Math Test describes a figure in words alone, your first step should be to make a quick sketch of the figure. Read the problem carefully, and label your sketch with the information you have been given.

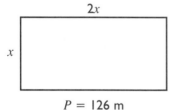

In this case, let x represent the width and $2x$ the length.

Now substitute the information you have into the formula and solve.

$$P = 2l + 2w$$
$$126 = 2(2x) + 2(x)$$
$$126 = 4x + 2x$$
$$126 = 6x$$
$$21 = x$$

> If the width (x) is 21 meters, then the length ($2x$) must be 42 meters.

Answer: The rectangular garden is **21 meters wide** and **42 meters long**.
Check: Make sure the dimensions meet the condition of the problem. Substitute the dimensions into the perimeter formula: $P = 2(21) + 2(42) = 42 + 84 = 126$ meters. The answer is correct.

Another common type of algebra problem involves the denominations of coins and bills. In this type of problem, you are told how many coins or bills there are in all. You are also given the denominations of the coins or bills used and the total amount of money. Your task is to find how many there are of each denomination.

▶▶ Learn how to solve denomination problems by studying this example.

Example: Marisa is taking a cash deposit to the bank. She has $10 bills and $5 bills in a deposit pouch. Altogether, she has 130 bills with a total value of $890. How many bills of each kind are in the pouch?

Let x represent the number of $10 bills in the bag. Next, use the same variable to represent the number of $5 bills. If there are 130 bills in all, then $130 - x$ represents the number of $5 bills.

Now you need to establish a relationship between the number of bills and their value. Using the expression above, the total value of the $10 bills is $10x$, and the total value of the $5 bills is $5(130 - x)$.

Write an equation and solve.

$$10x + 5(130 - x) = 890 \quad \longleftarrow \text{ Multiply both terms in parentheses by 5.}$$
$$10x + 650 - 5x = 890 \quad \longleftarrow \text{ Combine like terms.}$$
$$5x + 650 = 890 \quad \longleftarrow \text{ Subtract 650 from both sides.}$$
$$5x = 240 \quad \longleftarrow \text{ Divide both sides by 5 to get the}$$
$$x = 48 \qquad \text{number of \$10 bills.}$$
$$130 - x = 82 \quad \longleftarrow \text{ Subtract to find the number of \$5 bills.}$$

Answer: There are **48 ten-dollar bills** and **82 five-dollar bills.**
Check: $(48 \times \$10) + (82 \times \$5) = \$480 + \$410 = \$890$. The answer is correct.

SKILL PRACTICE

Solve each problem.

1. The length of a rectangle is 4 inches more than twice its width. If the perimeter of the rectangle is 38 inches, what is its width?

2. The perimeter of a right triangle is 60 cm. Side A is 2 cm less than half of Side B. Side C is 2 cm longer than Side B. Find the lengths of the three sides.

3. A bag contains a total of 200 quarters and dimes. If the total value of the bag's contents is $41.00, how many quarters and how many dimes are in the bag?

4. A school sold 300 tickets to a basketball game. Tickets were $9 for adults and $5 for children. If the total revenue was $2340, how many of each ticket type were sold?

HISTORY **Connection**

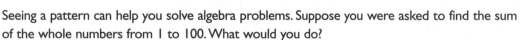

Seeing a pattern can help you solve algebra problems. Suppose you were asked to find the sum of the whole numbers from 1 to 100. What would you do?

In 1787, ten-year-old Carl Gauss was given this problem. As the other students began adding on their slates, Carl solved the problem mentally. Carl observed that by adding the highest and lowest numbers in the sequence and working toward the middle he could find pairs that equaled 101: $1 + 100 = 101$, $2 + 99 = 101, 3 + 98 = 101$, and so on. Carl knew there must be 50 pairings in all. He multiplied 101 by 50 and got 5050, the correct sum. Carl Gauss went on to become a famous mathematician.

Apply Carl's method here. **Find the sum of the even whole numbers from 2 to 40.**

Answers and explanations start on page 330.

PROGRAM 38: Introduction to Algebra

PART ONE DIRECTIONS: Choose the <u>one best answer</u> to each of the following problems. Use a calculator wherever necessary.

Question 1 refers to the following number line.

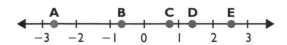

1. The variable x is greater than -2 and less than 0. Which of the points on the number line could be a true value for x?
   - **(1)** A
   - **(2)** B
   - **(3)** C
   - **(4)** D
   - **(5)** E

2. Which expression could be used to find 178 minus the sum of a and $7b$?
   - **(1)** $(a + 7b) - 178$
   - **(2)** $178 - (a + 7b)$
   - **(3)** $-178 + (7b - a)$
   - **(4)** $178 - 7ab$
   - **(5)** $178(a + 7b)$

3. What is the value of $8(-3)(2)(-2)$?
   - **(1)** -96
   - **(2)** -15
   - **(3)** 0
   - **(4)** 15
   - **(5)** 96

Question 4 refers to the following drawing.

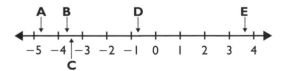

4. On this number line, which point represents $-\frac{25}{7}$?
   - **(1)** A
   - **(2)** B
   - **(3)** C
   - **(4)** D
   - **(5)** E

5. Lin began the month with $1450 in her savings account. She deposited $120 and $340. She transferred $845 to another account. Which expression would be used to find Lin's closing balance?
   - **(1)** $1450 − $120 − $340 + $845
   - **(2)** $1450 + $120 + $340 + $845
   - **(3)** $1450 + $120 + $340 − $845
   - **(4)** $1450 + (−$120) + (−$340) − $845
   - **(5)** $120 + $340 + $845 − $1450

6. Given the equation $a = 4b(c - 5)$, find a when $b = 2$, $c = 11$, and $d = -7$.
   - **(1)** 451
   - **(2)** 252
   - **(3)** 68
   - **(4)** 48
   - **(5)** 40

Question 7 and 8 refer to the following figure.

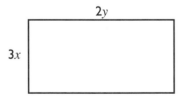

7. Which of the following expressions represents the perimeter of the rectangle?
   - **(1)** $5xy$
   - **(2)** $6xy$
   - **(3)** $3x + 2y$
   - **(4)** $6(x + y)$
   - **(5)** $2(2y) + 2(3x)$

8. If $x = 4$ and $y = 12$, what is the area in square units of the rectangle.
   - **(1)** 36
   - **(2)** 72
   - **(3)** 91
   - **(4)** 288
   - **(5)** 9216

9. What is the value of $-10(5 + 1)^2 - \frac{36}{4}$?
   (1) −369
   (2) −351
   (3) 351
   (4) 591
   (5) 3591

10. Delores has three cats—Rita, Sam, and Thunder. Sam weighs 4 pounds less than Rita, and Rita weighs 3 pounds more than Thunder. Thunder weighs 9 pounds. How much, in pounds, does Sam weigh?
    (1) 4
    (2) 6
    (3) 8
    (4) 10
    (5) 12

11. As a preparation for a marathon race, Eric ran on Monday and Tuesday. On Tuesday, he ran 5 miles less than twice the distance he ran on Monday. If his total distance for the two days was 22 miles, how many miles did he run on Monday?
    (1) 9
    (2) 12
    (3) 13
    (4) 16
    (5) 22

12. The distance from Earth to the star Toofla is 7.6×10^6 light-years away, and the distance from Earth to the star Quiza is 3.8×10^5 light-years away. Which of the following statements would be true regarding the stars' distances from Earth?
    (1) Toofla is 2 times farther than Quiza.
    (2) Quiza is 2 times farther than Toofla.
    (3) Toofla is 10 times farther than Quiza.
    (4) Toofla is 20 times farther than Quiza.
    (5) Toofla and Quiza are equal distances from the Earth.

13. The sum of three consecutive even numbers is 162. What is the greatest of the numbers? (*Hint:* If x represents the first number, then $x + 2$ represents the next consecutive number.)
    (1) 38
    (2) 46
    (3) 52
    (4) 56
    (5) 80

14. This year Celia's father is 39 years old. He is 5 years older than Celia's mother. If C represents Celia's age, which expression could be used to determine how old Celia is?
    (1) $39 = 3C$
    (2) $39 - 5 = 3C$
    (3) $39 = C - 5$
    (4) $39 = \frac{C}{5}$
    (5) Not enough information is given.

Question 15 is based on the following drawing.

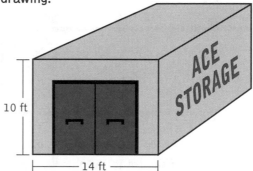

15. The formula for the volume of a rectangular container is $V = lwh$. The volume of the rectangular storage bin shown in the figure is 3500 cubic feet. What is the length of the bin in feet?
    (1) 25
    (2) 35
    (3) 70
    (4) 145
    (5) 250

16. Ricky's coin bank has 150 dimes and nickels, worth a total of $9.00. How many of each coin are in his bank?
    (1) 30 dimes and 120 nickels
    (2) 25 dimes and 130 nickels
    (3) 75 dimes and 75 nickels
    (4) 120 dimes and 30 nickels
    (5) Not enough information is given.

17. The width of Joni's rectangular yard is 3 meters less than half its length. If the perimeter of her yard is 120 meters, which equation could you use to find the length of Joni's yard in meters?
    (1) $x + (\frac{1}{2}x - 3) = 120$
    (2) $2x + 2(\frac{1}{2}x - 3) = 120$
    (3) $\frac{1}{2}x + 2x - 3 = 120$
    (4) $2(x + \frac{1}{2}x + 3) = 120$
    (5) $2x + 2(\frac{1}{2}x) - 3 = 120$

Question 18 refers to the following information.

┌─────────────────────────────────────┐
│   **BARGAIN THEATER TICKET PRICES** │
│   **ALL SHOWS**   │
│   Adults $6.00 • Children $3.00   │
└─────────────────────────────────────┘

18. Bargain Theater sold 100 tickets on Thursday. If the total revenue was $510, how many adult tickets were sold?
    (1) 20
    (2) 30
    (3) 50
    (4) 70
    (5) 80

19. The distance from the equator to the North Pole is about 6.2×10^3 miles. Which of the following numbers expresses the distance in miles in standard form?
    (1) 62
    (2) 620
    (3) 6,200
    (4) 62,000
    (5) 620,000

20. What is the value of y in the equation $7y + 6 = -15$?
    (1) -4
    (2) -3
    (3) -1
    (4) 1
    (5) 3

21. Barbara rode in a bike-a-thon to raise money for charity. She raised $25 for each kilometer that she rode plus $125 in other donations. If she raised $625 in all, how many kilometers did she ride?
    (1) 5
    (2) 20
    (3) 25
    (4) 30
    (5) Not enough information is given.

Question 22 refers to the following figure.

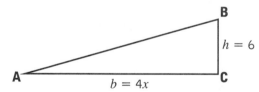

22. The area of △ABC is 72 square inches. What is the measure in inches of side AC? (Hint: Use the formula for finding the area of a triangle: $A = \frac{1}{2}bh$.)
    (1) 3
    (2) 6
    (3) 7.2
    (4) 12
    (5) 24

23. Three more than four times a number (n) is equal to three less than 5 times the number. Which of the following equations could be used to find the value of n?
    (1) $3(4n) = 5 - 3n$
    (2) $4n + 3 = 3n - 5$
    (3) $4n + 3 = 5n - 3$
    (4) $3n + 4 = 5n - 3$
    (5) $3n + 5n = 4 - 3$

Answers and explanations start on page 330.

Visit a loomhouse and find out how weavers create patterns with fiber. Then learn about the importance of patterns in math and how relationships between numbers can be shown on the coordinate plane.

BEFORE YOU WATCH

39

Special Topics in Algebra and Geometry

OBJECTIVES

1. Apply algebraic properties to find and graph the solutions to inequalities.

2. Solve problems involving patterns and functions.

3. Solve problems using the connection between algebra and the coordinate plane.

Based on your traveling speed, have you ever figured out how long it would take you to reach a destination? Have you ever figured out how getting a raise would affect your yearly wages? If you have, you have used algebraic thinking to understand mathematical patterns and functions.

The ability to work with algebra and geometry is important to your success on the GED Math Test. You will need to know how to solve and graph inequalities, recognize patterns and functions, and solve problems using the coordinate plane. Your work in this program will help you gain other math skills in the areas of applying number sense, solving equations, and using formulas.

On the following pages, you will find a brief exercise called *Sneak Preview*. It is designed to introduce you to the topics that will be featured in the video program and the corresponding lesson. After you complete the exercise and check your answers, turn to the vocabulary page. There you will find terms that will help you better understand the video and the lesson that follow. After reviewing page 272, you will be ready to watch Program 39.

For additional practice, visit *LiteracyLink* online at http://www.pbs.org/literacy.

Sneak Preview

This exercise previews some of the concepts from Program 39. After you answer the questions, use the feedback on page 271 to help set your learning goals.

COMMUNITY LINK: J.T. teaches classes on local history at the Piedmont Community Center. He assigns hands-on projects in geography and map reading. This week he is helping some students learn how to interpret the grids on a portion of the Piedmont County map, including symbols, distances, and landmarks.

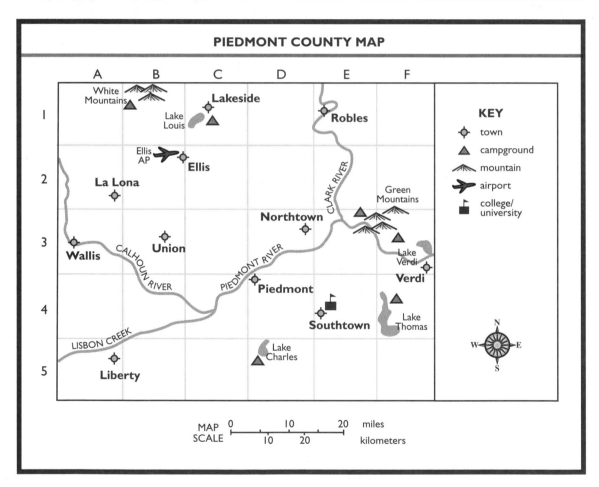

Answer these questions based on the map shown above.

1. J.T. explains that to find a specific grid square such as B-3, you trace your finger down the column labeled *B* and then across the row labeled *3* to the square where the column and row intersect. On this map, what town is shown in B-3?

    (1) Ellie
    (2) Wallis
    (3) Northtown
    (4) Union
    (5) Verdi

2. Carmen, one of J.T.'s students, will be camping in the Green Mountains during spring break. She would like to figure the distance "as the crow flies" (straight from point to point) from the mountains to her hometown. About how many miles is it from the Green Mountains to the town of Union?

   (1) between 3 and 5
   (2) between 30 and 50
   (3) between 50 and 100
   (4) between 200 and 300
   (5) between 300 and 400

3. One of J.T.'s students tells him about another nearby town. The student says that Midvale lies northeast of Piedmont and that the distance to Midvale is less than five miles more than twice the distance from Piedmont to Union. Let u equal the distance from Piedmont to Union. Which of the following inequalities could be written from the student's information about the distance from Piedmont to Midvale (m)?

   (1) $m > 2u + 5$
   (2) $m < 2u - 5$
   (3) $m < 2(u + 5)$
   (4) $m > u + 5$
   (5) $m < 2u + 5$

4. According to J.T.'s map, if you moved southwest from Southtown University, what is the first landmark you would encounter?

   (1) Piedmont
   (2) Northtown
   (3) Lake Charles
   (4) Lake Thomas
   (5) Green Mountains campgrounds

Feedback

- If you got all of the answers right...   you have a basic understanding of how to use grids and evaluate inequalities and distances.

- If you missed question 1...   you need to practice locating points on a coordinate plane.

- If you missed question 2...   you need to work on reading scales and symbols and figuring the distance between two points.

- If you missed question 3...   you need to learn about how to write inequalities.

- If you missed question 4...   you need to work with slope and functions of grids on a coordinate plane.

ANSWERS FOR SNEAK PREVIEW:

1. Choice (4)   2. Choice (2)   3. Choice (5)   4. Choice (3)

Vocabulary for *Special Topics in Algebra and Geometry*

compound inequality	a mathematical statement that combines two inequalities; for example, $3 < x < 10$.
coordinate plane	a flat surface divided by a horizontal number line and a vertical number line in order to form four quadrants, or sections; the number lines intersect at right angles at the point of origin
function	a rule that defines the relationship between two quantities
inequality	a mathematical statement that two expressions or numbers are not equal
linear equation	an equation with two variables and multiple solutions; its solution set forms a line when graphed on a coordinate plane
ordered pair	the pair of coordinates needed to locate a point on the coordinate plane; the coordinates are given in parentheses in the order (x,y)
origin	the point where the x-axis and y-axis cross on a coordinate plane; the coordinates of the point are $(0,0)$
quadratic equation	an equation in which a variable is squared or written to the second power
slope	the measure of the steepness or incline of a line
x-axis	the horizontal number line used to form the coordinate plane
y-axis	the vertical number line used to form the coordinate plane
y-intercept	the point at which the graph of a line crosses the y-axis on a coordinate plane

---

➡ **N O W   W A T C H   P R O G R A M   3 9 :**

This program introduces the coordinate plane and terms such as x-axis, y-axis, ordered pair, and origin. You'll also see how to graph an equation. Use the program as a foundation for additional information provided in the workbook.

After you watch the program, work on:

- pages 273–296 in this workbook
- Internet activities at http://www.pbs.org/literacy

Special Topics in Algebra and Geometry

On the following pages, you will learn more about the ideas discussed in the video program and have an opportunity to develop and practice your GED math skills.

Key Points to Think About

In the video program, you explored:

- How people use a combination of algebra and geometry to find solutions to special types of problems as workers, citizens, and family members.
- How inequalities are used to show the relationship between two expressions or numbers that are not equal.
- Everyday applications of algebra and geometry, such as those that deal with money, distance, and measurement.

On the GED Math Test:

- You will be expected to know how to solve problems involving functions and patterns.
- You should know how to use formulas to solve for the slope of a line and the distance between two points on the coordinate plane.
- You will use algebra and geometry to set up equations and inequalities to solve word problems.

As you work through the lesson for Program 39:

- Think about how the language of mathematics is used to clarify the relationship between numbers and expressions.
- Look for patterns in the examples and exercises, and think about how the properties of algebra are used to solve problems.
- Be aware of opportunities to use algebra and geometry to solve problems in your daily life, not just on the GED Math Test.

GED TIPS

When taking the GED Test, you should:

- Make sure your solution answers the question that was asked in the item. You may need to perform other steps before choosing an answer.
- In many algebra word problems, the information you need most is given last. Read the entire problem before you start to write an equation or inequality.
- Make a sketch and label it before you begin calculations on any problem describing a geometric figure.

Working with Inequalities

WORKPLACE LINK: Lenore is making arrangements for a sales conference. She can spend up to $500 for a conference room and lunch for 40 employees. A hotel charges $170 for a conference room. Using x to represent the cost of one meal, Lenore writes the inequality $170 + 40x \leq 500$ to find out the most she can afford to spend per meal.

Solving Inequalities

An inequality is a mathematical statement that two expressions or numbers are not equal. The symbols below are used to show the relationship between the two sides of an inequality.

Symbol	Meaning	Example	
$<$	is less than	$x < 5$	The variable x is a number less than 5.
$>$	is greater than	$10 > y$	Ten is greater than the value of y.
$\leq$	is less than or equal to	$5 \leq m$	Five is less than or equal to m.
$\geq$	is greater than or equal to	$n \geq -2$	The value of n is greater than or equal to -2.

Inequalities are solved much like equations. Your goal is to isolate the variable on one side of the inequality. To accomplish your goal, you can perform any operation as long as you do it to both sides of the inequality.

▸▸ See how Lenore's inequality is solved using the rules of algebra.

Example: In the situation above, Lenore wrote the inequality $170 + 40x \leq 500$ to find out how much she could afford to spend per meal for the sales conference. Solve for x.

Solve.	$170 + 40x \leq 500$
Subtract 170 from both sides of the inequality.	$170 - 170 + 40x \leq 500 - 170$
	$40x \leq 330$
Divide both sides by 40.	$\frac{40x}{40} \leq \frac{330}{40}$
	$x \leq 8.25$

Answer: Lenore can afford to spend any amount up to and including **$8.25** per meal for the conference guests.

Check: Substitute $8.25 for x in the original inequality.
Since $8.25 makes the cost equal $500, any lesser
amount will bring the total cost in under $500.

$$170 + 40x \leq 500$$
$$170 + 40(8.25) \leq 500$$
$$170 + 330 \leq 500$$
$$500 \leq 500$$

There is one difference between solving equations and solving inequalities. Whenever you multiply or divide both sides of an inequality by a negative number, you must reverse the inequality symbol.

MATHEMATICS

▶▶ Learn when to reverse the inequality symbol when solving an inequality.

Example: Solve the inequality: $-5n + 30 > 75$.

Solve.

Subtract 30 from both sides of the equation.

Divide both sides by -5. Change the inequality
symbol from "greater than" to "less than."

$$-5n + 30 > 75$$
$$-5n > 45$$
$$n < -9$$

Answer: The inequality is true for **any value of n that is less than –9.**

Check: The number -10 is less than -9. Try -10
in the original inequality. The answer makes sense.

$$-5(-10) + 30 > 75$$
$$50 + 30 > 75$$
$$80 > 75$$

Graphing Solutions to Inequalities

We can graph the solution to an inequality using a number line. A gold line is drawn over the portion of the number line that represents possible values for the variable. Study these examples.

$x < -9$

The open circle means that -9 is not included in the set of solutions.

$x \geq 3$

The closed circle means that 3 is included in the set of solutions.

$5 < x < 8$

This is a **compound inequality.** From the graph, we know that the value of x must be *between* 5 and 8. Neither 5 nor 8 is included in the solution set.

SKILL PRACTICE

Solve each inequality and graph the solution on a number line.

1. $x - 2 < 1$

2. $2n + 3 \geq 19$

3. $5d > 20$

4. $-6x > 24$

5. $-3z + 7 \geq 28$

6. $2x - 3 < x - 4$

7. A number n is greater than 2 and less than 7. Graph the solution set for n.

8. A number y is less than 3 and greater than -4. Graph the solution set for y.

Answers and explanations start on page 331.

Using Inequalities to Solve Word Problems

Many life situations can be represented using inequalities. When a problem can have a range of answers, the problem can usually be solved using an inequality.

Follow these steps to write inequalities:

1. Assign a variable to one of the numbers in the problem.
2. Use algebra to show how any other numbers in the problem are related to the variable.
3. Finally, connect the two sides of the inequality using the appropriate symbol: $<$, $>$, $\leq$, or $\geq$.

▶▶ See how to write and solve an inequality in this situation about saving for a large purchase.

Example: Seth wants to save at least $1500 for a down payment on a car. He plans to put part of his earnings each month into savings. What is the smallest amount of money he should plan to set aside each month so that he can reach his goal within a year?

Let x represent the amount he will save each month.

Then $12x$ represents the amount he will save in a year.

His annual savings must be greater than or equal to $1500: $12x \geq 1500$.

Solve:
$$12x \geq 1500$$
$$\frac{12x}{12} \geq \frac{1500}{12}$$
$$x \geq 125$$

Answer: Seth should set a goal of saving at least **$125** per month.
Check: Multiply: $125(12) = 1500$. If Seth saves $125 for 12 months, he will have $1500, which is enough for the down payment on a car.

Is it really necessary to use an inequality to solve this problem? Not really. Most people solve everyday situations like Seth's by using equations and common sense. You know that $125 times 12 *equals* $1500. Using common sense, you know that Seth can save even more if he puts a larger amount in savings each month. Thus, his savings must be *greater than or equal to* $125.

Even though you can use a combination of equations and common sense to solve inequality situations, you will need to know how to write inequalities to do well on the GED Math Test. Some problems will ask you to choose the best way to set up an inequality to solve a problem.

MATHEMATICS

▸▸ For this situation, choose the best set-up using the distance formula.

Example: Sharon is driving from Joplin to Great Bend, a distance of 316 miles. If she drives no faster than 55 miles per hour, which expression could be used to find the time (t) in hours that the trip will take?

(1) $55t < 316$

(4) $55t \geq 316$

(2) $55t > 316$

(5) $55t = 316$

(3) $55t \leq 316$

You're right if you chose **(4) 55t ≥ 316.** To solve the problem, use the formula $d = rt$, where d = distance, r = rate, and t = time in hours. If the rate of speed remains constant at 55 miles per hour, you can solve the problem using the equation $55t = 316$, or $t = \frac{316}{55}$. If Sharon ever drives slower than 55 miles per hour, the trip will take longer: $t \geq \frac{316}{55}$. Working backward, $55t \geq 316$.

SKILL PRACTICE

Solve each problem.

1. Three times a number (x) increased by 8 is greater than 20. Which of the following is a true statement?

   (1) $x \leq 4$ (4) $x < 3$
   (2) $x \geq 3$ (5) $x < 4$
   (3) $x > 4$

2. Mae earns $8.90 per hour. Write an inequality showing the amount of money she can expect to earn in a week if she works 40 or fewer hours per week.

3. A rectangle is 12 inches long, and its area is greater than 48 square inches. Which of the following inequalities can be used to find the width (w) of the rectangle in inches?

   (1) $48 > 12w$
   (2) $48 < 12w$
   (3) $48 \geq 12w$
   (4) $w > 12(48)$
   (5) $w < 12(48)$

PROBLEM SOLVER Connection

How do you graph a compound inequality such as "$x < 7$ <u>or</u> $x > 9$"?

Example: There are two types of jobs Rakseet could take at the parks department. There are jobs working in the gardens for under $7 an hour, depending on experience. Or Rakseet could work in the office and make more than $9 an hour. How would you graph $x < 7$ <u>or</u> $x > 9$?

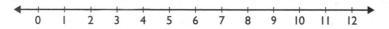

Step 1. Since the symbols $<$ and $>$ are used, draw open circles around each boundary number: 7 and 9.

Step 2. Shade the rays on either side of the boundary numbers. *Note:* A compound inequality that connects with "and" ($b > 3$ <u>and</u> $b < 8$) can be written as one inequality ($3 < b < 8$). One that connects with "or" ($b < 5$ <u>or</u> b > 10) cannot be written as one statement. Think of the "or" statement as saying that the solution lies on one side of a boundary number *or* on the other side of a second boundary number, not *between* the two boundaries as in an "and" statement.

Draw a number line and graph the solution to the inequalities $x < –2$ <u>or</u> $x > 3$.

Answers and explanations start on page 332.

Understanding Patterns and Functions

FAMILY LINK: Arturo's son is having trouble learning the multiplication facts for the number 6. To help him visualize how the multiplication tables work, Arturo writes the numbers from 1 to 100, putting 10 numbers in each row. Then he asks his son to count by 6s and circle every sixth number with a red crayon. Then they look for patterns together.

Recognizing Patterns and Functions

Mathematics can be called the science of patterns. Once you see the pattern in a series of numbers, you can predict what will come next. To recognize patterns, study the order of the numbers and the relationship between each pair of numbers in the series.

▶▶ Look for the pattern in this series of fractions.

Example: What comes next in this series: $\frac{1}{2}, \frac{1}{4}, \frac{1}{8}, \frac{1}{16}, \ldots$?

Study the series. Did you make these observations?

- The fractions decrease in size from left to right.
- Each fraction has the number 1 as the numerator.
- Each denominator is twice the denominator of the fraction on the left.

In fact, moving from left to right, each fraction is $\frac{1}{2}$ the size of the fraction on its left.

$$\frac{1}{2} \cdot \frac{1}{2} = \frac{1}{4} \qquad \frac{1}{4} \cdot \frac{1}{2} = \frac{1}{8} \qquad \frac{1}{8} \cdot \frac{1}{2} = \frac{1}{16} \qquad \frac{1}{16} \cdot \frac{1}{2} = \frac{1}{32}$$

Answer: The next fraction in the series is $\frac{1}{32}$.

A **function** is a rule that defines the relationship between two numbers. The distance formula from the GED formulas page is an example of a function. We say that distance is a function of time. What does this mean? Imagine taking a long car trip and traveling at the average rate of 55 miles per hour. How far will you travel in a day? It depends on how many hours you drive.

▶▶ See how looking for patterns can help you identify a function.

Example: The table below shows the number of hours Lillian worked each day during the week and her earnings for that day. Based on the data, is Lillian's pay a function of the number of hours she works?

Day	Hours Worked	Earnings
Monday	5	$45
Tuesday	4	$36
Wednesday	6	$54
Thursday	7	$63
Friday	8	$72

Put the data in order and look for a pattern. Is there a general rule that ties the hours worked to the earnings?

Answer: Yes, Lillian's pay is a function of the hours worked. Lillian must earn $9 per hour, since the pay is always 9 times the number of hours worked. The function could be written $p = rh$, where p = pay, r = rate, and h = hours.

Graphs are often used to express functions. The graph below shows distance as a function of time when the rate is 6 miles per hour.

See how the line on the graph is used to represent a function.

Example: Payson is in training for a marathon race. Each weekday he runs about 3 miles. On Saturday, he runs between 5 and 10 miles. If his average speed is 6 miles per hour, how long would it take him to run 15 miles?

The horizontal scale represents the time in hours Payson runs. The vertical scale represents the distance he runs. The line shows all the possible pairings between time and distance.

To find how long it would take Payson to run 15 miles, find 15 on the vertical scale and follow it across to the point on the line. Then go straight down from this point to the horizontal scale.

Answer: Payson could run 15 miles in **2.5 hours.** *Check:* Use the distance formula, $d = rt$: $15 = 6t$, so, $t = \frac{15}{6} = 2.5$ hours.

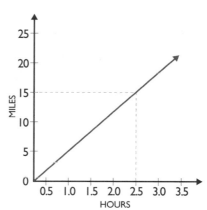

SKILL PRACTICE

For items 1 to 5, write the next number in the series. Then describe the pattern.

1. 8, 15, 22, 29, 36, 43, _____
   Pattern:

2. 1, 3, 6, 10, 15, _____
   Pattern:

3. 1, 3, 2, 4, 3, 5, 4, _____
   Pattern:

4. 1, 4, 9, 16, 25, _____
   Pattern:

5. 1, 1, 2, 3, 5, 8, 13, 21, _____
   Pattern:

For items 6 to 9, describe the function in each situation.

6. The cost of one bottle of craft glue is $1.20. Linda paid $6.00 for 5 bottles.

7. The area of a square with a side measuring 3 cm is 9 sq cm. The area of a square with a side measuring 4 cm is 16 sq cm.

8. The average clothes washer uses 50 gallons of water per load. Three loads use 150 gallons.

9. The cost of shipping on each catalog order is 7% of the merchandise total. The cost of handling is $5. On an order with a merchandise total of $65.00, Edna paid $9.55 for shipping and handling.

Use the graph to answer item 10.

10. Andrea's pay is a function of the value of the goods she sells. Using the graph, what value of goods must Andrea sell to earn $100?

Answers and explanations start on page 332.

Graphing a Function

One way to think about a function is to imagine a machine that carries out a certain mathematical procedure. For example, the machine shown here doubles the number that is put into the machine. We could say that for any number (x), the machine performs the function $2x$.

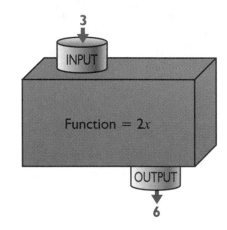

Input Number	Output Number
1	2
2	4
3	6

Graphing a function gives a visual image of how the function works. The graph is also useful for solving problems. On this graph, the horizontal scale shows possible input numbers. The vertical scale shows possible output numbers. The line shows the relationship between the input and output numbers.

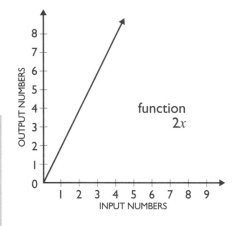

To graph a function:

1. Choose at least three input numbers.
2. Carry out the function and find the output numbers.
3. Plot the results on a graph by placing a dot, or point, at the intersection of each pair of input and output numbers.
4. Finally, draw a line to connect the points.

▸▸ See how to graph a function to find the cost of running a business.

Example: Sheila wants to start a home-based business to make handmade quilts. It will cost $60 for materials to make each quilt. She will need to spend $1000 for equipment. Make a graph to find the cost of making the quilts.

First, write a function rule to describe what is happening in the situation. The cost of equipment is fixed at $1000. The cost per quilt depends on the number of quilts. Let x equal the number of quilts.

The cost of making x quilts is $1000 + $60x$.

Choose three convenient input numbers. For this exercise, use 0, 5, and 10. Make a table of input numbers (number of quilts) and output numbers (cost of making x quilts). Construct a graph with a horizontal scale showing the number of quilts and a vertical scale showing the cost of making x quilts.

Input Number (number of quilts)	Output Number (cost of x quilts)
0	$1000
5	$1300
10	$1600

You can now use the graph to solve problems.

Example: Sheila can afford to spend $1400 on her business. How many quilts can she make for that amount?

Answer: Six quilts.

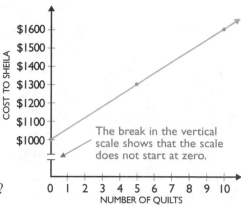

The break in the vertical scale shows that the scale does not start at zero.

COST TO SHEILA

NUMBER OF QUILTS

SKILL PRACTICE

Solve each problem.

1. For each input number x, a function machine multiplies the number by 2 and adds 1.

   a. Write the function as an algebraic expression.

   b. Find the outputs for the input numbers 0, 1, 2, and 3.

   c. Graph the function below.

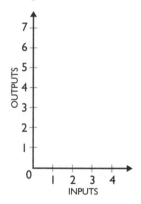

OUTPUTS

INPUTS

2. Sheila plans to charge $400 for each quilt that she makes. She knows that her total revenue (R) will depend upon the number (n) of quilts that she makes. In algebraic language: $R = $ function of $n = 400n$

   a. On a separate sheet of paper, make a graph showing Sheila's total revenue for up to 10 quilts.

   b. Sheila can find her profits by subtracting her costs from her revenue. Use the graph at the top of the page to find Sheila's cost for 10 quilts. Then use the graph you just made to find her revenue. How much will she show in profits after making and selling 10 quilts?

SCIENCE Connection

In this famous sequence (1, 1, 2, 3, 5, 8, 13, 21, . . .), each term in the pattern is the sum of the two previous terms. The mathematician Fibonacci discovered this pattern in 1202 when investigating how rabbits breed! There are many places in nature where patterns reflect this sequence. The bee family tree below exhibits Fibonacci numbers when tracing the ancestors of a male bee. *Note: Male bees have only a female parent (they are born of unfertilized eggs), while female bees have both male and female parents.*

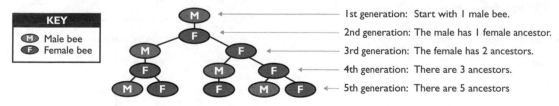

KEY
M Male bee
F Female bee

1st generation: Start with 1 male bee.
2nd generation: The male has 1 female ancestor.
3rd generation: The female has 2 ancestors.
4th generation: There are 3 ancestors.
5th generation: There are 5 ancestors

If you continued the chart, how many bees would be in the 6th and 7th generations?

Answers and explanations start on page 332.

Coordinate Geometry

WORKPLACE LINK: Irene is using a city map to plan a delivery system for her company. She divides the map into four equal sections by drawing a horizontal and a vertical line. Then she draws more lines to form a grid. Each customer's order will have an address and a grid location. The grid locations will help the drivers schedule deliveries and plan their time.

Understanding the Coordinate Plane

The grid below is called the **coordinate plane.** The plane is a flat surface that is divided by two lines into four quadrants. These two axis lines intersect at right angles. The horizontal line is called the **x-axis,** and the vertical line is called the **y-axis.**

The x-axis and y-axis are marked as number lines with positive and negative numbers. Notice that the positive numbers are to the right on the x-axis and upward on the y-axis. The point where the lines intersect is called the **origin,** which is located at zero on both number lines.

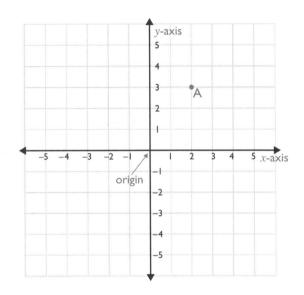

For every point on the grid, there is an address called an **ordered pair** that gives the coordinates for a point. The **x-coordinate** defines the position of the point on the x-axis. The y-coordinate defines the position of the point on the y-axis.

An ordered pair is always given in the order (*x*,*y*). The coordinates for point A are (2,3) because point A is above 2 on the x-axis and to the right of 3 on the y-axis.

▶▶ See how to use the coordinate plane to write the ordered pair for the location of a point.

Example: Write the ordered pairs for points B and C on the system below.

Sometimes the number lines on a grid are not marked. In such cases, count the lines from the point of origin (0,0).

For Point B: Count three spaces to the left of the origin and four spaces up. The x-coordinate is at −3, and the y-coordinate is at 4.

Answer: The ordered pair for point B is (−3,4).

For Point C: Count four spaces to the right of the origin and one space down. Point C is at 4 on the x-axis and at −1 on the y-axis.

Answer: The ordered pair for point C is (4,−1).

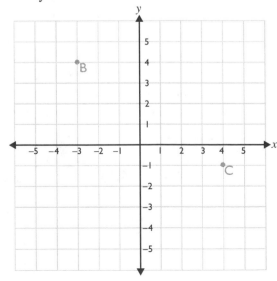

MATHEMATICS

Plotting Points

▶▶ See how to plot a point using its coordinates.

Example: Point D is found at $(-3, -2)$. Plot point D.

Start at the point of origin. Since the x-coordinate is negative, count 3 spaces to the left. The y-coordinate is also negative; count 2 spaces down. Plot the point at the intersection of the lines and label point D.

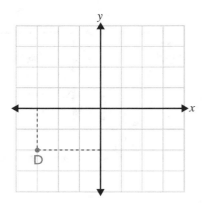

SKILL PRACTICE

Write the coordinates for the points shown on the coordinate system.

1. Point A

2. Point B

3. Point C

4. Point D

5. Point E

6. Point F

7. Point G

8. Point H

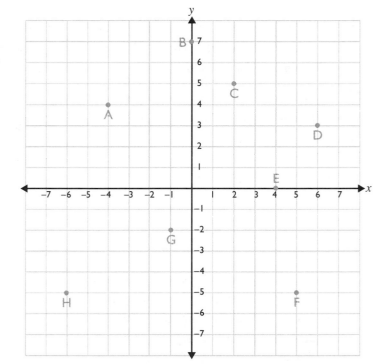

9. Plot the following points on the coordinate system.

   Point J = $(-2, 5)$

   Point K = $(1, 4)$

   Point L = $(-3, 1)$

   Point M = $(0, -6)$

   Point N = $(2, -1)$

10. Answer this question without plotting the points. Point N = $(-1, 3)$ and point P = $(3, -1)$. Do the two points lie in the same quadrant? How do you know?

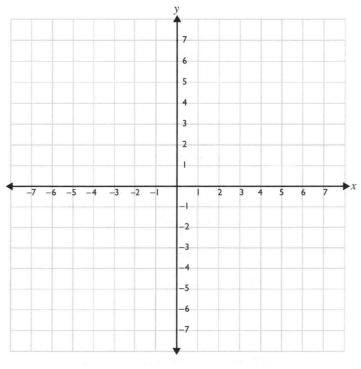

FAMILY LINK: Sadrac is two years older than his sister Lara. When Lara was 5, he was 7. Now that Lara is 8, he is 10. To help him learn a little about algebra, his mother helps him write the equation Sadrac = Lara + 2. Sadrac notices that each time the number for Lara's age changes, his own age changes. He wonders if he could make a graph to show the changes.

Graphing a Line

An equation can have more than one variable. Consider the equation $y = x + 3$. The value of y depends upon the value of x. By substituting different values for x, we can make a table of possible solutions for y. These x and y pairs can be used to write coordinates (x,y).

For the equation: $y = x + 3$ Coordinates:
If $x = 0$, then $y = 3$.   (0,3)
If $x = 1$, then $y = 4$.   (1,4)
If $x = 2$, then $y = 5$.   (2,5)
If $x = 3$, then $y = 6$.   (3,6)

> There is an infinite number of pairs of x and y values that will make the equation true.

We can also substitute negative numbers for x.
If $x = -1$, then $y = 2$ (−1,2)
If $x = -2$, then $y = 1$ (−2,1)

If these coordinates are plotted on a coordinate plane, they form a line. The line extends in both directions without ending. If we find the coordinates of any point on the line, those x and y values are members of the set of solutions for the equation. In fact, the line is the graph of the entire solution set for the equation $y = x + 3$. This type of equation is called a **linear equation** because its graph forms a line.

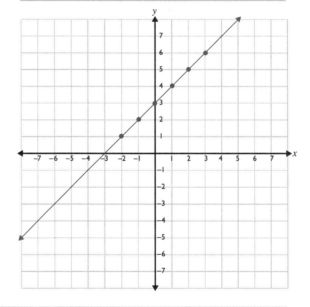

> **To graph a linear equation, follow these steps:**
>
> 1. Make a table of x and y values. Choose three values for x, then solve for y.
> 2. Use the resulting coordinates to plot points on a coordinate plane.
> 3. Draw a line connecting the points.

Apply your understanding of coordinates to graph another linear equation.

Example: Graph the solution to the equation: $y = -2x + 1$.

1. Make a table of values using any three values for x.
   (*Hint:* Although you can draw a line using only two points, finding a third point can help you avoid errors.)

x	y
0	1
2	−3
4	−7

MATHEMATICS

2. Plot the points.

3. Draw a line through the points.

Answer: The solution set to the equation is shown by the graph of the line.
Check: If the three points lie on the same line, you can be confident that you have the graphed the line correctly.

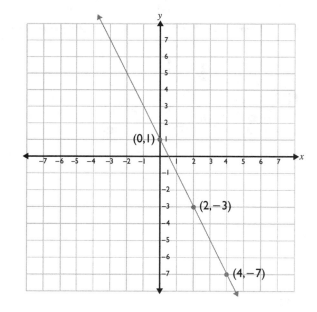

SKILL PRACTICE

Solve each problem.

1. Graph: $y = 2x - 4$.

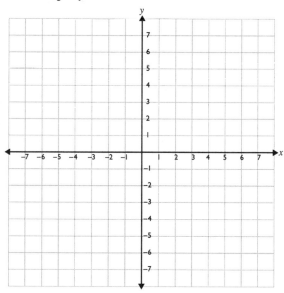

2. Graph: $y = -3x - 1$.

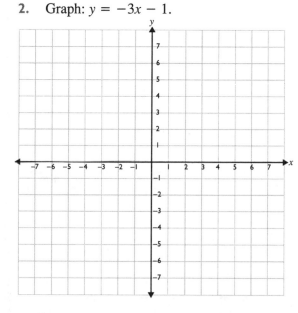

Use the diagram below to answer items 3 and 4.

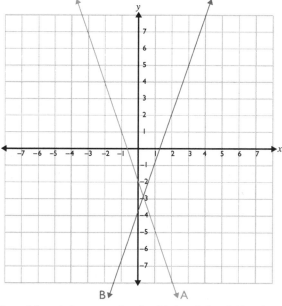

3. Line A is a graph of which of the following linear equations?

   (1) $y = 3x - 2$
   (2) $y = 3x - 4$
   (3) $y = -4x + 3$
   (4) $y = -3x - 2$
   (5) $y = 2x + 5$

4. Which of the following points lies on Line B?

   (1) $(4,3)$ **(4)** $(-2,4)$
   (2) $(3,5)$ **(5)** $(1,-5)$
   (3) $(3,2)$

Answers and explanations start on page 332.

Finding the Slope of a Line

Slope is the measure of the incline, or steepness, of a line. Slope is found by writing a ratio that compares the rise (the change up or down) to the run (the change right or left).

Look at the two ramps shown in the illustration. Both ramps cover the same distance, but the first ramp is much steeper than the second. In other words, the slope of the first ramp is greater than that of the second.

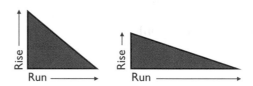

▶▶ See how to use a ratio to define the slope of a line.

Example: Find the slope of the line connecting points A and B.

Place your pencil on point A. To move from A to B, your pencil moves both up and right at the same time. In fact, it moves 4 spaces up as it moves 2 spaces to the right. We can describe the incline of the line by saying that the rise is +4 and the run is +2.

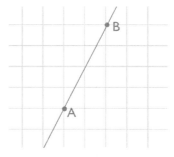

Answer: Written as a ratio, the slope of the line running through points A and B is $\frac{4}{2}$, which equals $\frac{2}{1}$, or 2.

Note: When slope is given as a whole number, the rise equals the whole number, and the run equals 1.

Slope can be positive or negative. On the coordinate plane, a line that goes up as you move from left to right has a positive slope. A line that goes down as you move from left to right has a negative slope.

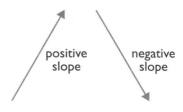

Note: The slope of a horizontal line is always 0. The slope of a vertical line is undefined, which means that we cannot measure its slope.

The GED Formulas Page shows a formula for finding the slope of a line when the coordinates of two points on the line are known.

slope of a line $\qquad m = \frac{y_2 - y_1}{x_2 - x_1}$; where (x_1, y_1) and (x_2, y_2) are two points in a plane

▶▶ See how to use a formula to find the slope of a line.

Example: Find the slope of a line that passes through the points $(-4,6)$ and $(6,1)$.

Assign one ordered pair to be (x_1,y_1) and the other to be (x_2,y_2). Let $(x_1,y_1) = (-4,6)$ and $(x_2,y_2) = (6,1)$.

Use the formula: $m = \dfrac{y_2 - y_1}{x_2 - x_1} = \dfrac{1 - 6}{6 - (-4)} = \dfrac{-5}{10} = \dfrac{-1}{2}$

Answer: The slope of the line is $\dfrac{-1}{2}$. Because the slope is negative, you know that it slopes downward from left to right.

Finding the *y*-Intercept

The **y-intercept** tells where a line crosses the *y*-axis. Knowing the *y*-intercept can be helpful in graphing a line. This graph shows the solution set for the equation $y = \dfrac{-1}{2}x + 4$. As you can see, the line crosses the *y*-axis at the coordinates (0,4).

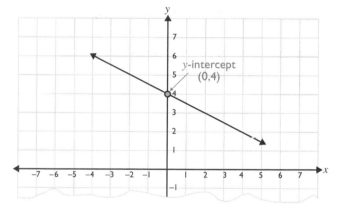

For any linear equation, you can find the *y*-intercept by substituting 0 for *x* and solving for *y*.

Example: Find the *y*-intercept for the line $y = 2x - 1$.

Let $x = 0$.
$$y = 2x - 1$$
$$y = 2(0) - 1$$
$$y = -1$$

Answer: The coordinates for the *y*-intercept are **(0,–1)**.

SKILL PRACTICE

Solve each problem.

1. Using the graph below, write the letter for the line that matches each of the following slopes.

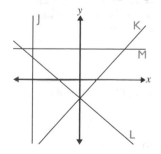

   a. $+\dfrac{3}{2}$

   b. 0

   c. −1

   d. undefined

2. Find the slope of the line that passes through each pair of points.

   a. $(-1,-1)$ and $(5,4)$

   b. $(1,7)$ and $(3,1)$

   c. $(1,-3)$ and $(-4,-3)$

3. For each linear equation, find the *y*-intercept.

   a. $y = x + 2$

   b. $y = \dfrac{-1}{4}x - 5$

   c. $y = 2x + 3$

   d. $y = -3x + 4$

Answers and explanations start on page 333.

Finding the Distance Between Points

Look at the coordinate plane to the right. You can find the distance between points A and B by counting the spaces. Point B is 6 spaces to the right of point A. Now count to find the distance between points B and C. Point C is 8 spaces above point B.

When two points lie on the same horizontal or vertical line, you can find the distance by counting the spaces. However, points A and C do not lie on a horizontal or vertical line. How can you find the distance between them?

One way is to apply the Pythagorean relationship shown on the GED Formulas page:

$c^2 = a^2 + b^2$, where c = hypotenuse, and a and b are the legs of a right triangle

Points A, B, and C, when connected, form a right triangle. You have already measured the lengths of the legs of the triangle. Now use the Pythagorean relationship to solve for the distance between points A and C.

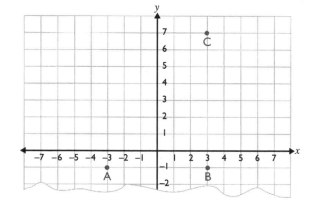

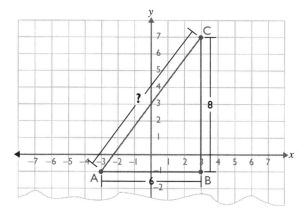

Solve:
$$c^2 = a^2 + b^2$$
$$c^2 = 6^2 + 8^2$$
$$c^2 = 36 + 64$$
$$c^2 = 100$$
$$c = 10$$

> **HINT:** On the GED Math Test, if you are given a graph showing points on a coordinated plane, the best way to find distance between points is to draw a right triangle. Then use the Pythagorean relationship. To review the Pythagorean relationship, see pages 180–181.

Answer: The distance between points A and C is **10.**

Another way to find the distance between two points is to use a formula from the GED formulas page.

distance (d) between $d = \sqrt{(x_2 - x_1)^2 + (y_2 - y_1)^2}$
two points in a plane where (x_1,y_1) and (x_2,y_2) are two points in a plane.

▶▶ Learn how to use the formula to find distance.

Example: The coordinates of two points are (6,4) and (2,1). Find the distance between the points.

Let $(2,1) = (x_1, y_1)$.
Let $(6,4) = (x_2, y_2)$.

Note: You can assign either pair of coordinates to be (x_1, y_1). As you gain experience, you may find that the calculations are simpler if you assign the pair with greater numbers to be the (x_2, y_2) pair.

Use the formula:
$$d = \sqrt{(x_2 - x_1)^2 + (y_2 - y_1)^2}$$
$$d = \sqrt{(6 - 2)^2 + (4 - 1)^2}$$
$$d = \sqrt{4^2 + 3^2}$$
$$d = \sqrt{16 + 9}$$
$$d = \sqrt{25}$$
$$d = 5$$

The square root of 25 can be either $+5$ or -5. However, since we are trying to find actual distance, $+5$ is the answer that makes sense.

Answer: The distance between points $(2,1)$ and $(6,4)$ is **5**.

The distance between two points will not always be a whole number. Suppose you get down to the last step in solving the equation and find that $d = \sqrt{39}$. How can you find the square root of 39?

You can approximate the square root:
Since $\sqrt{36} = 6$ and $\sqrt{49} = 7$, you know that $\sqrt{39}$ is between 6 and 7.

Or you can use your calculator:
Calculator: $\boxed{3}\ \boxed{9}\ \boxed{\sqrt{\ }}$. The display reads: $\boxed{\textbf{6.2449980}}$

> For a review of square roots, turn to page 180.

SKILL PRACTICE

Solve each problem.

Use the coordinate plane to answer items 1 and 2.

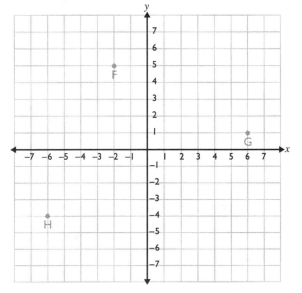

1. Which of the following represents the distance between points F and G?

   (1) between 7 and 8
   (2) between 8 and 9
   (3) between 9 and 10
   (4) between 10 and 11
   (5) between 11 and 12

2. What is the distance between points G and H on the coordinate plane?

   (1) 5   **(4)** 13
   (2) 10   **(5)** 25
   (3) 12

3. To the nearest tenth, what is the distance between points R and S if R is found at $(-2, -6)$ and S is found at $(7, -5)$?
   Hint: Use your calculator.

4. What is the approximate distance between points V and W if V is found at $(-6, -1)$ and W is found at $(2,6)$?

   (1) between 7 and 8
   (2) between 8 and 9
   (3) between 9 and 10
   (4) between 10 and 11
   (5) between 11 and 12

Answers and explanations start on page 333.

FAMILY LINK: Leon's son Kyle is worried about how well he will do on his algebra test tomorrow. Leon suggests a simple strategy for the multiple-choice test. "If you aren't sure of the correct answer for an equation, try each answer choice in the equation until you find the one that makes the equation true."

Finding the Solution to Quadratic Equations

When a variable is squared in an equation, there may be two solutions that make the equation true. For example, in the equation $x^2 = 9$, there is a positive and a negative solution that makes the equation true. Try substituting 3 and -3 for x. Multiplying two negative numbers yields a positive result: $(-3)(-3) = 9$. For the equation $x^2 = 9$, the variable x can equal 3 or -3.

In a **quadratic equation,** the variable is squared. On the GED Math Test, most will take the form $ax^2 + bx + c = 0$, where a, b, and c are integers.

▶▶ Learn to recognize quadratic equations by studying these examples.

Examples: $x^2 + 4x + 3 = 0$ $\qquad$ $x^2 - 3x - 4 = 0$ $\qquad$ $2x^2 + 6x - 8 = 0$

Quadratic equations are solved by factoring. To factor an equation, we look for two expressions that, when multiplied, will equal the equation. The factors of $x^2 + 4x + 3$ are $(x + 3)$ and $(x + 1)$.

To multiply expressions, multiply each term in the second expression by each term in the first expression. Think of the FOIL method. In other words, multiply the terms in this order: **F**irst, **O**utside, **I**nside, **L**ast.

$$(x + 3)(x + 1) = x(x) + x(1) + 3(x) + 3(1) = x^2 + x + 3x + 3 = x^2 + 4x + 3$$

(first, outside, inside, last)

When a quadratic equation equals zero and the factors are known, find the solutions by applying the zero-product rule: Any number multiplied by 0 is 0.

▶▶ Apply the zero-product rule to solve this quadratic equation.

Example: The factors of the equation $x^2 - 3x - 4 = 0$ are $(x + 1)$ and $(x - 4)$. Solve for x.

Since $(x + 1)(x - 4) = 0$, if either $(x + 1)$ or $(x - 4)$ is equal to 0, the entire equation will equal 0. Find the values for x that will make the factors equal 0.

$x + 1 = 0 \qquad x - 4 = 0$
$x = -1 \qquad\ \ x = 4$

Answer: If x is equal to **either -1 or 4,** the equation will be true.

Check: Substitute each solution (-1 and 4) into the original equation.

$x^2 - 3x - 4 = 0$	$x^2 - 3x - 4 = 0$
$(-1)(-1) - 3(-1) - 4 = 0$	$(4)(4) - 3(4) - 4 = 0$
$1 + 3 - 4 = 0$	$16 - 12 - 4 = 0$

Both solutions are correct. $\qquad$ $0 = 0$ $\qquad\qquad\qquad\qquad\qquad$ $0 = 0$

The GED Math Test will probably have no more than one item involving a quadratic equation. To make the best use of your time, you will be better off solving this problem by substituting the answer choices into the equation.

▶▶ See how to substitute answer choices to solve GED Math Test items.

Example: If $x^2 - 3x - 18 = 0$, what does x equal?

  (1) −9 and 2   **(4)** −3 and 6
  (2) −6 and −3   **(5)** −2 and 9
  (3) −6 and 3

Substitute each pairing until you find two solutions that make the equation true. Only values **−3 and 6** for x **(choice 4)** make the equation equal to 0.

SKILL PRACTICE

Solve each problem.

1. If $x^2 + 7x + 12 = 0$, what does x equal?

  (1) −6 and −2   **(4)** −3 and 4
  (2) −6 and 2   **(5)** 3 and 4
  (3) −3 and −4

2. If $x^2 - 2x - 8 = 0$, what does x equal?

  (1) −1 and 8   **(4)** 2 and −4
  (2) −2 and 4   **(5)** 4 and 8
  (3) 1 and −8

3. If $x^2 - 16 = 0$, what does x equal?

  (1) 4 only   **(4)** −4 and 4
  (2) −2 and 8   **(5)** −8 and 2
  (3) −4 only

4. If $x^2 + 4x + 4 = 0$, what does x equal?

  (1) −2 only   **(4)** −1 and 4
  (2) −2 and 2   **(5)** 1 and 4
  (3) −1 and −4

PROBLEM SOLVER Connection

On the GED Math Test, you can use the **guess-and-check method** for any long or difficult multiple-choice problem. Starting with the answer choice that seems most reasonable, substitute answer choices for the unknown in the problem until you find the correct choice. Keep in mind that this approach is time-consuming.

Example: The area of a rectangle is 55 square inches. If the length measures 1 inch more than twice the width, what is the width of the rectangle in inches?

  (1) 1   **(2)** 5   **(3)** 10   **(4)** 11   **(5)** 15

Think through the problem: You know that the width times the length will equal 55 square inches. If x represents the width, then $2x + 1$ represents the length.

Use the expression $2x + 1$ to evaluate the answer choices:
Choice 1: If $x = 1$ inch, then $2x + 1 = 3$ inches. Multiply: $3 \times 1 \neq 55$ square inches.
Choice 2: If $x = 5$ inches, then $2x + 1 = 11$ inches. Multiply: $5 \times 11 = 55$ square inches.
Choice (2) 5 is correct. There isn't any need to go through the remaining choices.

Use guess and check to solve this problem: In the equation $\frac{4}{3}x - 7 = 28 - x$ what does x equal?

  (1) 9   **(2)** 12   **(3)** 15   **(4)** 18   **(5)** 21

PART ONE DIRECTIONS: Choose the <u>one best answer</u> to each of the following problems. Use a calculator wherever necessary.

1. Janet is traveling from Fargo to Willston, a distance of 417 miles. If her speed does not exceed 65 miles per hour, which of the following inequalities could be used to find the amount of time the drive will take? (*Hint:* Use the formula: $d = rt$.)

(1) $65t \geq 417$ **(4)** $t \geq 417(65)$

(2) $65t \leq 417$ **(5)** $t \geq \frac{65}{417}$

(3) $65t < 417$

2. Which of the following is a possible solution for the inequality $3x < 150$?

(1) 56   **(4)** 50

(2) 54   **(5)** 48

(3) 52

<u>Questions 3 and 4</u> are based on the following diagram.

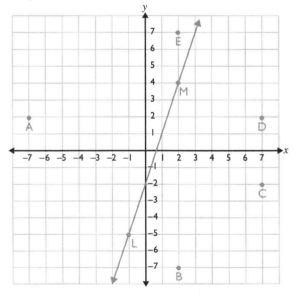

3. Which point has the coordinates $(2, -7)$?

(1) A   **(4)** D

(2) B   **(5)** E

(3) C

4. What is the slope of line LM?

(1) $\frac{1}{4}$ **(4)** 3

(2) $\frac{1}{2}$ **(5)** 4

(3) 2

5. A number x is greater than or equal to -2 and less than 4. Which of the following is a graph of the solution set for x?

(1)
(2)
(3)
(4)
(5)

6. Which of the following solution sets expresses the solutions to $x^2 - 2x - 8$?

(1) -2 and 2   **(4)** -4 and 2

(2) 6 and -8 **(5)** -6 and 8

(3) 4 and -2

<u>Question 7</u> is based on the following figure.

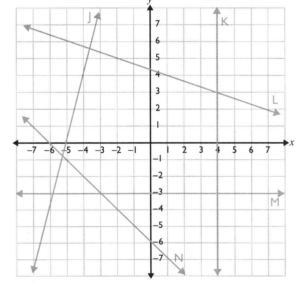

7. Which line has a slope that is undefined?

(1) J   **(4)** M

(2) K   **(5)** N

(3) L

SHARON'S WEEKLY COSTS

(graph: COST IN DOLLARS vs PAIRS OF EARRINGS)

8. Sharon makes and sells bead earrings at craft fairs. The cost of renting a space at a fair is $20.00 per week. Each pair of earrings costs $3.00 to make. If she rents a space, how much will Sharon spend during a week in which she makes 25 pairs of earrings?
   (1) $55
   (2) $75
   (3) $95
   (4) $110
   (5) Not enough information is given.

9. Sharon's weekly cost (C) is a function of the number of earrings (n) she makes. Which of the following equations represents the function shown on the graph?
   (1) $C = 3n - 20$
   (2) $C = 20 + 3n$
   (3) $C = 20 - 3n$
   (4) $C = n^2 - 3n + 20$
   (5) $C = 3n^2 + 20$

10. Which of the following is true when $b = 10$?
    (1) $2b + 3 \le 18$
    (2) $3b + 8 \ge 29$
    (3) $7b - 5 < 49$
    (4) $4b - 8 \le 30$
    (5) $12b + 9 > 135$

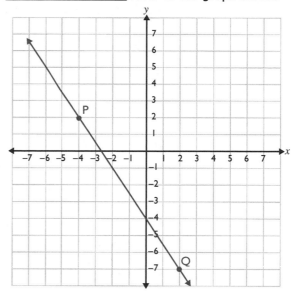

11. Line K passes through points P and Q. What is the approximate distance between P and Q?
    (1) between 7 and 8
    (2) between 8 and 9
    (3) between 9 and 10
    (4) between 10 and 11
    (5) between 11 and 12

12. What is the slope of Line K?
    (1) -5
    (2) $\frac{-3}{2}$
    (3) $\frac{-2}{3}$
    (4) $\frac{2}{3}$
    (5) $\frac{3}{2}$

13. Oscar draws a line to graph the solution set for the equation $y = 3x - 5$. Which of the following points is found on the line?
    (1) $(2, -4)$
    (2) $(1, -3)$
    (3) $(1, 2)$
    (4) $(4, 6)$
    (5) $(3, 4)$

14. If $x^2 + 2x - 3 = 0$, what does x equal?
    (1) -3 and 1
    (2) 3 and -1
    (3) -3 only
    (4) -2 and 3
    (5) 1 and 2

PART TWO DIRECTIONS: Choose the <u>one best answer</u> to each of the following problems.
You may not use a calculator on these problems.

15. Which of the following values is <u>not</u> in the solution set of $12z - 4 > 56$?

(1) 5
(2) 6
(3) 7
(4) 8
(5) 9

16. At Hill's Furniture sale, a love seat can be purchased for half price when a recliner is bought at regular price. Which of the following formulas could be used to find the total cost of the love seat and recliner, when l is the love seat's original price and r is the recliner's price?

(1) $2(l + r)$
(2) $l + 2r$
(3) $\frac{l + r}{2}$
(4) $\frac{l + 2}{r}$
(5) $r + \frac{l}{2}$

17. A line passes through points $(1, -2)$ and $(6, 5)$. Which of the following expressions could be used to find the slope of the line?

(1) $\frac{5 - 2}{6 - 1}$
(2) $\frac{5 - (-2)}{6 - 1}$
(3) $\frac{6 - 5}{1 - (-2)}$
(4) $\frac{6 - 1}{5 - (-2)}$
(5) $\frac{1 - 6}{-2 - 5}$

Questions 18 through 20 are based on the following figure.

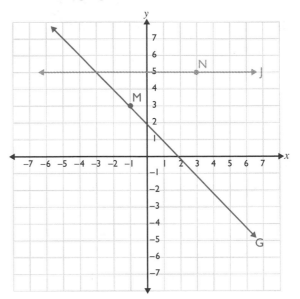

18. Point N lies on Line J, and point M lies on Line G. Which of the following expressions could be used to find the distance from point M to point N?

(1) $\frac{5 - 3}{3 - (-1)}$
(2) $\sqrt{(3 - 1)^2 + (5 - 3)^2}$
(3) $\sqrt{[3 - (-1)]^2 + (5 - 3)^2}$
(4) $\sqrt{[3 + (-1)]^2 + (5 + 3)^2}$
(5) $\sqrt{(3 - 3)^2 + [5 - (-1)]^2}$

19. Line H (not shown) has a y-intercept of -4 and a slope of $\frac{1}{2}$. At which of the following coordinates does Line L intersect Line G?

(1) $(5, -3)$
(2) $(4, -2)$
(3) $(3, -1)$
(4) $(2, 0)$
(5) $(1, 1)$

20. Line J is a graph of the solution set for which of the following equations?

(1) $y = x - 5$
(2) $y = 5x$
(3) $y = -x + 5$
(4) $y = x + 5$
(5) $y = 5$

MATHEMATICS

Answers and explanations start on page 333.

Alternate Math Formats

The questions below are based on the math skills in Programs 38–39. For more information on answering alternate format items, review pages 20–22.

Grid in the answers to questions 21 through 30.

21. Show the location of the point with the coordinates (−4,−3). Mark your answer on the coordinate grid at right.

22. Show the location of the point with the coordinates (5,−1). Mark your answer on the coordinate grid at right.

<u>Questions 23 and 24</u> refer to the following figure.

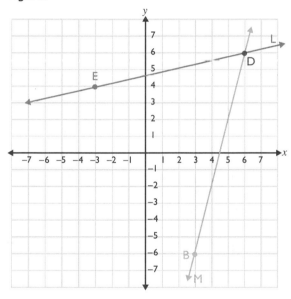

23. Line M passes through point D at coordinates (6,6) and point B at coordinates (3,−6). What is the slope of Line M?

24. Line L passes through points E and D. What is the slope of Line L?

21.

22.

23.

24.

25. Grid in a possible solution for the inequality $2.5 < x < 3.4$.

26. A line has a y-intercept of 2 and passes through a point with the coordinates $(3,5)$. What is the slope of the line?

<u>Questions 27 and 28</u> **refer to the following figure.**

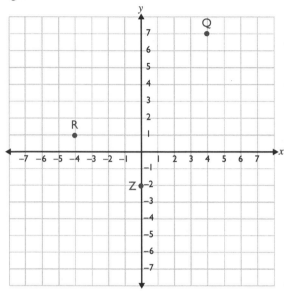

27. What is the distance between points Q and R?

28. What is the distance between points R and Z?

<u>Question 29</u> **refers to the following figure.**

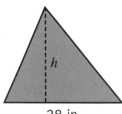

28 in

29. The area of the triangle is 336 square inches. What is the measure in inches of the height (h) of the triangle?

30. Given the equation $4x = 7y - 5z$, find the value of y if $x = 9$ and $z = 4$.

25.

26.

27.

28.

29.

30.

Math Practice Test—Part I

Write your answers on the answer sheet provided on page 303. You may use a calculator for any of the items in Part I, but some of the items may be solved more quickly without a calculator.

Some of the questions will require you to use a formula. The formulas you may need are given on page 340. Not all of the formulas on this page will be needed.

DIRECTIONS: Choose the <u>one best answer</u> for each question.

1. Onyeka's new computer cost $1768 (including tax). She paid $250 down and agreed to pay the balance in 24 monthly payments. How much will she pay each month?
   - **(1)** $147.33
   - **(2)** $84.08
   - **(3)** $73.67
   - **(4)** $63.25
   - **(5)** $10.42

Question 2 refers to the following drawing.

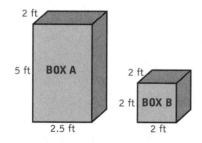

2. A moving company uses two sizes of cardboard boxes. Which of the following expressions could be used to find how many more cubic feet Box A holds than Box B?
   - **(1)** $5(2.5) - 2^2$
   - **(2)** $5(2.5)(2) - 2^3$
   - **(3)** $(5 + 2.5 + 2) - (2 + 2 + 2)$
   - **(4)** $(5 - 2)(2.5 - 2)$
   - **(5)** $5^3 - 2^3$

3. Kyle has his own painting business. He charges $3000 to paint a two-story home. Kyle will spend $\frac{1}{5}$ of the money on paint and supplies and $\frac{1}{3}$ to pay his assistants. What fraction of the money will he have left?
   - **(1)** $\frac{1}{8}$
   - **(2)** $\frac{7}{15}$
   - **(3)** $\frac{8}{15}$
   - **(4)** $\frac{7}{8}$
   - **(5)** $\frac{14}{15}$

4. Which of the following expressions is the equivalent of $-12 + 4(-5a - b)$?
   - **(1)** $-12 - 20a - 4b$
   - **(2)** $-12 - 20a + 4b$
   - **(3)** $-12 - 20ab$
   - **(4)** $40a + 8b$
   - **(5)** $-40a - 8b$

Question 5 refers to the following information.

TICKET CENTRAL Numbers of Tickets Sold by Event Type			
Month	**Concerts**	**Plays**	**Sporting Events**
May	5,428	4,312	10,672
June	6,350	5,971	12,985
July	12,642	9,820	15,738
Aug.	10,910	7,654	13,014
Sept.	9,852	11,056	16,931

5. Ticket Central sells tickets to concerts, plays, and sporting events. What was the company's mean ticket sales to sporting events for the 5-month period?
   - **(1)** 69,340
   - **(2)** 30,667
   - **(3)** 13,868
   - **(4)** 13,014
   - **(5)** 4,622

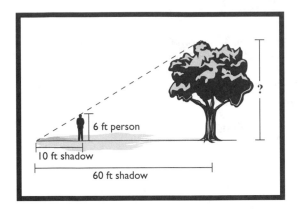

Note: Diagram is not drawn to scale.

6. Henry wants to find the height of the tree in his front yard. With his son's help, he measures the length of his shadow at 4 P.M. At the same time he measures the shadow cast by the tree. Using the information from the drawing, find the height of the tree.
   (1) 100
   (2) 40
   (3) 36
   (4) 15
   (5) Not enough information is given.

Question 7 refers to the following information.

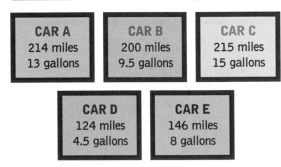

CAR A	CAR B	CAR C
214 miles	200 miles	215 miles
13 gallons	9.5 gallons	15 gallons

CAR D	CAR E
124 miles	146 miles
4.5 gallons	8 gallons

7. Becca wants to buy a car that gets good gas mileage. The information above shows how many miles five different cars can drive on a given number of gallons of gasoline. Which car gets the greatest number of miles per gallon of gasoline?
   (1) Car A
   (2) Car B
   (3) Car C
   (4) Car D
   (5) Car E

Question 8 refers to the following information.

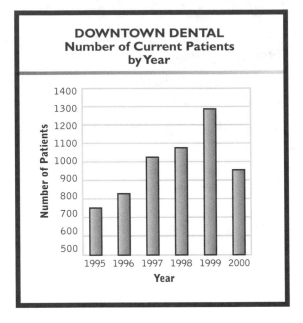

8. Downtown Dental has been in business since 1995. The graph shows the number of patients who visited the clinic each year. In which year was there an increase in patients of approximately 25% from the year before?
   (1) 1996
   (2) 1997
   (3) 1998
   (4) 1999
   (5) 2000

9. At a bicycle factory, Matt can build a brake assembly in 18 minutes. Which of the following expressions could be used to find how many <u>hours</u> of work it will take Matt to complete 25 brake assemblies?
   (1) $18(25)(60)$
   (2) $\frac{(60 \div 18)}{25}$
   (3) $\frac{60(25)}{18}$
   (4) $\frac{25}{18(60)}$
   (5) $\frac{18(25)}{60}$

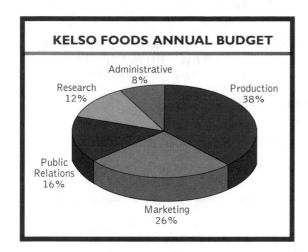

KELSO FOODS ANNUAL BUDGET

Administrative 8%
Research 12%
Production 38%
Public Relations 16%
Marketing 26%

10. What percent of the annual budget is left after marketing and research expenses are paid?

(1) 38%
(2) 62%
(3) 72%
(4) 74%
(5) 88%

Question 11 refers to the following figure.

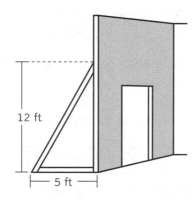

12 ft

5 ft

11. Community members are building a set for a play. The 16-foot-high walls must have a diagonal brace to keep the walls from swaying. Using the measurements given in the diagram, what is the length in feet of the brace?

(1) 12
(2) 13
(3) 17
(4) 30
(5) Not enough information is given.

12. The distance between Santa Fe and Roswell is 185 miles. If the two cities are $4\frac{5}{8}$ inches apart on a map, how many inches would represent 30 miles on the same map?

Mark your answer in the circles in the grid on your answer sheet on page 303.

13. Show the location of a point with the coordinates $(1, -4)$.

Mark your answer on the coordinate plane grid on your answer sheet on page 303.

Math Practice Test—Part II

You may not use a calculator for the questions in Part II. Some of the questions will require you to use a formula. The formulas you may need are given on page 340. Not all of the formulas on this page will be needed.

DIRECTIONS: Choose the <u>one best answer</u> for each question.

Question 16 refers to the following figure.

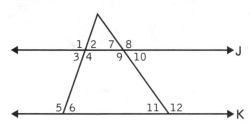

14. The Grahams, the Suddeths, and the Bowens went to an amusement park. Together, the families spent $350. The Grahams spent $100 less than the Suddeths, and the Suddeths spent twice as much as the Bowens. Which of the following equations could be used to solve for the amount the Bowens spent (x)?
    - **(1)** $x + 2x - 100 = 350$
    - **(2)** $3x = 350$
    - **(3)** $x + 2x + 2x = 350 - 100$
    - **(4)** $x + 2x + (2x - 100) = 350$
    - **(5)** $\frac{x + 2x + (2x - 100)}{3} = 350$

16. In the figure, lines J and K are parallel. If $\angle 5$ measures 107°, what is the measure of $\angle 12$?
    - **(1)** 73°
    - **(2)** 107°
    - **(3)** 120°
    - **(4)** 146°
    - **(5)** Not enough information is given.

Question 15 refers to the following drawing.

17. Two lines intersect at the coordinates $(-4, -5)$. Show the location of the point.

    Mark your answer on the coordinate plane grid on your answer sheet on page 303.

15. A container holds 16 marbles as shown in the drawing. To play a game, a marble is drawn at random from the container and replaced. For four consecutive turns, a black marble is drawn. What is the chance that a white marble will be drawn next?
    - **(1)** $\frac{1}{3}$
    - **(2)** $\frac{1}{2}$
    - **(3)** $\frac{2}{3}$
    - **(4)** $\frac{3}{4}$
    - **(5)** $\frac{9}{10}$

Question 18 refers to the following figure.

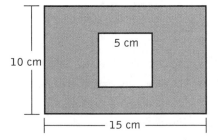

18. A square piece is cut from a rectangular piece of plastic. What is the area in square centimeters of the remaining portion of the plastic (the shaded portion of the figure)?

    Mark your answer in the circles in the grid on your answer sheet on page 303.

Questions 19 and 20 refer to the following information.

A grocery store is open 24 hours a day. The manager wants to find the typical amount shoppers spend between the hours of 10 P.M. and 6 A.M. The manager programs the registers to keep track of every 20th purchase until she has 25 items of data. She then records the information on the frequency table below.

SHOPPERS' TOTAL BILLS Between 10 P.M. and 6 A.M.	
$1–$20	XXXX
$21–$40	XXXXXXXXX
$41–$60	XXXXX
$61–$80	XXXX
$81–$100	XX
$101–$120	
$121–$140	
$141–$160	X

19. The manager decides that the median amount will best represent the data. Which of the following ranges includes the median grocery purchase?
   (1) $1–$20
   (2) $21–$40
   (3) $41–$60
   (4) $61–$80
   (5) $141–$160

20. What percent of the shoppers spent $61 or more during the hours included in the sampling?
   (1) 7%
   (2) 12%
   (3) 28%
   (4) 39%
   (5) Not enough information is given.

21. Kay Lynn bought a bedroom set from a friend for $700. She agreed to pay the amount owed plus 8% annual simple interest in 9 months. Which of the following expressions could be used to find the total amount she will pay her friend in nine months?
   (1) $700 \times 0.08 \times \frac{3}{4}$
   (2) $700 \times 0.08 \times 9$
   (3) $700 + (700 \times 8 \times \frac{3}{4})$
   (4) $700 + (700 \times 0.08 \times 9)$
   (5) $700 + (700 \times 0.08 \times \frac{3}{4})$

Question 22 refers to the following figure.

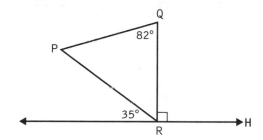

22. Point R of $\triangle$PQR lies on Line H. What is the measure of $\angle$QPR?
   (1) 43°
   (2) 55°
   (3) 63°
   (4) 98°
   (5) 145°

23. If $a = -2$ and $b = 3$, what is the value of $\frac{a^3 + b^2}{2(b - a)}$?
   (1) $-\frac{1}{2}$
   (2) $-\frac{1}{10}$
   (3) $\frac{1}{10}$
   (4) $\frac{1}{2}$
   (5) $1\frac{7}{10}$

Question 24 refers to the following information.

3, 6, 5, 10, 9, 18, 17, . . .

24. If the pattern continues, what will be the tenth number in the series?
    (1) 34
    (2) 42
    (3) 54
    (4) 65
    (5) 66

Question 25 refers to the graph below.

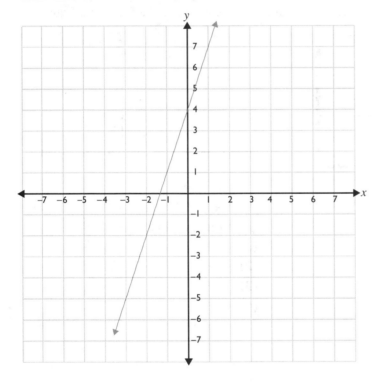

25. Which of the following values represents the slope of the line shown above?
    (1) −4
    (2) −3
    (3) 0
    (4) $\frac{1}{3}$
    (5) 3

Math Practice Test Answer Sheet

Part I

1. ① ② ③ ④ ⑤
2. ① ② ③ ④ ⑤
3. ① ② ③ ④ ⑤
4. ① ② ③ ④ ⑤
5. ① ② ③ ④ ⑤
6. ① ② ③ ④ ⑤
7. ① ② ③ ④ ⑤
8. ① ② ③ ④ ⑤
9. ① ② ③ ④ ⑤
10. ① ② ③ ④ ⑤
11. ① ② ③ ④ ⑤

12. (grid-in answer box: / / / with decimal points and digits 0–9)

13. (coordinate grid answer area, x and y axes labeled −6 to 6)

Part II

14. ① ② ③ ④ ⑤
15. ① ② ③ ④ ⑤
16. ① ② ③ ④ ⑤

17. (coordinate grid answer area, x and y axes labeled −6 to 6)

18. (grid-in answer box: / / / with decimal points and digits 0–9)

19. ① ② ③ ④ ⑤
20. ① ② ③ ④ ⑤
21. ① ② ③ ④ ⑤
22. ① ② ③ ④ ⑤
23. ① ② ③ ④ ⑤
24. ① ② ③ ④ ⑤
25. ① ② ③ ④ ⑤

Math Practice Test Answers and Explanations
Part I

1. **(4) $63.25** Subtract the down payment from the total cost of the computer:
   $1768 − $250 = $1518. Divide by 24 to find the amount of each monthly payment:
   $1768 ÷ 24 = $63.25.

2. **(2) 5(2.5)(2) − 2³** Use the formula for finding the volume of a rectangular container
   ($V = lwh$) and the formula for finding the volume of a cube ($V = s^3$). Substitute the values into
   the formulas, and subtract the volume of the cube from the volume of the rectangular container.

3. **(2) $\frac{7}{15}$** Add $\frac{1}{5}$ and $\frac{1}{3}$ to get $\frac{8}{15}$. Subtract 8/15 from 1 (or $\frac{15}{15}$) to find the fraction that
   is left: $\frac{15}{15} - \frac{8}{15} = \frac{7}{15}$.

4. **(1) −12 − 20a − 4b** The number 4 is multiplied by both of the terms in the parentheses.
   Remember to use the distributive property first to remove the parentheses. The expression
   cannot be simplified further.

5. **(3) $13,868** Add the numbers in the sporting events column and divide by 5:
   10,672 + 12,985 + 15,738 + 13,014 + 16,931 = 69,340, and 69,340 ÷ 5 = 13,868.

6. **(3) 36** Since the angle of the sun is the same for both Henry and the tree, two similar
   right triangles are formed. Set up a proportion and solve for the tree's height: $\frac{6}{10} = \frac{x}{60}$.
   Cross multiply: 6(60) = 10x, 360 = 10x, and $x = \frac{360}{10} = 36$.

7. **(4) Car D** Find the mileage (unit rate) for each car by dividing the number of miles driven by
   the number of gallons of gasoline used. Then compare the results:

   Car A: 16.5
   Car B: 21.1
   Car C: 14.3
   Car D: 27.6
   Car E: 18.25

   The greatest mileage is for Car D: 27.6 miles per gallon.

8. **(2) 1997** First, notice that the graph does not start at zero. You cannot solve the problem by
   looking at the heights of the bars alone. To solve the problem, estimate the height of each bar
   and divide by 4 to get 25%. Then add the amount represented by 25% and see if it matches
   the next year's bar. In 1996, the company has about 820 patients. 25% of 820 is 205.
   Add: 820 + 205 = 1025, approximately the height of the bar for 1997. The 25% increase
   occurred in 1997.

9. **(5) $\frac{18(25)}{60}$** Multiply the time for one brake assembly (18) by the number of brake assemblies
   (25). This will give the total minutes. Since 60 minutes = 1 hour, divide the product of 18 and
   25 by 60 to convert the time to hours.

10. **(2) 62%** The entire circle represents 100%. Add the percents for marketing and research and
    subtract from 100%: 26% + 12% = 38%, and 100% − 38% = 62%.

11. **(2) 13** Use the Pythagorean relationship to find the length of the brace:
    $c^2 = a^2 + b^2$
    $c^2 = 5^2 + 12^2$
    $c^2 = 25 + 144$
    $c^2 = 169$
    $c = \sqrt{169} = 13$

12. **0.75** or **.75** or $\frac{3}{4}$

Set up a proportion and solve:
$x:30 = 4\frac{5}{8}:185$. Change the fractions to decimals and do the work quickly on your calculator. $\frac{5}{8} = 0.625$, so $4\frac{5}{8} = 4.625$.

$$\frac{x}{30} = \frac{4.625}{185}$$

Cross multiply and divide:
$30 \times 4.625 \div 185 = 0.75$ or $\frac{3}{4}$ inch

13. Your answer is correct if you marked the coordinate plane grid as shown.

Part II

14. (4) $x + 2x + (2x - 100) = 350$ If x represents the amount the Bowens spent, then $2x$ represents the amount the Suddeths spent. The Grahams spent $2x - 100$. The sum of the three expressions is equal to 350.

15. (2) $\frac{1}{2}$ Since the marble is replaced, the probability of the current event does not depend on what happened before. There are 8 white marbles and 8 black marbles, so the chance of drawing a white marble is $\frac{8}{16}$, or $\frac{1}{2}$.

16. (5) Not enough information is given. Two legs of the triangle form transversals of parallel lines J and K. Knowing the measure of $\angle 5$, we can deduce that the measure of $\angle 6$ is 73°. Using this information, we can deduce the measures of $\angle 1$, $\angle 2$, $\angle 3$, and $\angle 4$. However, to find the remaining angles, we need to know either the measure of one of the angles formed by the rightmost transversal, or we need to know the measure of the unmarked interior angle of the triangle. We do not have enough information to solve the problem.

17. Your answer should appear as shown on the coordinate grid below.

18. 125

The area of the rectangle is 10(15) = 150 square cm.
The area of the square is 5^2 = 25 square cm.
Subtract: 150 − 25 = 125 square cm.

19. **(2) $21–$40** Since there are 25 values on the chart, the median (or middle) value must be the 13th. Counting from either the lowest to the highest or the highest to the lowest, find the 13th value. It is in the row labeled $21–$40.

20. **(3) 28%** Seven out of the 25 values are for $61 or more. $\frac{7}{25} = 0.28 = 28\%$. You can do the math mentally by thinking; "25 represents 100%. Since I need to multiply 25 by 4 to make it equal 100, I can multiply 7 by 4 to find the percent: $7 \times 4 = 28$."

21. **(5) 700 + (700 × 0.08 × $\frac{3}{4}$)** Use the formula for finding simple interest. The rate 8% must be expressed as a decimal, and the time 9 months must be expressed in terms of years: 9 months = $\frac{3}{4}$ year. The expression $700 \times 0.08 \times \frac{3}{4}$ is equal to the amount of interest Kay Lynn will owe, but she must pay her friend the amount borrowed plus the interest: $700 + (700 \times 0.08 \times \frac{3}{4})$.

22. **(1) 43** Side QR meets line h at a right angle (shown by the corner symbol in the diagram). Therefore, $\angle$PRQ is a complementary angle to the angle measuring 35°. $\angle$PRQ = 90 − 35° = 55°. You know that the sum of the interior angles of a triangle equals 180°. Solve the equation $\angle$PRQ + $\angle$PQR + $\angle$QPR = 180°: 55° + 82° + x = 180°. 137° + x = 180° and x = 43°.

23. **(3) $\frac{1}{10}$** Substitute the values and solve: $\frac{a^3 + b^2}{2(b-a)} = \frac{-8 + 9}{2(5)} = \frac{1}{10}$.

24. **(5) 66** The pattern alternately multiplies by 2 and subtracts 1. Continuing the pattern, we get 34, 33, 66, 65, and so on. The tenth number is 66.

25. **(5) 3** Use the formula for finding the slope (m) of a line.

$$m = \frac{y_2 - y_1}{x_2 - x_1}$$

$$m = \frac{-2 - 1}{-2 - (-1)}$$

$$m = \frac{-3}{-1} = +3$$

Using Your Practice Test Results

Circle your incorrect answers in Column 1 below. Read across. Column 2 tells you which skills you may still need to work on. Column 3 tells you which program you can use to study those skills.

Practice Test Questions	Skills Tested	Program
9	number sense, estimation, problem solving, multi-step word problems	28, 29
1, 7	understanding decimals, decimal applications	30
3	operations with fractions, problem solving with fractions	31
6, 8, 12, 20	ratio, proportion, and percent	32
18	standard English measurements, metric measurements, finding perimeter and area	33
2, 21	using formulas to solve problems, solving for other variables, using geometry formulas	34
11, 16, 22	working with lines, angles, triangles, and circles	35
5, 10, 19	reading tables, charts, and graphs; understanding data; mean, median, and mode	36
15	using data to draw conclusions, understanding chance, applying probability	37
4, 13, 14, 17, 23, 24, 25	signed numbers, expressions, equations, inequalities, patterns and functions, coordinate geometry	38, 39

Answer Key

PROGRAM 27: PASSING THE GED MATH TEST

GED Practice, page 16

(5) $131

Press: [1][5][+][2][2][+][9][4][=]

The display reads: | 131. |

GED Practice, page 17

(3) $1,428

Press: [2][3][8][×][6][=]

The display reads: | 1428. |

GED Practice, page 18

(5) $130

Press: [1][1][×][8][=][M+][7][×][6][=][M+][MR]

The display reads: | 130. |

GED Practice, page 19

1. **(4) $36**

   Press: [1][2][0][×][3][0][%]

   The display reads: | 36. |

2. **(3) between 6 and 7**

   Press: [4][2][√]

   The display reads: | 6.480740698 |

The whole-number part of the number is 6.
The decimal part represents a fractional amount. The square root of 42 is between 6 and 7.

GED Practice, page 20

Your grid may be slightly different. Remember, your answer can start in any column. For item 3, you do not have to show the leading 0 on the grid.

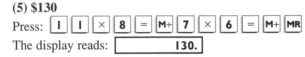

GED Practice, page 21

1.–4. You should have plotted the following points.

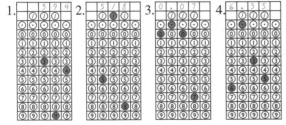

GED Practice, page 22

You should have graphed the point with coordinates (−4,1).

PROGRAM 28: NUMBER SENSE

Your Approach to Learning Math
Skill Practice, page 29

1. Your answer may vary. Sample answer:
   figuring the tip at a restaurant
   figuring out how much is left in the
      checking account
   buying groceries
   putting gas in the car
   shopping around to find the best price for
      pet supplies

2. Your answer may vary. Sample answer:
   d. I separate items into groups that cost about $10
      and add them.

3. Your answer may vary. Sample answer:
   d. I move the decimal point to find 10%,
      double it to get 20%, and then round down
      to the nearest quarter. I figure the amount
      is pretty close to 15%.

4. Your answer may vary. Sample answer:
   d. I make a list of instructions, but I always
      ask my friend for landmarks that will help me
      know if I have gone too far or the wrong way.

Understanding Our Number System
Skill Practice, page 31

1. five hundred
2. six million
3. one thousand
4. four hundred million
5. sixty
6. nine hundred thousand
7. −5
8. $+3\frac{1}{8}$
9. −100 ft
10. **(4) John has done more than he has left
    to do.** John has done 75%. If the whole job
    is 100%, John has 25% left to do. The only
    true statement is choice (4).

Skill Practice, page 33

1. False
2. True
3. True
4. True
5. False
6. True
7. **(5) ticket, hotel, food, car, parking**
Compare the place values of the digits from left to right. The correct order is $437.82, $238, $97.08, $87.52, and $15.
8. **(2) between $800 and $1,000**
Round to the hundreds place and add:
$400 + $200 + $100 + $100 + $0 = $800.

Estimating

Skill Practice, page 35

1. **(2) between 350 and 550** Using front-end estimation, think: $40 \times 9 = 360$. Using rounding, think: $50 \times 10 = 500$. Either way the answer is choice (2).
2. **(2) 2,000 miles** Estimate:
$400 + 500 + 200 + 700 + 200 = 2,000$
3. **(5) $100,000 − $8,000** To use front-end estimation, use the value of only the first digit. Don't round.
4. **(3) $27,000 + $28,000** $26,948 rounds to $27,000, and $28,125 rounds to $28,000.

Skill Practice, page 37

1. **(3) between $425 and $550**
Think: 96 is nearly 100. $100 \times $5 = 500, or $100 \times $5.25 = 525.
2. **(3) $7,384** Using front-end estimation: $900 \times 8 = $7,200$. The only answer choice close to this estimate is choice (3).

GED Practice, pages 38–40

1. **(1) All of these numbers can be divided evenly by 3.** Remember that any even number can be divided evenly by 2; any number ending in 5 or 0 can be divided evenly by 5; any number ending in 0 can be divided evenly by 10. However, only if the sum of the digits in a number is a multiple of 3 can the number be divided evenly by 3. (For example, the sum of the digits in $24 = 2 + 4 = 6$, which is a multiple of 3.)
2. **(3) Thorton and Winslow** Compare the values of the 1990 populations with the 2000 populations. Only Thorton's and Winslow's went down, or decreased.
3. **(5) Payson** Compare the values of the 1990 populations with the 2000 populations. Only Payson, Sunnydale, and Ft. James show increases. Mentally round the numbers to the thousands place and find the differences. Payson's population increased by about 8000. Sunnydale's increased by about 4000, and Ft. James's increased by about 1000. Payson's increase was greatest.

4. **(2) 38,000** Round to the nearest thousand by looking at the digit immediately to the right of the thousands place: 3. Since 3 is less than 5, change it and the remaining digits to the right of it to 0.
5. **(3) Winslow** Winslow's population in 1990 was 4009, which is about 4000 people. Winslow's population in 2000 was 3997, which is also about 4000 people.
6. **(4) One thousand eighty-five** Look carefully at the place value of each digit. Since zero occupies the hundreds place, there are no hundreds in the number.
7. **(2) between 150 and 325** Using front-end estimation, $20 \times 8 = 160$. Using rounding, 28 *yukata* round to 30. Multiply: $30 \times 8 = 240$, which is between 150 and 325.
8. **(2) 4 × $3.00** Each of the boxes of chocolates costs *about* $3, so the total would be about $4 \times 3.00.
9. **(5) 5000 ÷ 50** Marie could round $5106 to the nearest thousand (5000) and $55 to the nearest ten (50).
10. **(4) $200** Round 198 to the nearest ten. The digit to the right of the tens place is 8, so round up the 9 to the next largest number, 10, which turns 198 to 200. (200 also happens to be the nearest hundred.)
11. **(1) 3** The digit 3 is in the millions place and has a value of 3 million.
12. **(1) $2,356 − $1,884** To solve this problem, you would subtract the smaller number from the larger number.
13. **(4) 1,700,000** Round down from 1,742,000, because 4 is less than five. That the 1994 figure was 10,000 fewer voters is irrelevant to this problem.
14. **(4) Lawson's, Way's Photos, Shoe Tree, Café Ritz** You can write 1, 2, 3, and 4 next to the businesses as you compare the amounts donated. Note that the problem says "from largest to smallest."
15. **(3) $1,087** Round $30,430 to $30,000; round 28 to 30 and divide: $30,000 ÷ 30 = $1,000$. Choice (3) is the most reasonable.
16. **(4) 7, 14, 21, 28, 35, _____** Consider each pattern. In choice (1), the pattern increases by 1, so the next number should be 12. In choice (2), the pattern increases by 6, so the next number should be 36. In choice (3), the pattern increases by 4, then 5, then 6, and so on. The next number should be 33. In choice (4), the pattern increases by 7, so the next number should be 42. In choice (5), the pattern increases by 8, so the next number should be 52. Only choice (4) is correct.

17. **(3) 262,000 sq mi** The digit 1 is in the thousands place of the number 261,914. The digit to the right is 9. Add 1 to the thousands place and replace the digits to the right with zeros. The number 261,914 rounds to 262,000.

18. **(4) 8 hundred thousand** The place value for 8 in this number means $8 \times 100,000$, or 800,000.

19. **(4) $5,000 − $4,000** Use front-end estimation by looking only at the value of the first digit. Subtract the smaller number from the larger.

20. **(2) less than Karen Hall.** Comparing the values of the numbers given, you will see that $38,054 (Ed's commissions) is less than $38,450 (Karen's commissions).

21. **(3) $1,000** You can "eyeball" or estimate the difference by looking at the two salaries or rounding them to the nearest thousand: $43,000 − $42,000 = $1,000.

PROGRAM 29: PROBLEM SOLVING

Basic Operations Review
Skill Practice, page 47
1. 1,832
2. $931
3. 1,024
4. **(4) $10,608** Multiply: 136×78
5. 972
6. 11,190
7. 12,288
8. **(4) $16,613** Add: $13,940 + $1,145 + $1,528

Skill Practice, page 49
1. 82
2. 533 r1
3. 900
4. 853 r14
5. **28 chairs** Divide: $2,500 \div 89$. Ignore the remainder, since Laurie can't buy part of a chair.
6. **$671** Subtract: $1,000 − $329
7. **$1,338** Multiply: 223×6
8. **$1,420** Multiply to find the cost of the book trucks: $189 \times 5 = $945. Then add the cost of the cart: $945 + $475 = $1,420.
9. **(2) 690** Divide: $12,500 \div $18 = 694$ r8, which rounds to 690.

Skill Practice, page 51
You may use any letter for the variable.
1. **$25** $36 + x = $61 or x + $36 = $61
2. **$166** $624 − x = $458
3. **38 hours** $h \times $9 = 342 or $9 \times h = 342
4. **252 books** $b \div 6 = 42$

Problem Solver Connection, page 51
To count up from $185 to $500, think: $5 gets me to $190, $10 more gets me to $200. Then I need $300 to get to $500. Add: $5 + $10 + $300 = $315.

Solving Word Problems
Skill Practice, page 53
1. **(3) $20,707** Add: $13,682 + $7,025
2. **(5) Not enough information is given.** You would need the amount of the annual goal to find how much the association has left to raise.
3. **(2) $6,764** Subtract: $13,682 − $6,918

Skill Practice, page 55
1. **$324** $36 \times $9 = 324
2. **$179** $1432 \div 8 = 179
3. **144 bottles** $432 \div $3 = 144$
4. **440 miles** $55 \times 8 = 440$ miles
5. **(1) 575 miles per hour** Use the formula: $d = rt$. Substitute the values you know: $1725 = r \cdot 3$. Divide to find the rate: $1725 \div 3 = 575$ miles per hour.

Science Connection, page 55
9 psf Divide 1,620 pounds by 180 square feet.

Solving Multi-Step Problems
Skill Practice, page 57
1. 17
2. 31
3. 55
4. 30
5. 63
6. 141
7. **90 miles** $(15 \times 2) \times 3 = 90$
8. **82 miles** $(15 + 12 + 14) \times 2 = 82$

Skill Practice, page 59
1. **(3) 113 + 72 + 58** Add to find the total.
2. **(5) 5(15 − 8)** This problem applies the distributive property.
3. **(4) ($22,880 + $20,800) ÷ 12** Add their annual wages and divide by 12, the number of months in a year.
4. **(1) 12($23) + 28($14)** Apply the cost formula for each item and add the results.

Calculator Connection, page 59
(3) 2($150) − 2($25) This is the only expression that equals $250.

GED Practice, pages 60–62
1. **(5) $21** Since the shirts each cost the same amount, divide $84 by 4 shirts. The information about the jeans is unnecessary, or extraneous, for this calculation.
2. **(1) 84 ÷ 6** Divide the number of employees per team into the total number of employees.
3. **(1) 8 − 2½ − 4** Subtract the morning and the afternoon work periods ($2\frac{1}{2}$ and 4 hours) from the total number of seminar hours (8 hours).
4. **(2) $7.00** Subtract: $35 − $28 = $7.

5. **(3) three lemon trees**   This is a multi-step problem. Compute each answer choice and subtract each sum from $100 to see if at least $10 is left. Only the third choice fits this requirement.

6. **(5) $510**   It will take two buses to transport 80 students to the museum ($2 \times \$135 = \$270$). The admission for the students can be found by multiplying $3 by 80 students ($\$3 \times 80 = \$240$). The total of the amounts is the total cost: $\$270 + \$240 = \$510$.

7. **(4) ($102 − $24) ÷ 6**   First, subtract the cost of the souvenirs. The remaining amount is the cost of the tickets alone. Divide this number by 6, the number of tickets, to find the cost of one ticket.

8. **(5) 7576**   Add both attendance figures. The clue to addition here is "in total."

9. **(3) 4($14)**   The cost of one all-day children's pass is $14. Multiply by 4 to find the cost of the children's passes.

10. **(2) $44**   Be careful to use the correct information from the price list   the prices of the 4-hour passes. Multiply $4 \times \$8$ and add $12 for the answer of $44.

11. **(4) 40**   Note that the train made the *round trip* in 7 hours. Double the number of kilometers to 280. Then use the distance formula, $d = rt$. Substitute: $280 = r(7)$. Divide both sides of the equation by 7: $r = 40$.

12. **(3) between $100 and $200**   Do mental math to round the two figures to the nearest tens place: 852 becomes 850, and 696 becomes 700. Subtract, and the difference is approximately $150.

13. **(5) Not enough information is given.**   You would need to know how many hours Theo spent driving to find the number of miles per hour.

14. **(1) 1400 and 70**   Remember that compatible numbers make an expression easy to perform with mental math.

15. **(2) $\frac{32}{8}$**   Perform multiplication and division operations first, working from left to right.

16. **(3) $50(8 + 12)**   One way to solve the problem is to find the total number of VCRs repaired during the two months and then multiply by $50.

17. **(5) 68**   Use the formula $d = rt$. The distance is 340 miles, and the time is 5 hours. To solve for r, divide 340 by 5.

18. **(4) 137(6)**   Parentheses around the second number show multiplication. This expression can also be written with a raised dot: $137 \cdot 6$.

19. **(3) 6**   The mixture with the fastest boiling time is Mixture B. Mixture C has the slowest boiling point. Subtract to arrive at choice (3), a 6-minute difference in boiling times.

20. **(5) 20 − 5 − 5 − 4**   The amounts of the three mixtures should be subtracted from the total size of the jar.

21. **(5) Not enough information is given.**   The table provides no information on freezing points.

PROGRAM 30: DECIMALS

Skill Practice, page 69
1. 0.08
2. 5.2
3. 11.95
4. 0.169
5. 0.4
6. 132 cm
7. less than
8. **(3) C, B, D, A**   Add zeros so that all numbers have the same number of decimal places. Then compare from left to right: $1.255 < 1.775 < 1.800 < 1.850$.

Skill Practice, page 71
1. 2.598
2. 7.66
3. 9.25
4. 2.850
5. 204.37
6. 0.255
7. 172.165
8. 69.017
9. **(4) 4**   2.95 is nearly 3 pounds, and 0.875 is nearly 1 pound. Add: $3 + 1 = 4$ pounds.
10. **(3) 13.28**   Subtract: $30 − 16.72 = 13.28$.
11. **(4) 585.6**   Subtract to find the difference between two numbers: $41,839.2 − 41,253.6 = 585.6$.

Skill Practice, page 73
1. **8-inch wide poplar**   You do not need to perform any calculation to solve this problem. Simply compare the costs given on the table for the two boards: $\$2.65 < \$2.80$.
2. **$148.40**   Multiply the number of boards by the length of each board by the price for the 8-inch-wide boards: $7 \times 8 \times \$2.65$.
3. **Yes**   Poplar boards that are 8 inches wide sell for $2.65 per foot. To buy 24 feet of the lumber, Ray will spend $63.60 before tax. Multiply: $24 \times \$2.65 = \$63.60$.
4. **(3) 12 × 50 × 0.63**   To solve the problem, you need to multiply the number of feet in one board by the number of boards by the cost per foot (the amount shown on the chart).

Skill Practice, page 75

1. **60 miles per hour**   Divide: $210 \div 3.5 = 60$
2. **16 shirts**   Divide: $45 \div 2.75 = 16.4$. Ignore the remainder. You want to find out how many whole shirts Reggie can make.
3. **40 lots**   Write four-tenths as 0.4. Then divide: $16 \div 0.4 = 40$

Skill Practice, page 77

1. **(2) 8 hours 45 minutes**   Divide: $568.75 \div 65 = 8.75$. Since 0.75 is equal to 45 minutes, 8.75 hours is equal to 8 hours 45 minutes.
2. **(4) 0.75 × 70**   Forty-five minutes is equal to 0.75 hour. Multiply the cost per hour by the time worked to find the total labor cost.
3. **(4) 0.4, 2.5, 1.25**   Express all minutes as decimal fractions of an hour.
4. **Answers will vary.**   Divide any number of minutes by 60 to write the minutes as a decimal.

Skill Practice, pages 78–79

1. **a.** $3.8 + 4.2 + 6.75$
   b. $1.57 + 1.33 + 1.29 + 1.55 + 1.89$
   c. $18.5 + 25.75 + 18.5 + 25.75$ or $(18.5 \times 2) + (25.75 \times 2)$
2. **20.2 miles**   Subtract the sum of 10.4 and 8.5 from 39.1.
3. **198 miles**   Lee travels to work 5 times a week and returns home 5 times, for a total of 10 trips. Multiply: $19.8 \times 10 = 198$.
4. **0.4 mile**   Find the route through Clifton: $11.7 + 7 = 18.7$. Find the route through Downs: $8.7 + 10.4 = 19.1$. Subtract the shorter route from the longer route: $19.1 - 18.7 = 0.4$.
5. **The shortest route is from Downs to Healy to Clifton to Corwin.**   Add and compare:
   Downs to Hudson to Clifton to Corwin = 26.4 miles
   Downs to Kimeo to Corwin = 35.4 miles
   Downs to Healy to Clifton to Corwin = 20 miles

Problem Solver Connection, page 79

2.6 miles longer $(10.9 + 11.1) - (15.8 + 3.6) = 22.0 - 19.4 = 2.6$ miles

GED Practice, pages 80–82

1. **(2) 9.043, 9.058, 9.13, 9.135**   Since all the whole numbers are 9, compare the values of the numbers to the right of the decimal points.
2. **(5) $25.39**   Add the three amounts. The result is what she spent.
3. **(5) 2.0, 1.5, 1.1, 0.75, 0.5**   First group the weights by whole numbers (0, 1, and 2). Then order the numbers within each group by comparing the values to the right of the decimal points. Finally, arrange the weights in order, starting with the heaviest item.
4. **(4) $2.00**   Either round $22.95 to $24 and divide by 12 (they are compatible numbers), or divide $22.95 by 12 on your calculator and round the answer ($1.9125) to $2.00.
5. **(5) 0.6** $5 m - 2.2 m - 2.2 m$, or $5 - (2 \times 2.2) = 5 - 4.4 = 0.6$.
6. **(3) $6.21**   Common sense says that the first two choices are too much. Multiply: $\$0.29 \times 20 = \$5.80$. Add the tax: $\$5.80 + \$0.41 = \$6.21$.
7. **(3) 26.9**   Add 23.9 and 7.8, then subtract the sum from the total distance, 58.6.
8. **(5) 7.8 + 11.5 + 7.8 + 11.5**   By formula, the perimeter of a rectangle is the sum of all four sides.
9. **(1) 0.75 hour**   Subtract the lesser time (2.5) from the greater time (3.25).
10. **(4) Tyrone**   Divide George's time by 2 and round the answer: $3.55 \div 2 =$ about 1.75, which is Tyrone's time.
11. **(3) 3:15 P.M.**   George's time of 1.75 hours is equal to 1 hour 45 minutes (0.75×60 minutes $= 45$ minutes). Add 1 hour 45 minutes to the starting time of 1:30 P.M. The result is 3:15 P.M.
12. **(4) $17.01**   Sally plus her 9 coworkers equals 10. To divide a decimal by ten, move the decimal point one place to the left.
13. **(5) (3.4 + 2.8) − 4.6**   Drawing a picture can be helpful in solving this kind of problem. You need to add the two distances in the longer route and subtract the shorter route to find the difference. Only choice (5) performs the operations in the correct order. Remember, the parentheses show you which operation to perform first.
14. **(3) 3.75**   45 minutes is equal to 0.75 hour. Multiply: $0.75 \times 5 = 3.75$ hours
15. **(2) $19.75**   Mark needs to buy 5 dozen doughnuts ($60 \div 12 = 5$). Multiply: $\$3.95 \times 5 = \$19.75$.
16. **(5) $11.10** $0.89 times 10 cans is $8.90 (move the decimal point one place to the right). Subtract that amount from $20 to compute the change, $11.10.
17. **(2) 15**   Multiply: 2 tablets $\times$ 2.5 milligrams each $\times$ 3 times a day
18. **(4) 3.5**   Divide 60 miles by 17 miles per hour to get the result, 3.529, which is approximately 3.5 hours.
19. **(2) $28**   11:30 A.M. to 1:15 P.M. is 1.75 hours. Multiply by the rate: $\$16 \times 1.75 = \$28$.
20. **(4) 4.5**   Add the three times together: $0.5 + 2.25 + 1.75 = 4.5$.
21. **(4) $105**   Multiply $60 by the time of the third service call: $1.75 \times \$60 = \$105$.

22. **(2) 11:35 A.M.**   Add the driving time to the service call time. Remember, that 2.25 hours is equal to 2 hours 15 minutes. 20 minutes + 2 hours 15 minutes = 2 hours 35 minutes. Then compute when the second call would have ended: 2 hours 35 minutes after 9 A.M. would be 11:35 A.M.

23. **(5) (2 × 0.75) + 2.25**   Two service calls were 0.75 hr each. To find the total time for these calls, multiply 0.75 by 2. Then add the time for the sixth service call.

Alternate Math Formats, pages 83–84

24. **48**   (8 × 3) + (3 × 8) = $48

25. **1.9**   4.5 − (2 × 1.3) = 1.9 m

26. **18.4**   202 ÷ 11 ≈ 18.36, which rounds to 18.4 miles per gallon.

27. **583**   1333 − 750 = 583 ft

28. **32,000**   31,700 rounds to 32,000.

29. Answers may range from 6.41 to 6.49.

30. **5.6**   Round to the tenths place. 5.59432 rounds to 5.6.

31. **280**   Multiply the number of miles each way by the number of times Lee makes the trip each day by the number of days he worked. 28 × 2 × 5 = 280

32. **105**   15 × (3 + 4) = $105

33. **0.09**

34. **64**   159 ÷ 2.5 = 63.6, which rounds to 64 miles per hour.

35. **730**   5 × (73 × 2) = 730 miles

PROGRAM 31: FRACTIONS

Basic Operations with Fractions

Skill Practice, page 91

1. $\frac{3}{4}$

2. $\frac{4}{5}$

3. $\frac{2}{3}$

4. $\frac{1}{3}$

5. $\frac{1}{2}$

6. $\frac{1}{4}$

7. $\frac{1}{4}$ **of the trip**

8. $\frac{1}{6}$ **of the paint**   Make sure you add the gallons of enamel and latex paint before writing the fraction.

Skill Practice, page 93

1. $\frac{4}{5}$

2. $1\frac{1}{8}$

3. $2\frac{1}{4}$

4. $\frac{3}{8}$

5. $\frac{7}{15}$

6. $\frac{5}{18}$

7. **(4) +$1\frac{11}{16}$**   Change the fractions so that they all have a denominator of 16 and add. You may have noticed that the sum of $\frac{1}{4}$ and $\frac{3}{4}$ is 1. If so, write 1 as a whole number and add $\frac{5}{16}$ and $\frac{3}{8}$.

Skill Practice, page 95

1. $\frac{2}{9}$

2. $\frac{1}{4}$

3. $\frac{1}{2}$

4. $2\frac{1}{2}$

5. 30

6. 26

7. **6 boards**   The quotient is $6\frac{2}{5}$, but the problem asks you to find the number of whole boards you can cut from 16 feet. Drop the remainder. You can cut 6 whole boards.

Science Connection, page 95

$\frac{4}{5}$ 39 eagles is close to 40. Simplify $\frac{40}{50}$ to $\frac{4}{5}$.

Problem Solving with Fractions

Skill Practice, page 97

1. **(4) 4 × $2\frac{5}{8}$**   Since there are four packages, each weighing the same amount, you can find the total by multiplying.

2. **(4) $30\frac{1}{2} ÷ \frac{3}{4}$**   You need to find out how many times the amount of fabric for one frame ($\frac{3}{4}$ yd) can divide into the total amount of fabric ($30\frac{1}{2}$ yd).

3. **(2) 50 − ($2\frac{3}{4}$ + $5\frac{2}{3}$)**   The total amount of chain is 50 yards. You need to subtract both of the lengths that were sold. You could subtract them one at a time: $50 - 2\frac{3}{4} - 5\frac{2}{3}$. Another way to think about the problem is to add the lengths of the chains that were sold and subtract that total from 50. This is the method shown in choice (2). Both methods give the same result.

Skill Practice, page 99

1. $\frac{3}{4}$ **is greater.** $\frac{3}{4}$ = 0.75 and $\frac{5}{7}$ ≈ 0.714. Since 0.75 > 0.714, $\frac{3}{4}$ is greater than $\frac{5}{7}$.

2. $\frac{3}{10}$ **is less.** $\frac{1}{3}$ ≈ 0.33 and $\frac{3}{10}$ = 0.3. Since 0.3 < 0.33, $\frac{3}{10}$ is less than $\frac{1}{3}$.

3. **a.** $\frac{4}{5}$

    b. 0.8

4. $\frac{1}{2}$ Change all fractions to decimals: $\frac{1}{2} =$
0.5, $\frac{7}{8} = 0.875$, and $\frac{4}{7} \approx 0.571$. Then compare
the decimals. Think of 0.5 as 0.500.
Remember you can add zeros to the right of
a decimal number without changing its value.
The decimal 0.571 is much nearer 0.500
than it is 0.875, so $\frac{4}{7}$ is closer to $\frac{1}{2}$.

5. **9** Change $\frac{3}{4}$ to a decimal by dividing:
$3 \div 4 = 0.75$. Then multiply: $0.75 \times 12 = 9$

Calculator Connection, page 99
$4\frac{3}{8}$ hours

Everyday Fractions
Skill Practice, page 101
1. **$4.65** The regular price of the clay is $18.60.
Multiply by $\frac{1}{4}$ to find the amount of the
discount: $18.60 \times \frac{1}{4} = \$4.65$. Remember,
multiplying by $\frac{1}{4}$ is the same as dividing by 4.
You can quickly solve the problem on your
calculator by dividing: $18.60 \div 4 = \$4.65$.

2. **$15.60** Multiply to find the original cost of
four brushes: $5.20 \times 4 = \$20.80$. Find the
amount of the discount: $20.80 \times \frac{1}{4} = \$5.20$.
Subtract the discount to find the sale price:
$20.80 - \$5.20 = \$15.60$. In other words, the
customer bought 4 brushes for the price of 3.

3. **$53.71** This is a good problem to solve with
your calculator. Don't forget to subtract the
coupon.

4. **(4) $\frac{1}{5}$** Write a fraction comparing the
amount spent on food to the monthly take-
home pay: $\frac{420}{2000}$, which reduces to $\frac{21}{100}$. Then
compare this fraction to the answer choices.
Since $\frac{1}{5} = \frac{20}{100}$, $\frac{1}{5}$ is the fraction closest in
value. You can also use a calculator to change
the fractions to decimals: $\frac{420}{2000} = 0.21$ and
$\frac{1}{5} = 0.2$.

5. **(2) Rent and Transportation** Find $\frac{1}{2}$ of the
take-home pay: $2000 \times \frac{1}{2} = \$1000$. Now
find the totals of the items in each answer
choice. Only choice (2) has items that total
more than $1000: rent and transportation, or
$750 + \$300 = \$1050$.

Skill Practice, page 103
1. $\frac{5}{12}$ 10 hours $= \frac{10}{24} = \frac{5}{12}$ day

2. $\frac{1}{4}$ 3 months $= \frac{3}{12} = \frac{1}{4}$ year

3. **(4) $1200 \times \frac{1}{2} \times 0.08$** 6 months is $\frac{6}{12}$ or
$\frac{1}{2}$ of a year.

4. $\frac{7}{12}$ 7 inches $= \frac{7}{12}$ foot

5. $\frac{3}{4}$ **or .75** 12 ounces $= \frac{12}{16} = \frac{3}{4}$ pound,
or 0.75 pound

6. **(2) $\frac{1}{5}$** $\frac{1000}{5280}$ is close to $\frac{1000}{5000}$, or $\frac{1}{5}$. You
can also evaluate the fractions by converting
them to decimals using your calculator.

Science Connection, page 103
$\frac{11}{16}$ to $\frac{13}{16}$ **ounce** The fraction $\frac{3}{4}$ is equal to $\frac{12}{16}$.
Add and subtract the error tolerance.

GED Practice, pages 104–106
1. **(3) $\frac{7}{10}$** Divide $3\frac{1}{2}$ or $\frac{7}{2}$ acres by 5 plots:
$\frac{7}{2} \times \frac{1}{5} = \frac{7}{10}$.

2. **(3) $40.50** Subtract one-fourth of the original
price from the original price: $54.00 - \frac{1}{4}(\$54.00)$
$= \$54.00 - \$13.50 = \$40.50$.

3. **(2) $144.00** This is a multi-step problem,
and there are several ways to approach it.
Method 1: Start by finding the total regular
price for 4 tires. The regular price for all four
tires is $54 \times 4 = \$216$. The discount is $216
$\frac{1}{3} = \$72$. Subtract to find the sale price:
$216 - \$72 = \$144$.
Method 2: Start by finding the sale price of
one tire. The regular price for 1 tire is $54.
The discount is $54 \times \frac{1}{3} = \$18$. Subtract:
$54 - \$18 = \$36$. Now multiply by 4 to find
the sale price of four tires: $36 \times 4 = \$144$.

4. **(3) $14\frac{1}{2}$** Divide the numerator by the
denominator, and write the remainder over the
denominator: $58 \div 4 = 14\frac{2}{4}$. Reduce to $14\frac{1}{2}$.

5. **(4) $\frac{4}{5}$** Add the total run by this relay team
to get the entire distance of the race:
$1.7 + 1 + 2.3 = 5$. Then add the number
of miles Terri and Marco ran ($1.7 + 2.3 = 4$),
and set up the fraction: $\frac{4}{5}$.

6. **(2) $2\frac{3}{10}$** Read the decimal in number words
("two and three-tenths") to find its equivalent
fraction: $2\frac{3}{10}$.

7. **(5) Not enough information is given.** The
problem does not indicate how fast any of the
relay runners ran, only how far they each ran
and how long it took them to finish the race
altogether.

8. **(1) $\frac{1}{10}, \frac{1}{4}, \frac{2}{7}, \frac{3}{10}, \frac{1}{3}$** Convert the fractions
into equivalent decimals (on the calculator
when necessary), and order them from smallest
to greatest: 0.1, 0.25, 0.286, 0.3, 0.333.

9. **(2) $2\frac{3}{4}$** Use fractions to express the amount
of time Sam read, and add the fractions:
$\frac{1}{2} + 1 + \frac{3}{4} + \frac{1}{2} = 2\frac{3}{4}$.

10. **(1) $\frac{23}{18 + 23}$** The number of amber beads sold
becomes the numerator, while the total beads
sold ($18 + 23$) becomes the denominator.

11. **(4) Between 16 and 17 weeks** The number
of pounds of flour in a sack is unnecessary
information. Divide: $11 \div \frac{2}{3} = 11 \times \frac{3}{2} = 16\frac{1}{2}$.

12. **(3) 70** Multiply the number of tons a month
times the number of months in a year times
$2\frac{1}{2}$ years: $2\frac{1}{3} \times 12 \times 2\frac{1}{2} = \frac{7}{3} \times \frac{12}{1} \times \frac{5}{2}$.
Cancel twice to get $\frac{7}{1} \times \frac{2}{1} \times \frac{5}{1} = 70$.

13. **(2) $\frac{1}{3}$** At the time he stopped to talk with his
uncle, Hans had cleaned for 15 of the 45 minutes
necessary to finish the job: $\frac{15}{45} = \frac{1}{3}$.

14. **(4) 18**   To obtain the lowest common denominator, think of the multiples of the denominators 6, 3, 9, and 2, and choose the lowest common multiple.

15. **(4) $19\frac{1}{2}$**   Multiply: $3\frac{1}{4} \times 6 = \frac{13}{4} \times \frac{6}{1} = \frac{78}{4} = 19\frac{1}{2}$

16. **(1) a pedicure**   Find the amount of time needed to complete 1 permanent and 2 haircuts: $1\frac{1}{4} + \frac{1}{2} + \frac{1}{2} = 2\frac{1}{4}$. Subtract from 3 hours: $3 - 2\frac{1}{4} = \frac{3}{4}$. Evaluate each of the choices to see which will take $\frac{3}{4}$ hour (45 minutes) or less. Choice (1) will take $\frac{2}{3}$ of an hour, or 40 minutes.

17. **(3) 1:10 P.M.**   There are several ways to approach the problem, but whatever method you use, you will eventually have to change the fractions of an hour to minutes.
    Method 1: Add the times from the chart: $\frac{1}{4} + 1\frac{1}{4} + \frac{2}{3} = 1\frac{7}{6} = 2\frac{1}{6}$ hour. Since there are 60 minutes in an hour, $\frac{1}{6}$ hour = 10 minutes. The work takes 2 hours 10 minutes. Since Tracy began at 11:00 A.M., she is finished at 1:10 P.M.
    Method 2: Change the times to minutes from the start: $\frac{1}{4}$ hour = 15 minutes, $1\frac{1}{4}$ hour = 1 hour 15 minutes, $\frac{2}{3}$ hour = 40 minutes. Add the amount of time: 15 min + 1 hr 15 min + 40 min = 1 hr 70 min = 2 hr 10 min. Tracy is finished at 1:10 P.M.

18. **(2) $\frac{15}{6} - \frac{2}{6}$**   Subtract the whipped cream used for the topping from the total whipped cream by converting the unlike fractions into like fractions with the lowest common denominator of 6.

19. **(4) $\frac{2}{5}$**   The artisans have already woven 45 out of 75 rugs, which means they have 30 left to weave. $\frac{30}{75}$ reduces to $\frac{2}{5}$.

20. **(1) 5**   You need to divide 42 by $7\frac{1}{2}$ inches. You can use either decimals or fractions.
    Using decimals: Divide: $42 \div 7.5 = 5.6$. Ignore the decimal remainder, since the situation calls for whole lengths of the pipe.
    Using fractions: Divide: $42 \div 7\frac{1}{2} = 42 \div \frac{15}{2} = 42 \times \frac{2}{15} = \frac{84}{15} = 5\frac{9}{15} = 5\frac{3}{5}$. Again, ignore the fraction.

21. **(3) $0.97**   Remember that a dollar has 100 parts, and think in terms of fractions of a hundred. Convert the fractions to decimals, then add: $\frac{1}{4} + \frac{3}{10} + \frac{2}{5} + \frac{1}{50} = $0.25 + $0.30 + $0.40 + $0.02 = 0.97.

PROGRAM 32: RATIO, PROPORTION, AND PERCENT

Working with Ratios
Skill Practice, page 113
1. **a. 3:5**   Reduce $\frac{75}{125}$.
    b. 3:8   Reduce $\frac{75}{(75+125)}$.

2. **a. 11:12**   He missed 4 items, so he got 44 correct. 44:48 = 11:12
    b. 1:12   Reduce 4:48.
    c. 11:1   Reduce 44:4.

3. **a. 3:1**   Reduce 246:82.
    b. 41   246 customers/6 hours = 41 customers per hour

4. **(5) $\frac{$855}{(36+40)}$**   Divide the amount of money earned by the total hours.

Working with Proportions
Skill Practice, page 115
1. **(3) 17** $\frac{\text{width}}{\text{length}}$ $\frac{6}{10} = \frac{10}{x}$ $10 \times 10 \div 6 = 16\frac{2}{3}$
2. **(1) 2** $\frac{\text{flour}}{\text{butter}}$ $\frac{6}{3} = \frac{4}{x}$ $3 \times 4 \div 6 = 2$
3. **(4) $350.00** $\frac{\text{dollars}}{\text{hours}}$ $\frac{218.75}{25} = \frac{x}{40}$
    $218.75 \times 40 \div 25 = 350$
4. **(5) $\frac{300 \times 5}{50}$** $\frac{\text{savings}}{\text{earnings}}$ $\frac{5}{50} = \frac{x}{300}$
5. **(1) $\frac{34.14 \times 7}{3}$** $\frac{\text{cost}}{\text{gallon}}$ $\frac{$34.14}{3} = \frac{x}{7}$

Skill Practice, page 117
1. **7 cm** $\frac{\text{cm}}{\text{km}}$ $\frac{1}{25} = \frac{x}{175}$
2. **198 miles** $\frac{\text{inch}}{\text{miles}}$ $\frac{1}{36} = \frac{5\frac{1}{2}}{x}$
3. **40 children** $\frac{\text{children}}{\text{people}}$ $\frac{5}{(5+2)} = \frac{x}{56}$
4. **20 shop sales** $\frac{\text{shop sales}}{\text{total sales}}$ $\frac{1}{(1+8)} = \frac{x}{180}$

Geography Connection, page 117
Water covers about 1,725 square miles in North Dakota.   Cross multiply, then divide: $69,000 \times 10 \div 400 = 1,725$.

Working with Percent
Skill Practice, page 119
1. 252
2. 315
3. $88.20
4. 80%
5. 90%
6. 75%
7. 64 children
8. 30%
9. **(4) $\frac{25 \times 272}{100}$**

Skill Practice, page 121
1. **8 hours**   Solve for the whole: $\frac{2}{0.25} = 8$.
2. **15%**   Solve for the percent: $\frac{1.2}{8} = .15 = 15\%$.
3. **(1) 6×0.2**   Solve for the part using the percent formula: Whole × Rate = Part. Use 0.2 for 20%.
4. **(3) $\frac{16}{40}$**   Solve for the rate using the percent formula: Part ÷ Whole = Rate.
5. **(2) $\frac{26.4 \times 100}{55}$**   Set up a proportion to solve for the whole: $\frac{55}{100} = \frac{26.4}{x}$.

Skill Practice, page 123

1. **15%** Make sure you use $65 as the original charge in the proportion. $\frac{10}{65} = \frac{x}{100}$.

2. **60%** Set up a proportion: $\frac{2500}{4200} = \frac{x}{100}$.

3. **6%** Set up a proportion: $\frac{2,800}{49,500} = \frac{x}{100}$.

4. **Current price: $55.35** Overall rate of decrease: 32.5% or $32\frac{1}{2}$%

Problem Solver Connection, page 123

To find 25% of a number, divide by 4. Example: 25% of 48 = 12 because 48 ÷ 4 = 12.

To find 20% of a number, find 10% by moving the decimal point one place to the left, then multiply by 2. Example: To find 20% of 250, first find 10%. 10% of 250 = 25. Then multiply by 2: 25 × 2 = 50, so 20% of 250 = 50.

GED Practice, pages 124–126

1. **(2)** $\frac{38.94 \times 8}{3}$ Set up the ratios comparing dollars to number of CDs, with x as the missing term: $\frac{38.94}{3} = \frac{x}{8}$. Cross multiply and then divide by the remaining term to get the correct expression.

2. **(4) $50.40** Multiply 840 × 6% to get the commission. The number of hours and days Marla works is unnecessary information.

3. **(3)** $10\frac{1}{2}$ The proportion set-up is $\frac{8}{14} = \frac{6}{x}$. Cross multiply and divide by the remaining term: 84 ÷ 8 = $10\frac{1}{2}$ inches long.

4. **(5) Not enough information is given.** You do not know how many total ounces or pounds of sculpting compound Cindy needs for two sculptures, so you cannot figure the amount of sand needed for the compound.

5. **(5) 280** Set up your proportion and compute: $\frac{(1.5 + 2) \times 80}{1}$ = 280. You might also estimate with rounding: 3.5 inches × 80 miles is going to be between 240(3 × 80) and 320(4 × 80) miles, which only leaves choice (5).

6. **(4)** $\frac{1 \times 300}{80}$ Set up your proportion and write the expression for the cross products.

7. **(1) $12 ÷ 4** A shortcut to finding 25% of something is to divide it by 4.

8. **(3) $94.50** In this multi-step problem, you first add the cost of the three items: $60 + $15 + $15 = $90. Now find 5% (the shipping charge) of $90. Set up a proportion: $\frac{x}{90} = \frac{5}{100}$. Solve: 90 × 5 ÷ 100 = $4.50. Add the shipping charge to the cost of the order: $90 + $4.50 = $94.50.

9. **(3) $57.60** Remember, in successive percent markdowns, do first one step, then the second. Do NOT add the two successive percents together. The original price of the quilt is $80. Find the first discount: 20% of $80 is $16. Subtract: $80−$16 =$64. After the first discount, the price of the quilt is $64. **Find the second discount:** 10% of $64 is $6.40. Subtract: $64−$6.40=$57.60.

10. **(4) 43%** Set up the proportion: $\frac{30}{70} = \frac{3}{7} = \frac{x}{100}$. Cross multiply, then divide by the remaining term, to get 42.8%. You can check your answer by reasoning that the number of cousins is less than half (50%) of 70, so the answer in percent will be less than, but close to, 50%.

11. **(4) $293.25** Find the discount: 15% of $345 is $51.75. Subtract to find the sale price at Factory Warehouse: $345 − $51.75 = $293.25.

12. **(1) $368.00** Set up a proportion: $\frac{\$142.60}{15.5} = \frac{x}{40}$. Cross multiply, then divide by the remaining term: $142.60 × 40 ÷ 15.5 = $368.

13. **(3)** $\frac{24}{1} = \frac{390}{x}$ Set up a proportion with the measurement fact (24 hours in one day) as the first ratio. Be sure to write the second ratio in the same order.

14. **(4) 81%** Add to find the total percent spent on painting and carpeting: 11% + 8% = 19%. Then subtract from 100%: 100% − 19% = 81%. You can also solve the problem by adding the percents to be spent on items other than painting and carpeting: 60% + 21% = 81%.

15. **(3) $3,150** Find 21% of $15,000: $\frac{21}{100} = \frac{x}{15,000}$, so 15,000 × 100 ÷ 21 = $3,150.

16. **(3) 2:15** Set up the ratio in the correct order and reduce to lowest terms: 8:60 = 2:15.

17. **(3) Between 120 and 125** You will need to multiply the unit rate (number of miles per gallon) by the number of gallons. Because the problem says "Approximately," estimating works well here. 24.6 is between 24 and 25. Using number sense (think of quarters in a dollar), you know that 25 × 5 = 125 and 24 × 5 is 5 less than that, or 120. The answer is between 120 and 125.

18. **(2) $1,200** Set up your proportion: $\frac{\text{interest}}{\text{account balance}}$ $\frac{5.5}{100} = \frac{66}{x}$

19. **(5) 3:8** There were 33 hardcover books sold out of a *total* of 88 books sold. 33:88 reduces to 3:8.

20. **(4) 45%** Find the difference between the regular price and the sale price: $125 − $68.75 = $56.25. Then set up a proportion: $\frac{\text{difference}}{\text{original amount}}$ $\frac{\$56.25}{\$125.00} = \frac{x}{100}$ Solve to find the percent: $56.25 × 100 ÷ $125 = 45. Add a percent sign: 45%.

Alternate Math Formats, pages 127–128

21. **455** Set up a proportion and solve: $\frac{1}{140} = \frac{3.25}{x}$. $x = 3.25 \times 140 \div 1 = 455$ miles.

22. $\frac{1}{6}$ Brad worked 4 hours, and $\frac{4}{24} = \frac{1}{6}$ hour.

23. **11** If 2 gallons cover 440 sq ft, then 1 gallon covers 220 sq ft. Set up a proportion and solve: $\frac{1}{220} = \frac{x}{2325}$. $x = 2325 \times 1 \div 220 = $ about 10.57 gallons. Since you can't buy 0.57 gallon, round up to 11.

24. $\frac{19}{16}$ Remember, you may not enter mixed numbers on the grid. Always enter mixed numbers as improper fractions. If Caroline used $\frac{3}{4}$ of the fabric, she has $\frac{1}{4}$ left. Find $\frac{1}{4}$ of $4\frac{3}{4}$ by multiplying: $\frac{1}{4} \times 4\frac{3}{4} = \frac{1}{4} \times \frac{19}{4} = \frac{19}{16}$.

25. **21.25** (grid in **21.25**)   The Bonillas budget $425 for food. Set up a proportion to find a 5% increase: $\frac{x}{425} = \frac{5}{100}$. $425 \times 5 \div 100 = 21.25$.

26. **$41.25** (grid in as **41.25**)   Multiply: 15% of $275 = 0.15 \times 275 = \$41.25$.

27. $\frac{1}{6}$ Multiply the fraction of registered voters who voted by the fraction who voted on the referendum. $\frac{1}{2} \times \frac{1}{3} = \frac{1}{6}$

28. $\frac{3}{8}$ To halve a recipe, multiply the amounts by $\frac{1}{2}$. $\frac{3}{4} \times \frac{1}{2} = \frac{3}{8}$ teaspoon salt

29. $\frac{3}{10}$ If $\frac{3}{5}$ work part-time, then $\frac{2}{5}$ work full-time. To find $\frac{2}{5}$ of $\frac{3}{4}$, multiply: $\frac{2}{5} \times \frac{3}{4} = \frac{6}{20}$, which reduces to $\frac{3}{10}$.

30. **6%** $21 is what percent of $350? Set up a proportion and solve: $\frac{21}{350} = \frac{x}{100}$, so $x = 21 \times 100 \div 350 = 6$.

31. **$0.15** (grid in as **0.15** or **.15**)   Divide the price by the number of ounces to find the price per ounce. Brand B is least per ounce at $0.15 per ounce.

32. $\frac{25}{4}$ (you may also grid in the answer **6.25**) Set up a proportion and solve: $\frac{2\frac{1}{2}}{4} = \frac{x}{10}$, so $x = 2\frac{1}{2} \times 10 \div 4 = \frac{25}{4}$.

PROGRAM 33: MEASUREMENT

Skill Practice, page 135

1. **(5) ounces**   The only measures of weight among the choices are ounces and pounds. Compare a deck of cards to benchmarks you know. The cards are clearly less than a pound and will be weighed in ounces.

2. **(3) 42**   There are 4 quarts in a gallon. Set up a proportion and solve: $\frac{4 \text{ qt}}{1 \text{ gal}} = \frac{x \text{ qt}}{10.5 \text{ gal}}$ Cross multiply and then divide: $4 \times 10.5 \div 1 = 42$.

3. **(2) 138**   Since there are 3 feet in a yard, divide 415 by 3. $415 \div 3 = 138\frac{1}{3}$, which rounds to 138 yards.

4. a. **Less**   Since you are changing from a smaller unit (yards) to a larger unit (miles), the number will be smaller.

   b. You know there are 5,280 feet in a mile. You also know there are 3 feet in a yard. First, convert 10,560 yards to feet by multiplying by 3. Then divide the result by 5,280 to get the number of miles. You could also find out how many yards are in a mile by dividing 5,280 by 3. 5,280 feet = 1,760 yards = 1 mile. Then divide 10,560 by 1,760 to find the number of miles in 10,560 yards.

Skill Practice, page 137

1. **15 clients**   You can solve this using minutes to measure the time.

2. **8 bags**   Express 3 pounds as ounces: $3 \times 16 = 48$ ounces. Then divide by the number of ounces in each treat bag: $48 \div 6 = 8$ bags.

3. **100 cups is the greater amount.**   Use the equivalencies you know to find how many cups equal 1 gallon (16). Then divide 100 cups by that number: $100 \div 16 = 6.25 = 6$ gallons 1 quart.

4. **(4) 5**   Convert 3 lb 12 oz to ounces. 3 lb 12 oz = $(16 \times 3) + 12 = 60$ oz. Divide by the number of ounces per meal: $60 \div 12 = 5$.

Calculator Connection, page 137

1. **$6\frac{1}{4}$ hours or 6 hours 15 minutes** Divide: $375 \div 60 = 6.25$.

2. **$9\frac{1}{2}$ pounds or 9 pounds 8 ounces** Divide: $152 \div 16 = 9.5$.

Skill Practice, page 139

1. meters (m)
2. kilograms (kg)
3. milliliters (mL)
4. kilometers (km)
5. millimeters (mm)
6. liters (L)
7. 0.5 kg, 650 g, 1.4kg, 1500 g
8. **(2) 295 mL**   First, change 3.54 liters to milliliters by multiplying by 1000. To multiply by 1000, move the decimal point 3 places to the right: 3.54 L = 3540 mL. Then divide by 12: $3540 \div 12 = 295$ mL.
9. **(1) 3**   Luis ran 4 laps of 750 meters. Multiply: $750 \times 4 = 3000$ meters. Since 1 kilometer = 1000 meters, Luis ran 3 kilometers.
10. **Your friend is right.** Here's how to figure it out. A kilometer is equal to 1,000 meters, and 1 meter is equal to 1,000 millimeters. $1,000 \times 1,000 = 1,000,000$ millimeters

Skill Practice, page 141

1. **225 grams** $1.825 - 1.6 = 0.225$ kilograms. Multiply by 1000 to get the number of grams.
2. **0.29 meter**   Divide: $1.16 \div 4 = 0.29$.
3. **3360 milliliters**   Set up a proportion and solve: $\frac{22 \text{ g}}{240 \text{mL}} = \frac{308 \text{ g}}{x \text{ mL}}$. Cross multiply and then divide: $240 \times 308 \div 22 = 3360$ mL.
4. **3 grams is greater than 505 milligrams.** Remember, 1 g = 1000 mg, so 3 g = 3000 mg. Find the difference: $3000 - 505 = 2495$ milligrams or 2.495 grams.

Science Connection, page 141

Every year, our measurement estimate of 365 days is off by about 0.26 of a day. After 4 years, we are off by about 1 day, since $0.26 \times 4 = 1.04$ day. You may have realized that leap year doesn't completely correct the problem, since 0.26×4 is a little more than 1 day. Therefore, every 100 years (except years that are evenly divisible by 1000), scientists eliminate 1 leap day to get back on track.

Skill Practice, page 143

1. **$A = 225$ square inches** $A = s^2 = 15^2 = 225$
   $P = 60$ inches $P = 4s = 4 \times 15 = 60$.

2. **The width is 3 cm, and the length is 16 cm.**
   Only 3 and 16 result in a perimeter of 38 and an area of 48.

3. **(3) $2(5) + 2(1.5)$**   Use the formula $P = 2l + 2w$. Substitute the numbers from the problem, and compare to the answer choices.

4. **a. Lacrosse**   The area of a lacrosse field is 8400 sq yd. The area of a field hockey field is 6000 sq yd.
   b. 2400 sq yd   Subtract to find the difference: $8400 - 6000 = 2400$.

5. **(2) 5.4**   Find the perimeter of the table: $2(165) + 2(105) = 540$ cm = 5.4 m.

Skill Practice, page 145

1. **(5) $60 + 60 + 50$**   Add the sides that are parallel to and opposite side x.

2. **(1) 600**   Add all measurements. Use deductive reasoning to find any missing measurements.

3. **(2) 15,500**   Break the irregular shape into one square (60 yd $\times$ 60 yd) and one rectangle (170 yd $\times$ 70 yd). Find the area of each regular shape and add to find total area. Note: You can also break the shape into three rectangles, but this will require an extra calculation. Try to choose problem-solving approaches that will save time.

Problem Solver Connection, page 145

46 square yards   To convert square feet to square yards, divide by 9. $414 \div 9 = 46$

GED Practice, pages 146–148

1. **(3) seconds**   A common benchmark for measuring time in seconds is to add a word or a brief phrase, such as "elephant" or "one thousand" between the consecutive numbers 1, 2, 3, and so on.

2. **(1) 2.5**   From Call Box 1 to Call Box 6 is 5 units of 0.5 mile each. Multiply: $5 \times 0.5 = 2.5$. You may find it helpful to sketch problems of this type before you begin calculations.

3. **(1) 259**   Divide the hours by the number of hours in one day: $6216 \div 24 = 259$.

4. **(3) 19**   Start by finding the total number of cups of lemonade Lauren needs: $1\frac{1}{2} \times 200 = 300$ cups. Since 4 cups = 1 quart and 4 quarts = 1 gallon, you know that there are 16 cups in 1 gallon. Divide: $300 \div 16 = 18\frac{3}{4}$ gal. To the nearest whole gallon, Lauren needs to make 19 gallons.

5. **(3) Wheeler Peak**   There are 5,280 feet in a mile. Since the altitudes in the table are given in feet, find out how many feet are in $2\frac{1}{2}$ miles: $2\frac{1}{2} \times 5,280 = 13,200$ feet. Wheeler Peak, with an altitude of 13,161 feet, is closest to $2\frac{1}{2}$ miles.

6. **(5) $(20,320 - 11,239) \div 5,280$**   This is a multi-step problem. First find the difference in height between the highest and lowest mountains ($20,320 - 11,239$). Then divide by the number of feet per mile (5,280) so the answer will be in miles.

7. **(3) 2,800**   There are 1,000 meters in a kilometer, so you need to multiply 2.8 by 1,000. Move the decimal point three places to the right: 2.8 km = 2,800 m.

8. **(2) 3.92**   Multiply the number of milligrams of sodium in 1 serving (280) by the number of servings in a box (14): $280 \times 14 = 3920$. There are 1000 milligrams in 1 gram, so you need to divide 3920 by 1000. Move the decimal point three places to the left: 3920 mg = 3.92 g.

9. **(1) $600 - 70 - 100 - 150$**   Your number sense tells you that it would be easier to convert all the amounts of time into minutes and then subtract the amounts already worked from the amount promised.

10. **(4) 7**   First find the distance around the painting. You can use the formula for finding the perimeter of a rectangle:
    $P = 2l + 2w$
    $P = 2(24) + 2(18)$
    $P = 48 + 36$
    $P = 84$ inches
    Then convert 84 inches to feet by dividing by 12: $84 \div 12 = 7$ feet.

11. **(4) $1\frac{1}{4}$**   Remember that 1 c = 8 fl oz. Garth will need to add 10 fluid ounces of the syrup to the water in the punchbowl (4×2.5). Convert to cups: 10 ounces = $1\frac{1}{4}$ cups.

12. **(2) 3.425**   The number of meters gives the whole-number part of the measurement. Centimeters and millimeters are fractions of a meter. Metric measurements are expressed using decimals. 42 centimeters is $\frac{42}{100}$, or 0.42 meter. 5 millimeters is $\frac{5}{1000}$ or 0.005 meter. Together, the measurement is 3.425.

13. **(3) 2 ft 2 in**   Subtract the two lengths ($98 - 72 = 26$) and then convert from inches to feet: 26 in = 2 ft 2 in. Another way to express this amount would be $2\frac{1}{6}$ ft.

14. **(4) 8**   The formula for the perimeter of a rectangle is $P = 2l + 2w$. Substitute: $2(98) + 2(48) = 196 + 96 = 292$. Then, to convert to yards, divide the total inches by 36: $292 \div 36 = 8.111$, which is approximately 8 yd.

15. **(1) 8 lb 13 oz**   You can convert the weights to ounces on your calculator and subtract the smaller run from the larger run: Or you can subtract longhand, regrouping from the pounds column:

$$
\begin{array}{r}
32 \text{ lb} \quad 8 \text{ oz} \\
- \ 23 \text{ lb} \quad 11 \text{ oz} \\
\hline
\end{array}
$$

$$
\begin{array}{r}
31 \text{ lb} \quad 24 \text{ oz} \ (8 + 16) \\
- \ 23 \text{ lb} \quad 11 \text{ oz} \\
\hline
8 \text{ lb} \quad 13 \text{ oz}
\end{array}
$$

16. **(1) 10**   Divide 50 by $4\frac{5}{8}$. Remember, to divide by a mixed number, change the mixed number to an improper fraction. Then invert the fraction you are dividing by, and multiply. $50 \times 4\frac{5}{8} = 50 \div \frac{37}{8} = 50 \times \frac{8}{37} = \frac{400}{37} = 10\frac{30}{37}$ Since it doesn't make sense to make a fraction of a dress, discard the fractional remainder. Annika can make 10 whole dresses from the fabric.

17. **(3) 2 hr 20 min**   Divide 7 hours by 3 jobs to get $2\frac{1}{3}$ hours. Your number sense tells you that this number is the same as 2 hr 20 min.

18. **(5) 375**   If you use the fact that 1 km = 1000 m, then Tamara can run 3000 meters in 8 minutes. Set up a proportion: $\frac{3000 \text{ m}}{8 \text{ min}} = \frac{x \text{ m}}{1 \text{ min}}$. Cross multiply and then divide: $\frac{3000(1)}{8} = 375$ m.

19. **(4) 22**   Convert 5 yards to inches: $5 \times 36 = 180$ inches. Divide by 8 to get 22.5 lengths of string. Ted cannot use half a length in his seminar, so he really has only 22 full lengths of string.

20. **(2) 340**   Add the outside measurements of the garden: $80 + 90 + 50 + 70 + 30 + 20 = 340$ feet.

21. **(4) 5**   The dimensions of the vegetable garden are 50 feet by 70 feet. Find the area by multiplying: $50 \times 70 = 3500$. Divide by 800 to find the number of bags of fertilizer: $3500 \div 800 = 4$ r 300. The neighbors will need 4 whole bags of fertilizer plus part of a 5th bag. They will need to buy 5 bags to cover the garden.

22. **(1) 16 × 12**   The formula for the area of a rectangle is $A = lw$.

PROGRAM 34: FORMULAS

Skill Practice, page 155

1. **$44.91** $c = nr$ Substitute and solve: $c = 9(4.99)$.

2. **15 miles** $d = rt$ Express 45 minutes as a fraction of an hour: $d = 20(0.75)$ or $20(\frac{3}{4})$.

3. **$2496** $i = prt$ Express 48 months as 4 years: $i = 7800(0.08)(4)$.

4. **162 miles** $d = rt$ Substitute and solve: $d = 30(5.4)$.

5. **a. Plan B**   Find the interest for each plan, and compare the two amounts:
   Plan A: $(1499)(.03)(5) = \$224.85$
   Plan B: $(1499)(.04)(3) = \$179.88$
   b. $1723.85   cost + interest = $1499 + 224.85 = \$1723.85$

6. **$11.50** $c = nr$ Substitute and solve: $c = 50(0.23)$.

7. Both formulas multiply rate by some other quantity.

Skill Practice, page 157

1. **(5) base and height**   The formula is $A = \frac{1}{2}bh$.

2. **(2) $A = lw$**   The garden will be in the shape of a rectangle. You need to find its area.

3. **(4) $V = lwh$**   To answer "how much the box will hold," you need a volume formula.

4. **(1) $P = 4s$**   "The distance around" means the perimeter of this square.

Technology Connection, page 157

1. In D3: $= $ **B3*C3**

2. In D4: $= $ **D2 + D3**

Skill Practice, page 159

1. **4%**
$$
\begin{aligned}
i &= prt \\
198 &= 1650(r)3 \\
198 &= 4950r \\
\frac{198}{4950} &= .04 = 4\% = r
\end{aligned}
$$

2. **18 in**   You have enough information to find the area of the square: $12^2 = 144$ sq in. This is the same area as the area of the rectangle. Substitute the value in the area formula for a rectangle ($A = lw$ or $\frac{A}{w} = l$): $\frac{144}{8} = 18$.

3. **(2) 16**
$$
\begin{aligned}
d &= rt \\
52 &= r(3.25) \\
r &= \frac{52}{3.25} = 16 \text{ mph}
\end{aligned}
$$

4. **$67.95**   Use the total cost formula and solve for rate: $c = nr$ or $r = \frac{c}{n}$. Substitute and solve: $\frac{339.75}{5} = \$67.95$.

5. **405 feet**
$$
\begin{aligned}
P &= 2l + 2w \\
1270 &= 2l + 2(230) \\
1270 - 460 &= 2l \\
810 &= 2l \\
l &= 405 \text{ ft}
\end{aligned}
$$

6. **About $4\frac{1}{2}$ hours**
$$
\begin{aligned}
d &= rt \\
275 &= 60t \\
t &= \frac{275}{60} = 4.58
\end{aligned}
$$
Rounded to the nearest half hour, $4.58 \approx 4.5 = 4\frac{1}{2}$ hr.

7. **(3) 18**   Use $P = 4s$. Express the perimeter in inches (6 feet = 72 inches):
$$
\begin{aligned}
72 &= 4s \\
s &= \frac{72}{4} = 18 \text{ inches}
\end{aligned}
$$

Skill Practice, page 161

1. $\dfrac{51.05 + 42.50 + 68.62}{3}$ Add the three bills, then divide by the number of bills.

2. $\dfrac{17.26}{12.6}$ Use the total cost formula: $c = nr$. Solve for the rate: $r = c/n$.

3. $\dfrac{340}{55}$ Use the distance formula: $d = rt$. Solve for time: $t = d/r$.

4. **(4)** $\dfrac{480}{24}$ Use the formula $A = lw$.
$$480 = 24w$$
$$w = \dfrac{480}{24}$$

Social Studies Connection, page 161

In January, the average temperature is about 25° in Grand Junction and about 42° in Atlanta.
The average temperature is higher in Atlanta.

Skill Practice, page 163

1. **80 square feet** $A = bh = 8(10) = 80$
2. **60 square feet** $A = \frac{1}{2}bh = \frac{1}{2}(12)(10) = 6(10) = 60$ sq ft
3. **37.6 feet** $P = a + b + c = 10 + 15.6 + 12 = 37.6$ feet
4. **180 square feet** Find the area of the larger path: $A = 12(10) = 120$. Add the area of the path to the area of the flower garden (from item 2): $A = 120 + 60 = 180$ sq ft.

Skill Practice, page 165

1. **432 cubic feet** $V = lwh = 6(8)(9) = 432$ cu ft
2. **42.875 cubic centimeters** $V = s^3 = (3.5)^3 = 42.875$ cu cm
3. **9 cubic yards** First find the number of cubic feet in one cubic yard. Since 1 yd = 3 ft, 1 cu yd $= 3^3 = 27$ cu ft in one cubic yard. Next, convert the volume of the storage unit to cubic yards: 243 cubic feet ÷ 27 = 9 cubic yards.
4. **9072 cubic inches** Remember to change 1.5 feet to 18 inches before multiplying: $V = lwh = 36(18)(14) = 9072$ cu in.

Problem Solver Connection, page 165

After 3 hours of travel, the train would have traveled 360 km. Since the train actually traveled less than 3 hours, choice (5) can be eliminated.
Choice (4) 330 must be correct.

GED Practice, pages 166–168

1. **(5)** $A = \frac{1}{2}bh$ Since the figure is a triangle, the appropriate formula to solve the problem is $A = \frac{1}{2}bh$, where b = base and h = height.

2. **(4)** $\dfrac{49}{3.50}$ Isolate the unknown variable, number of units (rolls of masking tape), in the total cost formula, $c = nr$. To do this, divide both sides of the equation by r, giving you $\frac{c}{r} = n$. Substitute the known numbers.

3. **(2) 10.75** Remember to compute the mean, or average, by adding all the units and dividing by the number of units: $\dfrac{(12.75 + 16 + 3.5)}{3} = \dfrac{32.25}{3} = 10.75$.

4. **(2) $0.39** Using the formula $c = nr$, solve for r: $\frac{c}{n} = r$. Substitute the known values and divide: $\frac{9.36}{24} = 0.39$.

5. **(4) $725(0.04)(4)** The correct choice is the simple-interest formula, $i = prt$, with its variables replaced by the known numbers from Plan B.

6. **(3) $833.75** Remember that the simple interest formula is $i = prt$. Substitute the Plan A values you know: $i = \$725(0.06)(2.5)$. Multiply: $i = \$108.75$. The question asks how much Nuyen will pay "in all," so add the principal to the simple interest: $\$725 + \$108.75 = \$833.75$.

7. **(3) 58** Add to find the number of miles from Lakewood to Marion: $103 + 42 = 145$ miles. The time is $2\frac{1}{2} = 2.5$ hr. Using the formula $d = rt$, solve for rate (r): $r = \frac{d}{t}$, so $r = \frac{145}{2.5} = 58$ miles per hour.

8. **(2) 4** Using the formula for perimeter, $P = 2l + 2w$, substitute your known terms: $P = 2(14) + 2(10)$. Multiply and then add: $28 + 20 = 48$. Remember to convert inches to the measurement unit asked for in the problem, <u>feet</u>: $\frac{48}{12} = 4$ feet.

9. **(1) 1463** Use the distance formula, $d = rt$, and substitute the known terms: $d = 418(3.5) = 1463$.

10. **(5) Not enough information is given.** The problem does not state how many miles Ariel walked on the fourth day, Saturday.

11. **(5)** $V = s^3$ Because all the dimensions in a cube are the same (10 cm, in this case), cube the length of one side, s, to find the volume.

12. **(3) 10** Add all five ages $(4 + 7 + 11 + 14 + 14 = 50)$, and divide by the number of children: $\frac{50}{5} = 10$.

13. **(4) 11** The median is the middle number in the list of children's ages: 4, 7, 11, 14, 14.

14. **(2)** $\dfrac{10.35}{2.3}$ Isolate the length in the area formula of a rectangle: $A = lw$, so $l = \frac{A}{w}$. Divide the total area by the one known side.

15. **(4) 2(16) + 2(12)** Substitute the known terms into the perimeter formula for a rectangle.

16. **(3) 150** You know the time (5 hours) and the rate (60 miles per hour). Substitute the values in the distance formula to find distance driven round-trip: $d = rt = 60 \times 5$. Luisa drove 300 miles <u>round-trip</u>. That means the distance <u>one way</u> from Sierra to Clayton is half that amount, or 150 miles. The information that Luisa drove on both Tuesday and Thursday is unnecessary, or extra information.

17. **(3) 320** Multiply the length by the width to find the area of a rectangle: $20 \times 16 = 320$ square feet.

18. **(1) 8(4)(6)** The volume of a rectangular container is found by multiplying the length by the width by the height.

19. **(4) Elm Place**   Use number sense to solve this problem. In each column, Elm Place has the most expensive homes sold compared to the other three streets, so it will also have the highest mean, or average, price.

20. **(3) $67,350**   Put all 12 selling prices in order from greatest to least or least to greatest. The two middle prices in the list are $68,200 and $66,500. To find the median, find the mean of these two prices: 68,200 + 66,500 = 134,700, and $\frac{134,700}{2}$ = $67,350.

21. **(4) 12**   You would divide by the number of homes sold, which is 4 streets × 3 homes each = 12.

PROGRAM 35: GEOMETRY

Skill Practice, page 175
1. **120°** $180° - 60° = 120°$
2. **45°** $\frac{1}{2} × 90° = 45°$
3. **68°** $180° - 112° = 68°$
4. **40°** $90° - 50° = 40°$
5. **60°** $180° - 90° - 30° = 60°$
6. **130°** $180° - 50° = 130°$
7. **90°** $180° - 90° = 90°$
8. **True**   Angle ABF measures 180°, which is the sum of three angles: ∠ABC, ∠CBE, and ∠EBF. The sum of the known angles is 80°, so the remaining angle, ∠CBE, must measure 100°.

Skill Practice, page 177
1. *a, d, e, h, i, k,* and *l*
2. 140°
3. *g, j,* and *n*
4. **(4) Angle *f* measures 50°.**   Angle *f* corresponds to ∠*m*, which is the vertical angle to a 50° angle. Therefore, ∠*f* also measures 50°.

Science Connection, page 177
The star is 25° above the horizon.   It is midway between the mark for 20° and the mark for 30°.

Skill Practice, page 179
1. **$1\frac{1}{4}$ inch or 1.25 inch**   Set up a proportion: $\frac{4}{5} = \frac{1}{x}$. Solve: $5 × 1 ÷ 4 = 1\frac{1}{4}$ or 1.25.
2. **9.6**   The base of the larger triangle is 16. The leg of the larger triangle is 8 + 12, or 20. Set up a proportion comparing the larger triangle to the smaller similar triangle: $\frac{16}{20} = \frac{x}{12}$. Solve: $16 × 12 ÷ 20 = 9.6$.
3. **No**   Remember that the sum of the interior angles of a triangle is 180° and that a right angle measures 90°. Thus, the missing angle in triangle A must measure 40°, and the missing angle in triangle B must measure 60°. Because they have different angles, the triangles cannot be similar.

4. **(4) ΔDEF is an isosceles triangle.**   The triangles are similar, which means they both are the same shape with equal corresponding angles, but they are different in size. Since ΔABC has two equal sides, ΔDEF also has two equal sides, making it an isosceles triangle.

Skill Practice, page 181
1. To solve each problem, use the Pythagorean relationship and insert the values you are given.
   a. **15** $c^2 = 9^2 + 12^2$, so $c^2 = 81 + 144 = 225$, and $c = \sqrt{225} = 15$.
   b. **24** $10^2 + b^2 = 26^2$, so $b^2 = 676 - 100 = 576$, and $b = \sqrt{576} = 24$.
   c. **7** $a^2 + 24^2 = 25^2$, so $a^2 = 625 - 576 = 49$, and $a = \sqrt{49} = 7$.
2. **(3) Between 11 and 12 inches**   Use the Pythagorean relationship:
$$8^2 + 8^2 = c^2$$
$$64 + 64 = c^2$$
$$128 = c^2$$
You know the square of 11 is 121 and the square of 12 is 144. Therefore, the square root of 128 must be between 11 and 12.

Calculator Power, page 181
10.3 cm   Use the Pythagorean relationship: $5^2 + 9^2 = c^2$.
Calculator: | 5 | x^2 | + | 9 | x^2 | = | ▭ 106. |
Press the square root key to get 10.29563. Round to the nearest tenth, or 10.3.

Skill Practice, page 183
1. **$471.00**   First find the area of the patio: $A = \pi r^2 = 3.14 × 5^2 = 78.5$ square feet. Then find the total cost: $c = nr = 78.5 × 6 = \$471$.
2. **17.27 feet**   Use the circumference formula: $C = \pi d = 3.14 × 5.5 = 17.27$ feet.
3. **The rectangular cake has the greater area.** The rectangular cake has an area of 117 square inches (9 × 13). The circular cake has an area of about 113.04 square inches ($3.14 × 6^2$). (The radius of a 12-inch pan is 6 inches.)
4. a. **about 18.84 meters**   Use the circumference formula: $C = \pi d = 3.14 × 6 = 18.84$.
   b. **about 28.26 meters**   The diameter of the outer circle is 9 meters (6 + 1.5 + 1.5). Use the circumference formula: $C = \pi d = 3.14 × 9 = 28.26$.
   c. **about 35.3 square meters**   To find the area of the walkway, find the area of the pool and walkway combined, then subtract the area of the pool. Use these facts: The diameter of the pool is 6 meters, so the radius is $\frac{6}{2}$, or 3 meters. The width of the walkway is 1.5 meters. Combine to find the radius of the entire figure: 3 + 1.5 = 4.5 meters. Use the formula $A = \pi r^2$ to find the area of the pool and walkways combined:

A = 3.14×4.5^2.

   = 3.14×20.25

   = 63.585 square meters

Now find the area of the pool using the same formula and 3 meters for the radius:

A = 3.14×3^2

   = 3.14×9

   = 28.26 square meters

Subtract to find the difference: $63.585 - 28.26 = 35.325$. Rounded to the nearest tenth, the area of the walkway is 35.3 square meters. *Note:* If you rounded as you worked, your answer might be slightly different. Each time you round, your answer becomes less accurate.

Skill Practice, page 185

1. **about 50.24 cubic feet**   Use 2 feet for 24 inches: $V = r^2h = 3.14 \times 2^2 \times 4 = 50.24$.

2. **about 6.28 cubic meters**   Use a radius of 0.5 meter: $V = r^2h = 3.14 \times 0.5^2 \times 8 = 6.28$.

3. **about 2826 cubic inches**   Use 36 inches for 3 feet: $V = r^2h = 3.14 \times 5^2 \times 36 = 2826$.

4. **6 cubic yards**   Find the volume in feet: $V = r^2h = 3.14 \times 5^2 \times 2 = 157$. Then divide by 27 to convert to cubic yards: $\frac{157}{27}$ is about 5.815. Round to 6 cubic yards.

History Connection, page 185

A circle's circumference is slightly more than three times the size of its diameter.

GED Practice, pages 186–188

1. **(3) 43.96**   On your calculator, use the circumference formula, $C = \pi d$, where $\pi = 3.14$: $C = 3.14(14) = 43.96$.

2. **(1) similar**   The two triangles have the same shape and the same corresponding angles; their corresponding sides are in proportion to each other.

3. **(3) 40°**   In an isosceles triangle, the two angles opposite the two equal sides are equal. Thus, $\angle b = 70°$. To find $\angle a$, subtract the sum of $70° + 70°$ from 180° (the total of the three angles in a triangle) for a remaining 40° angle. Since $\angle d$ and $\angle a$ are equal angles, $\angle d = 40°$.

4. **(5) 3.14 × 6²**   Use the formula for finding the area of a circle: $A = \pi r^2$. Find the radius of the circle by dividing the diameter by 2: $\frac{12}{2} = 6$ feet. Substitute the values from the problem into the formula using 3.14 for pi: $A = 3.14 \times 6^2$.

5. **(3) 16**   Using the formula for circumference of a circle, substitute the known terms: $C = \pi d$, so $d = \frac{C}{\pi} = \frac{50.24}{\pi}$. On your calculator, divide 50.24 by pi, 3.14. The result is 16 feet.

6. **(5) Not enough information is given.**   Look at the formula for volume of a cylinder. You need the height of the cylinder to compute its volume.

7. **(3) 122°**   Since angles 4 and 5 combine to form a line, their sum is 180°. Subtract to find the missing angle: $180° - 58° = 122°$.

8. **(4) 67°**   Remembering that complementary angles total 90°, subtract: $90° - 23° = 67°$.

9. **(3) 24**   An equilateral triangle has sides of equal length, so 3 sides × 8 inches = 24 inches.

10. **(1)** $r^2 = \frac{50.24}{3.14}$ If $A = \pi r^2$, then $r^2 = \frac{A}{\pi} = \frac{50.24}{3.14}$.

11. **(4) 15**   The path Ana's team jogs is a right triangle. Because you are looking for the hypotenuse of this triangle, you can use the formula for the Pythagorean relationship: $c^2 = a^2 + b^2$. Substitute and solve: $c^2 = 9^2 + 12^2 = 81 + 144 = 225$. To solve for c, find the square root of 225: $\sqrt{225} = 15$. However, notice that the measurements of this triangle can reduce to the common 3:4:5 ratio. Both legs have been multiplied by 3, so the missing hypotenuse must be 5 × 3, or 15.

12. **(3) 300**   Set up a proportion and solve: $\frac{\text{post height}}{\text{post shadow}} = \frac{\text{building height}}{\text{building shadow}}$, so $\frac{4\text{ m}}{1.6\text{ m}} = \frac{h}{120\text{ m}}$. Cross multiply: $4(120) = 1.6h$. Divide: $\frac{480}{1.6} = 300$.

13. **(4)** $\angle$ **PQT**   The sum of two supplementary angles is equal to 180°, or the measure of the degrees in a straight line. You know that points P, Q, and R lie on a straight line. $\angle$ TQR forms one portion of the line. The angle that completes the line when combined with $\angle$ TQR is $\angle$ PQT.

14. **(3)** $17^2 - 3^2 = b^2$ Use the Pythagorean relationship: $c^2 = a^2 + b^2$. Substitute the known amounts, and isolate the unknown variable.

15. **(2) 3.14**   First use the formula for the circumference for a circle: $C = \pi d$. Substitute and solve for the diameter: $d = \frac{6.28}{3.14} = 2$. The radius of a circle is half its diameter: $\frac{2}{2} = 1$. Now that you know the radius, you can solve for the area: $A = \pi r^2 = 3.14(1)^2 = 3.14$ square meters.

16. **(4) between 15 and 20 inches**   Estimate the circumference of the circle as 3 (pi rounded) times its diameter (twice the radius, or 3 inches × 2 = 6): 3 × 6 = 18. This approximation falls between 15 and 20 inches.

17. **(3) 78°**   Angles 1 and 5 have the same measure, given as 102°. Since angles 5 and 6 are supplementary angles, you can find the measure of $\angle$ 6 by subtracting from 180°: $180° - 102° = 78°$.

18. **(2)** $\angle$ **3**   Line Z is a transversal to the parallel lines X and Y. When a transversal crosses parallel lines, groups of corresponding and vertical angles are formed. Angles 1 and 5 are corresponding angles. Angle 7 is a vertical angle to $\angle$ 5, and $\angle$ 7 corresponds to $\angle$ 3. Thus, angles 1, 3, 5, and 7 all have equal measures, but only one of these appears among the answer choices: $\angle$ 3.

19. **(5) 75**   The question asks for an approximation, so round pi to 3 and use the area formula: $A = \pi r^2 \approx 3(5)^2 = 3(25) = 75$.

20. **(3) right**   The sum of the interior angles of a triangle is 180°. You can find the missing angle by adding the known angles and subtracting from 180°: $33° + 57° = 90°$, and $180° - 90° = 90°$. The missing angle is a right angle; therefore, the triangle must be a right triangle.

21. **(1) 8**   Sketch a picture of lines G and H and the perpendicular intersecting line A. Remember that line A will cross *both* lines G and H, by definition of a line. Eight angles are formed, all of which will be right angles, or 90-degree angles.

22. **(5) Neither∠Y nor∠Z equals 36°.**   In a scalene triangle, there are no equal angles (or equal sides). Since ∠X equals 36°, the other angles must have different measures.

23. **(4) 500**   Use the formula for volume of a cylinder: $V = \pi r^2 h$. Since you need an approximate answer, round pi to 3. Substitute and solve: $V = 3 \times 4^2 \times 10 = 3 \times 16 \times 10 = 480$. You know the answer will be a bit more than 480, so your best choice is (4).

Alternate Math Formats, pages 189–190

24. **2.6**   Divide 2600 by 1000, since 1000 m = 1 km.

25. **7**   18 in × 6 = 108 in, but you need the amount in feet. Since 12 in = 1 ft, 108 in = 9 ft. Subtract to find the remaining amount: 16 ft − 9 ft = 7 ft.

26. **144**   Find the missing distances. The total length of the diagram is 44 ft (28 + 16), so the missing length at the bottom of the diagram must be 44 − 24 = 20 ft. The total width is 28 ft (20 + 8), so the missing width at the top of the diagram must be 28 − 20 = 8 ft. Add all measurements: $20 + 28 + 8 + 16 + 20 + 24 + 8 + 20 = 144$ ft.

27. **816**   Break the space into three rectangles. The measurements are 20 by 16 ft, 20 by 20 ft, and 12 by 8 ft. You will need to use the other measurements on the diagram to calculate the length and width of the smallest rectangle. Find the area of each rectangle using the formula $A = lw$: $20 \times 16 = 320$
$20 \times 20 = 400$
$12 \times 8 = 96$
Then add the areas: $320 + 400 + 96 = 816$ sq ft.

28. **156**   Use the formula for finding simple interest: $i = prt = 650 \times 0.08 \times 3 = \$156$

29. **50.2**   Use the formula for finding the area of a circle: $A = \pi r^2$. The radius is 4 cm, which is half the diameter. $A = 3.14 \times 4^2 = 3.14 \times 16 = 50.24$. Round to the nearest tenth.

30. **12**   Use the Pythagorean relationship: $c^2 = a^2 + b^2$. $13^2 = 5^2 + b^2$
$169 = 25 + b^2$
$144 = b^2$
$12 = b$

31. **23**   The sum of the interior angles of a triangle is always 180°. You know that one angle is a right angle measuring 90°. The measure of another angle is given as 67°. Solve for the missing angle:
$180 = 90 + 67 + x$
$180 = 157 + x$
$23 = x$

32. **42.3**   Use the formula for finding the area of a square: $A = s^2 = 6\frac{1}{2} \times 6\frac{1}{2} = 42.25$. Round to the nearest tenth.

33. **1296**   Use the formula for finding the volume of a rectangular container:
$V = lwh = 18 \times 6 \times 12 = 1296$ cubic feet.

34. **95**   The sum of supplementary angles is 180°. Subtract to find the unknown angle measurement: $180° - 85° = 95°$.

35. **1140**   Divide 3.42 by 3, then multiply by 1000 to convert your answer to milliliters.

PROGRAM 36: DATA ANALYSIS, PART ONE

Skill Practice, page 197

1. a. **True**
   b. **False**
   c. **False**
   d. **True**

2. **New York**   You can quickly see that only New York and Los Angeles increased by more than 3,000,000 from 1900 to 1990. Subtract to find the exact difference for each city.

3. **(5) $4\frac{1}{2}$**   Use a calculator to divide New York's population by Houston's. You can also round to the hundred thousands place and estimate an answer. Houston's population rounds to 1,600,000, and New York's rounds to 7,300,000. Compare the numbers 16 and 73. The number 73 is about $4\frac{1}{2}$ times greater than 16.

4. **Memphis**   This city's population dropped by 6%. The next smallest change was Nashville's, with an increase of 7%.

5. **No**   The chart does not give you any information about the actual size of the population of the cities.

Skill Practice, page 199

1. **$1,125,000**   Multiply $4\frac{1}{2}$ by $250,000.

2. **(4) $1,875,000**   The row for basketball players contains $7\frac{1}{2}$ symbols more than the row for football players. Multiply $7\frac{1}{2}$ by $250,000.

3. a. **False**
   b. **False**
   c. **True**
   d. **True**   Each symbol represents $250,000, so compare the number of symbols and see if the difference is less than 1:
   $5\frac{1}{4} - 4\frac{1}{2} = 5\frac{1}{4} - 4\frac{2}{4} = \frac{3}{4} = 0.75$.

Problem Solver Connection, page 199
There are two item sets on page 197. Items 1 through 3 are based on the first table. Items 4 and 5 are based on the chart.

Skill Practice, page 201
1. **About 140 customers**   Both bars fall between 60 and 80. The 19149 bar falls short of the halfway mark and probably represents 65. The 19136 bar represents about 75. Add: $65 + 75 = 140$.
2. **19136**   The 19124 bar represents about 40 customers. Look for the bar that is closest to 80 customers.
3. **About $1600**   The food booths earned about $4400, and the rides earned about $2800. Subtract: $4400 − $2800 = 1600. Consider your answer correct if it is between $1400 and $1800.
4. **Rides**
5. **Family videos**
6. **(4) The ratio of drama to family videos was about 3:2.**   Evaluate the truthfulness of each statement. There were about 60 drama rentals, compared with 40 family rentals. The ratio 60:40 reduces to 3:2.

Skill Practice, page 203
1. About $82
2. **CTR stock**   You are looking for the greatest change in price, not the highest price.
3. **$450**   Multiply $90 by 5.
4. **CTR stock**   The line representing CTR is climbing faster than the line for ARL. The CTR line is likely to cross the ARL line in the very near future.
5. About $20

Social Studies Connection, page 203
The statement is false.   Look at the two bars labeled Ms. Black. Although the bar for the 18th District is about twice the length of the bar for the 12th District, the bar for the 18th District represents about 600 votes, while the bar for the 12th District represents about 400 votes. The number 600 is not two times 400.

Skill Practice, page 205
1. **6 times**   The 29% for housing is close to 30%. That is about 6 times greater than 5% for savings.
2. **Yes**   You can set up a proportion: The ratio of 29% to $826.50 is equal to the ratio of 14% to what number? You can also use your knowledge of percent. Since 29% is equal to $826.50, what was the Miller's monthly income? Use your calculator to divide $826.50 by 0.29, or write a proportion. The Miller's monthly income was $2850. Now you can use this amount, the value of the whole circle, to find the value of any of the sections.

3. **Transportation**   The fraction $\frac{1}{10}$ is equal to 10%, which is closest to the percent for transportation.
4. **$12.50**   One-fourth of each dollar (25 cents, or 25%) is spent on the library, and $\frac{1}{4}$ of $50 is $12.50.
5. **$\frac{2}{3}$**   Subtract $\frac{1}{3}$, the fraction sold to adults, from 1, the whole (total ticket sales).

Skill Practice, page 207
1. **$\frac{3}{10}$** $30\% = \frac{30}{100} = \frac{3}{10}$
2. **160**   Find 25% of 640, the total books donated.
3. **352**   Add the other sections: $20\% + 25\% + 10\% = 55\%$. Find 55% of the total donated: $640 \times 0.55 = 352$ books.
4. **20%**   The 15% section on the present graph represents 96 books: $640 \times 0.15 = 96$. On the new graph, the science section will represent 136 books: $96 + 40 = 136$. The total of all books will increase from 640 to 680. Find what percent 136 is of 680: $136 \div 680 = 0.2 = 20\%$.

Technology Connection, page 207
Answers will vary. Each graph has a different emphasis. The graph with multiple bars makes it easy to compare the data from the three stores. You can easily see which store had the greatest sales in each quarter. The three-dimensional graph emphasizes how much better the store in the east did during the third quarter. The line graph is useful for seeing trends in how the stores are doing over time.

GED Practice, pages 208–210
1. **(4) Central States and New England States**   Use addition to evaluate each of the options. Only the Central States maps (about 2,300 units sold) and the New England States maps (about 2,800 units sold) total about 5,000.
2. **(3) 2.5**   The company sold twice as many this year as last year, so you need to find half of this year's sales of the map. Mentally draw a line from the end of the bar to the scale to see that 5 thousand units were sold this year. Divide by 2: $\frac{5}{2} = 2.5$.
3. **(2) $0.01**   Read the key to learn that Murphy's Gas is represented by the dashed line. Find March 4 (3/4) on the bottom scale and move your finger up to where the dashed line crosses, at $1.08. The solid line represents Gas & Go, which crosses March 4 at $1.07. The difference is $1.08 − $1.07 = 0.01.
4. **(5) 15($1.09)**   Multiply the number of gallons (15) by the price of gas at Gas & Go on March 5 ($1.09).
5. **(5) Not enough information is given.**   You do not know how many gallons of gasoline were sold by each station or to each customer.

6. **(3) $3500** Because each symbol in the pictograph represents $1000 worth of rentals, the $3\frac{1}{2}$ symbols across from the July label represent $3\frac{1}{2} \times \$1000$, or $3500.

7. **(2) June** By scanning the graph, you note that the most symbols—and therefore the most rental money received—are in the month of June.

8. **(2) $3000** In Stan's best month, June, he had rentals of $4500; in his worst month, September, he had rentals of $1500. (*Note* that $\frac{1}{2}$ of a symbol is worth $\frac{1}{2}$ of $1000.) Subtract for your answer.

9. **(3) 200,000** The bar for Lawrence County for May is at 800; the bar for March is at 600. Subtract: $800 - 600 = 200$. The scale is marked in thousands of pounds, so multiply by 1,000: $200 \times 1,000 = 200,000$.

10. **(4) April** Look closely at the unshaded bars, which represent Mansfield County. The bars climb steadily until the bar for April, when its value drops slightly.

11. **(2) 25%** Work with the amounts shown by the bars. You don't need to multiply by 1000 to solve this problem, because the proportions will stay the same. For Lawrence County, recycling in March was at 600. The bar for April is at about 750. Subtract to find the amount of change: $750 - 600 = 150$. Then set up a proportion: $\frac{150}{600} = \frac{x}{100}$. Solve: $150 \times 100 \div 600 = 25\%$.

12. **(3) 17 million** Read the labels on the stacked bar graph carefully. Find the month of May and combine the two sections for round and square widgets. Together, they reach between 16 and 18 million units: about 17 million.

13. **(5) 10 million** Compare only the triangle portions of the bar for April and July. In April, the triangle portion goes from 13 to 31 on the scale, representing 18 million. In July, the triangle portion goes from 20 to 28, representing 8 million. Subtract to find the difference: $18 - 8 = 10$ million.

14. **(2) 31 million** Add only the portions of the bar representing the square widgets: 4 million (April), 10 million (May), 2 million (June), and 15 million (July). $4 + 10 + 2 + 15 = 31$.

15. **(3) 25%** Add to find the total spent on Office Supplies and Fund-Raising Expenses: $1,000 + \$2,000 = \$3,000$. Then find what percent $3,000 is of $12,000, the total of the service club's expenses. You can also solve the problem by looking carefully at the graph. Mentally combine the sections for Office Supplies and Fund-Raising Expenses. These sections make up about $\frac{1}{4}$ of the entire circle. Since $\frac{1}{4} = 25\%$, the best answer is 25%.

16. **(5) Friday** Run one finger down each column for both Icies and Slushies, and compare day by day.

17. **(1) Monday** For each day, mentally add the Smoothies sold to the Snowcones sold. Combined, the most sold were on Monday.

PROGRAM 36: DATA ANALYSIS, PART TWO

Skill Practice, page 217

1. convenience sampling

2. **2:1** Self-serve copying has 12 tally marks, and color copying has 6. Reduce the ratio 12:6 to lowest terms.

3. **76%** Find what percent 19 is of 25.

4. **(5) Not enough information is given.** The frequency table and line plot show different types of information. Although all 25 customers are included on both, there is no way to tell how the data values on the frequency table and the line plot are related.

5. **(3) $\frac{1}{4}$** Six out of 25 is 24%, which is close to 25%. You can also think that 6 out of 25 is almost the same as 6 out of 24, which reduces to $\frac{1}{4}$.

Skill Practice, page 219

1. $20

2. $80

3. **$70** Subtract: $80 - \$10 = \$70$.

4. **20%** Four out of 20 donations were more than $40: $\frac{4}{20} = \frac{1}{5} = 20\%$.

Social Studies Connection, page 219

Three percent of 125,300 is 3,759. The actual population may be as low as 121,541.

Skill Practice, page 221

1. **$87,110** The sum of the selling prices is $871,100. Divide by 10, the number of data values, to find the mean.

2. **$86,300** The two middle prices are $87,600 and $85,000. Find the sum and divide by 2.

3. **$72,000** This is the only price that occurs more than once.

4. **The mode** The mode is also the lowest price. This is more likely to be a coincidence than an indicator that $72,000 is the typical selling price.

5. **The mean will be affected the most.** The value $130,000 is much higher than most of the other values in the list. The new mean would be about $91,009, a change of nearly $4,000. The new median would be $87,600, a change of a little more than $1,000. An outlier generally affects the mean more than the median.

Skill Practice, page 223

1. **$475** Reynaldo wanted to pay $500 per month for six months. He has paid a total of $2525. Subtract to find the amount he has to pay in the sixth month: $3000 - \$2525 = \$475$.

2. **86 points** Ninety points multiplied by five assignments is 450 points. Maggie already has 364 points. She needs 86 more to get an A.

3. **$15,288** She averages $294 per week. Multiply: $294 × 52 = $15,288.

4. **They are over budget by $180.** Multiply $120 by 12 to find the amount they should have spent. Subtract to find the difference.

5. **No** He needed 5 more sales. Multiply 17 by 5 to find the number of sales he made in the 5-day period. Then compare the result with his goal.

Problem Solver Connection, page 223

Count the digits on the right. There are 9 scores represented on the plot. Since the number of scores is an odd number, you know that there will be a single score in the middle. Using the numbers in the right column, work towards the middle. You may want to cross off the scores as you go. First, cross off 1 (for 91) from the top row and 9 (for 69) from the bottom. Next, cross off 1 (for 91) from the top row and 0 (for 80) from the 2nd row. Keep going. Cross off 3 (for 83) and 9 for (89) from the second row. Finally, cross off 3 (for 83) and 7 (for 87). The score in the middle is 83.

```
9 | 1 1
8 | 0 3 3 3 7 9
7 |
6 | 9
```

GED Practice, pages 224–226

1. **(4) 147** You can calculate this one on your calculator. Add the scores and divide by 5 for the mean, or average, score.

2. **(2) Spanish** This choice has the fewest tally marks.

3. **(3) German** Add the total number of tally marks (30) and multiply by 20% (or find $\frac{1}{5}$ of 30) to arrive at 6. The language with 6 tally marks next to it is German.

4. **(2) $60.25** Add the two middle values: $55.27 + $65.23 = $120.50. Divide this sum by 2, which will give you the median, the value halfway between the two middle values: $\frac{\$120.50}{2} = \$60.25$.

5. **(4) 1 hour 42 minutes** Add the three waiting times (23 + 41 + 38 minutes) to get 102 minutes. Remember to convert into hours: 102 = 1 hour (60 minutes) and 42 minutes.

6. **(5) $\frac{23 + 41 + 38 + 22}{4}$** Add all four rides' waiting times together and divide by 4.

7. **(5) Pace** In evaluating the data, you can determine that 4,000 of 30,000 votes is about 13%. The candidate who received 13% of the vote is Pace.

8. **(2) 6,000** If you add up all five candidates' percentages, they equal 100% of the vote. Therefore, just divide 30,000 (total number of votes) by 5 (number of candidates who received votes): 30,000 ÷ 5 = 6,000 votes.

9. **(4) $20.14** The median is the middle value of a set of values. If you have an even number of values, find the average, or mean, of the two middle values. The middle values are $19.69 and $20.59. Add: $19.69 + $20.59 = $40.28. Divide by 2: $40.28 ÷ 2 = $20.14.

10. **(2) mode** The mode is the value that occurs most often in a set of data. In this case, analyzing the line plot will show that the mode is the size 12 dress. *Note* that *average* and *mean* are the same thing.

11. **(4) Medium sizes are more popular than small or large sizes.** The medium sizes are size 10 and 12. Combined, more dresses of these sizes were sold than any other grouping.

12. **(4) 9** Analyzing the line plot, determine that in May Ming-Yi sold 3 of this dress in size 14. In June she sold 3 times as many: 3 × 3 = 9.

13. **(2) 2** There is a gap at $300 and another from $1200 to $1300.

14. **(5) $1400** The single value at $1400 is much greater than the other values on the plot and is separated from the rest of the values by a gap.

15. **(2) $600** There are 25 values on the plot, so the 13th value is the median, or middle value. Count off the 13 values starting at either the lowest or highest value on the plot. The middle value is in the column labeled $600.

16. **(3) 10** Add all five ages (4 + 7 + 11 + 14 + 14 = 50), and divide by the number of children: $\frac{50}{5} = 10$.

17. **(4) 11** The median is the middle number in the list of children's ages: 4, 7, 11, 14, 14.

18. **(5) $\frac{131}{7}$** Add all of the Rosarian family members' ages together (remember, two twins at age 14): 4 + 7 + 11 + 14 + 14 + 38 + 43 = 131. Divide by the number of family members now being analyzed, which is 7.

19. **(2) 4** Since Pat's age is 43 and the middle child (median) is 11, divide: $\frac{43}{11} = 3.9$, or approximately 4. Or you can estimate before dividing: $\frac{43}{11}$ is close to $\frac{44}{11}$, which equals 4.

PROGRAM 37: STATISTICS AND PROBABILITY

Skill Practice, page 233

1. **(4) The number of crimes in the small town is too small to draw a meaningful conclusion.**

2. The library committee wants to find out what community members think of the library, yet they plan to survey only those people who choose to use the library. This plan will completely ignore the views of those who have chosen not to use the library because of their dissatisfaction with its services. The survey should be administered to include members of the community that do not currently use the library.

3. The students may be making progress. Even though the test scores have declined, the margin of error for the test results is plus or minus 4%. Depending on the ability of the test to accurately measure performance, students' reading ability for 1997 may have been as low as 80% and their reading ability for 1999 may have been as high as 86%. The teachers would be wise to give their observations at least as much weight as the test scores.

4. **Yes** Considering the margin of error, math performance for 1997 could have been as high as 80%, and math performance for 1999 may have been as low as 82%. Even considering the possibility of error, the scores show an increase of at least 2 percentage points.

Skill Practice, page 235

1. $\frac{1}{4}$ $\frac{10}{40} = \frac{1}{4}$, or 25%

2. $\frac{3}{10}$ Add the number of blue and green outcomes, and place the sum over 40. $8 + 4 = 12$, and $\frac{12}{40} = \frac{3}{10}$, or 30%

3. $\frac{3}{5}$ You can either count the spins that are not black, or count black and subtract from 40: $40 - 16 = 24$, and $\frac{24}{40} = \frac{3}{5}$, or 60%.

4. Your sections may be in a different order, but each color should take up about the same fraction of the total circle as shown to right.

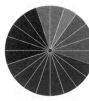

Skill Practice, page 237

1. **(3)** $\frac{3}{10}$ Count the combinations that contain neither C nor F. Then write a ratio comparing that number to 20, the number of possible combinations: $\frac{6}{20} = \frac{3}{10}$, or 30%.

2. $\frac{5}{18}$ **or 28%**   There are 36 possible dice rolls. Remember that the combination 2 and 3 is different than 3 and 2, even though the sums are the same. Count the number of rolls that total more than 8, and compare to 36, the number of possible rolls: $\frac{10}{36} = \frac{5}{18}$, or about 28%.

3. $\frac{1}{100}$ **or 1%**   Write a probability ratio and reduce: $\frac{3}{300} = \frac{1}{100}$, or 1%.

Science Connection, page 237

The possible pairings are R_1R_2, R_1r_2, r_1R_2, and r_1r_2. One out of the four offspring will be white.

Skill Practice, page 239

1. $\frac{1}{8}$ For each coin, the probability that the toss will come up tails is $\frac{1}{2}$. Multiply to find the combined probability: $\frac{1}{2} \times \frac{1}{2} \times \frac{1}{2} = \frac{1}{8}$.

2. $\frac{10}{21}$ Before a card is drawn, 5 out of 7 cards are hearts. Assume the first card is a heart. Of the cards that are left, 4 out of 6 are hearts. Multiply the two probabilities: $\frac{5}{7} \times \frac{4}{6} = \frac{20}{42} = \frac{10}{21}$.

3. $\frac{1}{4}$ Of the 8 equal sections, 2 are labeled "2," and $\frac{2}{8}$ reduces to $\frac{1}{4}$.

4. $\frac{25}{64}$ On either spin, there is a $\frac{5}{8}$ chance of not spinning 4. Multiply: $\frac{5}{8} \times \frac{5}{8} = \frac{25}{64}$.

5. $\frac{9}{64}$ The only way to get a sum of 8 in two spins is by spinning two 4s. The question is really asking, "What is the probability of spinning two 4s?" On any spin, the probability of spinning a 4 is $\frac{3}{8}$. Multiply: $\frac{3}{8} \times \frac{3}{8} = \frac{9}{64}$.

6. $\frac{1}{6}$ Hasina needs to draw the $20 and $10 bills in order to end up with $30. The possibility of getting either the $20 or $10 bill on the first draw is $\frac{2}{4}$, or $\frac{1}{2}$. Assume she gets either of those bills. The chance of drawing out the other on the second draw is $\frac{1}{3}$. Multiply: $\frac{1}{2} \times \frac{1}{3} = \frac{1}{6}$.

7. **(2)** $\frac{1}{11}$ After Grant's name is drawn, 11 cards are left, and only one is Anna's.

8. **(5) The chance of getting a sum of 11 is $\frac{1}{18}$.** Out of the 36 possible combinations, there are only two that total 11: $5 + 6$ and $6 + 5$. Two out of 36 reduces to $\frac{1}{18}$.

Skill Practice, page 241

1. $\frac{7}{8}$ The chance of all coming up heads is $\frac{1}{2} \times \frac{1}{2} \times \frac{1}{2} = \frac{1}{8}$. Subtract $\frac{1}{8}$ from 1. The difference is $\frac{7}{8}$.

2. **(5)** $\frac{3}{5}$ A total of six cards are labeled with either a 1 or a 2. Write the probability ratio and reduce: $\frac{6}{10} = \frac{3}{5}$.

3. $\frac{1}{2}$ Four sections are labeled with even numbers, and four are labeled with odd. The probability is the same for both. Write the probability ratio and reduce: $\frac{4}{8} = \frac{1}{2}$.

Technology Connection, page 241

About $\frac{1}{4}$ of the 500 bags would have a fourth-place game piece: $\frac{1}{4} \times 500 = $ **125.** It is about **twice as hard** (half as likely) to win $500 as to win $100, since 1:18,000 is half the frequency of 1:9,000.

GED Practice, pages 242–244

1. **(3)** $\frac{1}{4}$ One dime among four coins has a 1-in-4 chance of being randomly chosen: $\frac{1}{(1+1+2)} = \frac{1}{4}$.

2. **(3) Wearhouse**   Focus on the data in the "Medium" column, rounding the statistics: $2(30 + 10 + 20) = 120$. Since Wearhouse sold 120 medium-sized sweaters, it sold about twice as many as the other stores combined. You can also use number sense. The store that sold twice as many as all the others combined would have to be the store with the greatest sales of that size.

3. **(5) 1 in 6**   The chance of getting a collector's card is $\frac{5,000}{30,000}$, which reduces to $\frac{1}{6}$.

4. **(3)** $\frac{22}{25}$ Note that you want the chance of Lee picking an orange that is _not_ starting to rot. Find the probability of $25 - 3$ fresh oranges among a total of 25 oranges: $\frac{(25-3)}{25} = \frac{22}{25}$.

5. **(2) 2%**   Waldo has 8 chances out of 400 for the winning ticket, so he has 2 chances out of 100, or a 2% probability of holding the winning ticket.

6. **(5) The ratio of blue tokens to white tokens is probably 3:1.**   By sampling the contents of the bag, Mike can predict its contents. By analyzing the data from the experiment, Mike can see that there are probably more blue tokens than white tokens in the bag, eliminating choices (1) through (4). Since the ratio of blue to white tokens during the experiment is 9:3, which reduces to 3:1, Mike can conclude that the ratio of tokens in the bag is probably 3:1.

7. **(2) $\frac{1}{4}$**   There are 40 tiles in the box, and 10 are red. Thus, $\frac{10}{40}$ of the tiles are red, which reduces to $\frac{1}{4}$.

8. **(5) $\frac{5}{8}$**   There are 25 tiles that are either red or white, so 25 out of 40 tiles are red or white. The chance of drawing a red or white tile is $\frac{25}{40}$, which reduces to $\frac{5}{8}$.

9. **(4) Add 20 red tiles.**   For the chance of drawing red to be 50%, half of the tiles in the box must be red. There are already 15 white and 15 blue, for a total of 30 nonred tiles. Adding 20 red to the 10 red already in the box would increase the total tiles in the box to 60, and the total red tiles to 30. 30 red tiles out of 60 would be 50% red.

10. **(4) $\frac{2}{9}$**   There are two possible chances to pick a red candy out of nine remaining candies. Be sure to subtract the one chosen candy from the original number of candies in the jar: $\frac{2}{(5+3+2-1)} = \frac{2}{9}$.

11. **(3) $\frac{1}{6} \times \frac{1}{6}$**   Each spin has the same chance of being an "A," a one-in-six probability. Since this is a dependent event (spinning one "A" after the other), the ratios are multiplied: $\frac{1}{6} \times \frac{1}{6}$.

12. **(2) $83\frac{1}{3}\%$**   To win a prize, Karen will have to spin "B" on her second spin, a probability of 1 in 6. Her chance of not spinning "B" is 5 in 6, or $\frac{5}{6}$, which equals $83\frac{1}{3}\%$.

13. **(1) 1470 to 1530**   The number of voters who said yes to the proposition was 1500. The survey's margin of error is 2% (plus or minus two percentage points of 1500, which is 30 voters), making the range 1500 minus 30 to 1500 plus 30, or 1470 to 1530.

14. **(3) $\frac{1}{24}$**   The probability that the first man will get the right hat is $\frac{1}{4}$. Now 3 men and 3 hats are left. The probability that the second man who tries will get his own hat is $\frac{1}{3}$. The probability for the third man is $\frac{1}{2}$. Of course, if the first three men get their own hats, then the fourth or last man must get his hat, the only hat left. The total probability is found by multiplying all these events together. $\frac{1}{4} \times \frac{1}{3} \times \frac{1}{2} \times 1 = \frac{1}{(4 \times 3 \times 2 \times 1)} = \frac{1}{24}$, or 1 in 24

15. **(2) $\frac{35}{100}$**   This set-up solution can be read, "There are 35 out of 100 chances that the bird is a goose." Notice that the answer choices were not reduced in this case.

16. **(4) $66\frac{2}{3}\%$**   Eight of the 12 sections are labeled with numbers less than 5 (1, 2, 3, or 4): $\frac{8}{12} = \frac{2}{3}$, which is a $66\frac{2}{3}\%$ chance.

17. **(2) 2 in 3**   Rethink the problem: Four of the six faces are <u>not</u> 3 or 6, so the probability is 4 in 6. Reduce to 2 in 3.

18. **(5) $\frac{3}{7}$**   There are 15 chances out of 35 that a jar of spaghetti sauce will be chosen: $\frac{15}{(15+20)} = \frac{15}{35} = \frac{3}{7}$.

19. **(3) 1 in 20**   If 5% of the shirts do not pass inspection, then 5 out of 100, or 1 out of 20, do not pass.

20. **(3) 1 in 13**   The chances of picking any one of the 4 aces are 4 in 52, or 1 in 13.

Alternate Math Formats, pages 245–246

21. **$104** $2 \times 4 \times \$13 = \$104$

22. **$11.20** $\frac{(\$9+\$8+\$11+\$15+\$13)}{5} = \$11.20$

23. **35**   Put the weights in order and find the middle value.

24. **$\frac{1}{4}$**   There are 1000 cards in all. The chance of drawing a Dodger card is 250 out of 1000, or 1 in 4.

25. **$\frac{3}{4}$**   There are 4 red sections and 2 white sections, so the number of favorable outcomes is 6. The chance of drawing either of the colors is 6 out of 8, or $\frac{3}{4}$.

26. **83°**   Add the temperatures and divide the total by 6, the number of measurements taken.

27. **Any value between $150 and $200 would be correct.**   Note that the points on the graph form a line. Mentally connect the points and determine where the line would cross the 4-hour mark. If you gridded in a value between 150 and 200, consider your answer correct.

28. **Any value between 70 and 80 would be correct.**   Each year the enrollment increases by about 20%. A good estimate for Year 6 is an enrollment of 78 players, an increase of 20% from Year 5. Consider an answer between 70 and 80 correct.

29. **Any value between 75 and 80 would be correct.**   As the price per family ticket increases, the number of tickets sold decreases. Mentally draw a line through the existing points. If the ticket price is raised to $30, the number of tickets sold will probably be between 75 and 80.

PROGRAM 38: INTRODUCTION TO ALGEBRA

Skill Practice, page 253

1.	6	6.	0
2.	−47	7.	30
3.	−15	8.	3
4.	−8	9.	$11\frac{3}{4}$
5.	51	10.	3.7

Skill Practice, page 255

1. 32
2. 18
3. -60
4. -24
5. 4
6. -25
7. -3
8. **17**   Subtracting $\frac{(-4)}{2}$ is equivalent to adding $\frac{4}{2}$, or 2.
9. **30**   Subtract inside the parentheses first: $-6(-5) = 30$.
10. **4**   Evaluate the exponent, then add inside the parentheses: $\frac{(8^2 + -20)}{11} = \frac{(64 + -20)}{11} = \frac{44}{11} = 4$.

Problem Solver Connection, page 255

$6 - 4 + 2 - 3 = 1$ or $6 + (-4) + 2 + (-3) = 1$

Skill Practice, page 257

1. $9a - 3b - 4$
2. $7x - 3$
3. $3x + 42$
4. $2m^2 - 2m + 12$
5. $13a^2 - 3b - 5b^2$
6. **$x + 2y$**   Do the division and multiplication first: $\frac{4y}{2} = 2y$ and $2(x - 2y) = 2x - 4y$. Then simplify by combining all like terms.
7. 22
8. 108
9. -4
10. 48
11. 70
12. 42
13. -4
14. 8
15. **-2**   First find the numerator: $2x^2 + y = 2(9) + 2 = 20$. Then find the denominator: $5x - (-5) = 5(-3) + 5 = -10$. Divide: $\frac{20}{-10} = -2$.
16. **12,000**   Instead of computing fractions of p, you can start by combining terms: $4p + 1.25p + 0.75p = 6p$. Substitute and solve: $100 \times 6p = 100 \times 6 \times 20 = 12,000$.

Skill Practice, page 259

1. 4^9
2. b^{11}
3. 10^{10}
4. m^6
5. 3^3
6. n^8
7. x (*Note:* $x^1 = x$)
8. 10^2
9. 10^{12}
10. y^{10}
11. 2^{18}
12. a^{12}
13. **2.1×10^{-3}**   In standard form, $2.1 \times 10^{-3} = 0.0021$ and $3.2 \times 10^{-2} = 0.032$.

14. **3.6×10^5**   In standard form, $3.6 \times 10^5 = 360,000$ and $9.4 \times 10^4 = 94,000$.
15. 2.09970×10^5 sq mi
16. $3,614,000$ sq mi
17. **25,000,000,000,000 miles**   This number is read "25 trillion."
18. **10 times**   Since our place value system is based on tens, a difference of 1 in the exponent changes the number by a factor of 10.
19. 2×10^{-3}

Skill Practice, page 261

1. **$y = 4$**
$$2y - 7 = 1$$
$$2y = 8$$
$$y = 4$$

2. **$x = -2$**
$$\frac{-10}{x} + 14 = 19$$
$$\frac{-10}{x} = 5$$
$$-10 = 5x$$
$$-2 = x$$

3. **$n = -1$**
$$5n - 4 = -9$$
$$5n = -5$$
$$n = -1$$

4. **$b = 3$**
$$-4b + 18 = 2b$$
$$18 = 6b$$
$$3 = b$$

5. **$a = 30$**
$$\frac{a}{6} - 5 = 0$$
$$\frac{a}{6} = 5$$
$$a = 30$$

6. **$x = 8$**
$$4x + \frac{x}{2} = 36$$
$$8x + x = 72$$
$$9x = 72$$
$$x = 8$$

7.
$$3x + 6 = 42$$
$$3x = 36$$
$$x = 12$$

8.
$$5x - 9 = -14$$
$$5x = -5$$
$$x = -1$$

9.
$$\frac{32}{x} + 5 = 1$$
$$\frac{32}{x} = -4$$
$$32 = -4x$$
$$-8 = x$$

10.
$$2x - 22 = 4$$
$$2x = 26$$
$$x = 13$$

Skill Practice, page 263

1. **The numbers are 18 and 39.**
first number $= x$, second number $= 2x + 3$
$$x + 2x + 3 = 57$$
$$3x + 3 = 57$$
$$3x = 54$$
$$x = 18$$

2. **Erin is 24.**
Paula's age $= x$, Erin's age $= 2x - 8$
$$2x - 8 + x = 40$$
$$3x - 8 = 40$$
$$3x = 48$$
$$x = 16$$

3. **Lyle earned $672.**
   Roy's earnings = x, Lyle's earnings = $4x$
   $$4x + x = 840$$
   $$5x = 840$$
   $$x = 168$$

4. **155, 156, 157, and 158**
   $$x + x + 1 + x + 2 + x + 3 = 626$$
   $$4x + 6 = 626$$
   $$4x = 620$$
   $$x = 155$$

5. **110**
   adult tickets = x, children's tickets = $5x$
   $$x + 5x = 132$$
   $$6x = 132$$
   $$x = 22$$

6. **$17**
   Carlo's contribution = x, Grace's contribution = $2x$
   $$x + 2x = 51$$
   $$3x = 51$$
   $$x = 17$$

7. **Mia is 13 years older than Fahi.**
   Mia's age = x, Fahi's age = $\frac{3}{4}x$
   $$\frac{3}{4}x + x = 91$$
   $$1\frac{3}{4}x = 91$$
   $$x = 52$$
   Mia is 52 and Fahi is 39.
   $$52 - 39 = 13$$

8. **31 and 33**
   $$x + x + 2 = 64$$
   $$2x + 2 = 64$$
   $$2x = 62$$
   $$x = 31$$

9. **10 and 13**
   first number = x, second number = $8 + \frac{1}{2}x$
   $$x + 8 + \frac{1}{2}x = 23$$
   $$1\frac{1}{2}x + 8 = 23$$
   $$1\frac{1}{2}x = 15$$
   $$x = 10$$

10. **(3) 28**
    Tia's hours = x, Julius's hours = $x - 2$,
    Adena's hours = $2(x - 2)$
    $$x + x - 2 + 2(x - 2) = 58$$
    $$x + x - 2 + 2x - 4 = 58$$
    $$4x - 6 = 58$$
    $$4x = 64$$
    $$x = 16$$
    Substitute 16 for x in the expression for Adena's hours.

Skill Practice, page 265

1. **5 inches**
   width = x, length = $2x + 4$
   $$P = 2l + 2w$$
   $$38 = 2(2x + 4) + 2x$$
   $$38 = 4x + 8 + 2x$$
   $$38 = 6x + 8$$
   $$30 = 6x$$
   $$5 = x$$

2. **The sides of the triangle measure 10, 24, and 26 cm.**
   side B = x, side A = $\frac{1}{2}x - 2$, side C = $x + 2$
   $$P = a + b + c$$
   $$60 = \frac{1}{2}x - 2 + x + x + 2$$
   $$60 = 2\frac{1}{2}x$$
   $$24 = x$$
   Side B is 24 cm. Substitute 24 cm for x in the expressions for sides A and C.

3. **140 quarters and 60 dimes**
   number of quarters = x
   number of dimes = $200 - x$
   $$0.25x + 0.10(200 - x) = 41$$
   $$0.25x + 20 - 0.10x = 41$$
   $$0.15x = 21$$
   $$x = 140$$

4. **210 adult tickets and 90 children's tickets**
   number of tickets sold to adults = x
   number of tickets sold to children = $300 - x$
   $$9x + 5(300 - x) = 2340$$
   $$9x + 1500 - 5x = 2340$$
   $$4x = 840$$
   $$x = 210$$

History Connection, page 265

840 There are 20 pairings of even numbers from 2 to 40 that have the same sum. $2 + 40 = 42$, $4 + 38 = 42$, $6 + 36 = 42$, and so on. Multiply: $42 \times 20 = 840$.

GED Practice, pages 266–268

1. **(2) B** Since x is greater than -2, it must lie to the right of -2. Since x is less than 0, it must lie to the left of 0. Only point B is both greater than -2 and less than 0.

2. **(2) $178 - (a + 7b)$** The quantity of a plus $7b$ will be a sum, which is to be subtracted from 178.

3. **(5) 96** Remembering that two negative numbers multiplied together result in a positive product, your answer is 96.

4. **(2) B** First convert $-\frac{25}{7}$ to $-3\frac{4}{7}$, which you can estimate is a little more than $-3\frac{1}{2}$. Being a negative number, $-3\frac{4}{7}$ will be just to the left of $-3\frac{1}{2}$.

5. **(3) $1450 + $120 + $340 - $845** Each deposit represents a positive; the transfer represents a negative.

6. **(4) 48** Substitute the known values. ($d = -7$ is extraneous information.)
   $$a = 4(2)(11 - 5)$$
   $$a = 8(6) = 48$$

7. **(5) $2(2y) + 2(3x)$** The formula for finding the perimeter of a rectangle is $P = 2l + 2w$. Substitute $2y$ for l and $3x$ for w.

8. **(4) 288** The formula for finding the area of a rectangle is $A = lw$. The length of the rectangle is $2y$ or $2(12)$, which equals 24. The width of the rectangle is $3w$ or $3(4)$, which equals 12. Thus, the area of the rectangle is $A = 24(12) = 288$.

9. **(1) –369** Follow the order of operations:
$$-10(5 + 1)^2 - \frac{36}{4}$$
$$-10(6)^2 - \frac{36}{4}$$
$$-10(36) - \frac{36}{4}$$
$$-360 - \frac{36}{4}$$
Reduce your fraction: $-360 - 9 = -369$

10. **(3) 8** Jot down R, S, and T to represent the cats' weights. You know that $T = 9$, so work backward from there: $R = 9 + 3 = 12$. $S = 12 - 4 = 8$.

11. **(1) 9** Write an equation: Let x = the distance Eric ran on Monday and $2x - 5$ equal the distance he ran on Tuesday. Write an equation in which the sum is equal to 22 miles: $x + 2x - 5 = 22$. Solve for x.
$$x + 2x - 5 = 22$$
$$3x - 5 = 22$$
$$3x = 27$$
$$x = 9 \text{ miles}$$

12. **(4) Toofla is 20 times farther than Quiza.**
In this scientific notation problem, the first factor in Toofla's distance from Earth is twice Quiza's first factor. But Toofla's second factor is ten times greater than Quiza's ($10^6 - 10^5 = 10^1 = 10$). Altogether, the distance is $2 \times 10 = 20$ times greater.

13. **(4) 56** The three numbers can be represented by x, $x + 2$, and $x + 4$. Write an equation and solve for x.
$$x + x + 2 + x + 4 = 162$$
$$3x + 6 = 162$$
$$3x = 156$$
$$x = 52$$
The consecutive even numbers are 52, 54, and 56. The problem asks for the greatest number, so choice (4) is correct.

14. **(5) Not enough information is given.**
You do not know the relationship of Celia's age to either her father's or her mother's.

15. **(1) 25** You are given the height and width of the storage bin. Using the formula, substitute the known variables and solve the equation for length (l).
$$V = lwh$$
$$3500 = l(14)(10)$$
$$3500 = l(140)$$
$$\frac{3500}{140} = l$$
$$25 = l$$

16. **(1) 30 dimes and 120 nickels** Set up and solve an equation in which x represents the number of dimes: $10x + 5(150 - x) = 900$. *Note:* You are dealing in cents (1 dime = 10 cents; 1 nickel = 5 cents), so change \$9.00 to 900 cents.
$$10x + 5(150 - x) = 900$$
$$10x + 750 - 5x = 900$$
$$5x = 150$$
$$x = 30$$
In a similar GED Math Test problem, you might also quickly figure the answers among the choices to see which one offers 150 coins equal to \$9.00.

17. **(2) $2x + 2(\frac{1}{2}x - 3) = 120$** Let x be the length of Joni's yard; then $\frac{1}{2}x - 3$ is the width. Using the formula for perimeter, you can use choice (2) as your algebraic expression.

18. **(4) 70** Let x equal the number of adults' tickets sold and $100 - x$ equal the number of children's tickets sold. Write an equation and solve:
$$6x + 3(100 - x) = 510$$
$$6x + 300 - 3x = 510$$
$$3x + 300 = 510$$
$$3x = 210$$
$$x = 70$$

19. **(3) 6200** Move the decimal point 3 places to the right, adding zeros as necessary: 6.2×10^3 is equal to 6200.

20. **(2) –3** Use inverse operations to isolate the variable.
$$7y + 6 = 15$$
$$7y = -21 \quad \text{Add } -6 \text{ to both sides of the equation.}$$
$$y = -3 \quad \text{Divide both sides by 7.}$$

21. **(2) 20** Let x equal the number of kilometers she rode. Write an equation and solve:
$$25x + 125 - 625$$
$$25x = 500$$
$$x = 20$$

22. **(5) 24** Substitute the numbers and variables from the figure into the formula:
$$A = \frac{1}{2}bh$$
$$72 = \frac{1}{2}(4x)(6)$$
$$72 = 2x(6)$$
$$72 = 12x$$
$$6 = x$$
The problem asks you to find the length of side AC, the base. From the diagram, you learn that side AC is equal to $4x$. Since $x = 6$, $4x$ is equal to $4(6)$, or 24.

23. **(3) $4n + 3 = 5n - 3$** Carefully translate the words from the problem into an equation. "Four times a number" is written $4n$. "Three more" means to add 3: $4n + 3$. "Five times a number" is written $5n$. "Three less" means to subtract 3: $5n - 3$. The two expressions are equal, so they are connected using the = symbol: $4n + 3 = 5n - 3$.

PROGRAM 39: SPECIAL TOPICS IN ALGEBRA AND GEOMETRY

Skill Practice, page 275

1. $x < 3$
2. $n \geq 8$
3. $d > 4$
4. $x < -4$
5. $z \leq -7$
6. $x < -1$
7. $2 < n < 7$
8. $3 > y > -4$

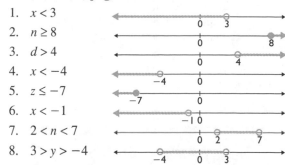

Skill Practice, page 277

1. **(3) $x > 4$**
   $3x + 8 > 20$
   $3x > 12$
   $x > 4$

2. **$\$8.90x \leq \$356$** Let x (or any variable) equal the number of hours Mae works. If she works 40, the maximum number of hours, her pay will be 40($\$8.90$), which equals $356. Set up the inequality so that the wage times the number of hours is equal to or less than $356.

3. **(1) $48 > 12w$** Use the formula $A = lw$. Substitute the known quantities: $48 = 12w$. Finally, change the equation to an inequality to represent the problem: $48 > 12w$.

Problem Solver Connection, page 277
Graph of the inequalities $x < -2$ or $x > 3$:

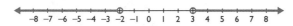

Skill Practice, page 279

1. **50** Each number is 7 greater than the number before.
2. **21** Add 2, then 3, then 4, and so on.
3. **6** Add 2, then subtract 1, add 2, subtract 1, and so on.
4. **36** Add 3, then 5, then 7, then 9, and so on.
5. **34** Each new number is the sum of the two numbers that came before.
6. To find the total cost (c), multiply the unit cost, or rate (r), by the number of bottles of glue (n): $c = nr$.
7. To find the area (A), square the measure of the side (s): $A = s^2$.
8. To find the total water usage (U), multiply 50 gallons by the number of loads (n): $U = 50n$.
9. To find the amount for shipping and handling (S), multiply the merchandise total (t) by 0.07 and add $5: $S = 0.07t + 5$.
10. **$2000** Find $100 on the vertical scale and follow it over to a point on the line. The point is directly over the amount $2000 on the horizontal scale.

Skill Practice, page 281

1. a. $2x + 1$
   b. input 0, output 1
      input 1, output 3
      input 2, output 5
      input 3, output 7
   c.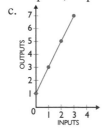

2. a.
      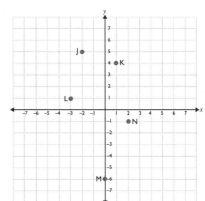
   Your graph should be similar to this one. You should have two scales: one showing the number of quilts and the other showing the amount of revenue in dollars.
   b. **$2400** Sheila's cost for 10 quilts is $1600. Her revenue is 400(10), or $4000. Her profits after making and selling 10 quilts are $4000 − $1600 = $2400.

Science Connection, page 281
The 6th generation will have 8 bees. The 7th generation will have 13.

Skill Practice, page 283

1. $(-4,4)$
2. $(0,7)$
3. $(2,5)$
4. $(6,3)$
5. $(4,0)$
6. $(5,-5)$
7. $(-1,-2)$
8. $(-6,-5)$
9.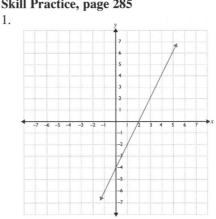

10. **No** Point N has a negative value for x, and point P has a positive value for x. The points must fall in different quadrants. (*Note:* The signs for the y-coordinates also differ.)

Skill Practice, page 285

1.

2.

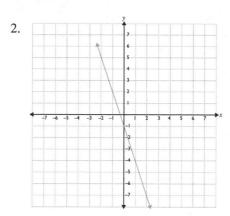

3. **(4)** $y = -3x - 2$ Find the coordinates of any point on line A. For example, line A passes through the coordinates $(-1,1)$. Then substitute the x and y values from the coordinates into each equation.

4. **(2)** **(3,5)**   Find the location on the grid for each set of coordinates. Only choice (2) lies on line B.

Skill Practice, page 287

1. **a.** K
   b. M
   c. L
   d. J

2. **a.** $\frac{5}{6}$ $m = \frac{4 - (-1)}{5 - (-1)} = \frac{5}{6}$
   b. -3 $m = \frac{1 - 7}{3 - 1} = \frac{-6}{2} = -3$
   c. 0 $m = \frac{-3 - (-3)}{-4 - 1} = \frac{0}{-5} = 0$

3. To find each y-intercept, substitute zero for x and solve for y.
   a. 2
   b. -5
   c. 3
   d. 4

Skill Practice, page 289

1. **(2) between 8 and 9**   Use the Pythagorean relationship. Draw a right triangle to connect points F and G. The legs of the triangle measure 4 and 8 spaces.
   $c^2 = a^2 + b^2$
   $c^2 = 4^2 + 8^2$
   $c^2 = 16 + 64$
   $c^2 = 80$
   $c = \sqrt{80}$ Since $\sqrt{81} = 9$, you know that the $\sqrt{80}$ is a little less than 9.

2. **(4) 13**   Use the Pythagorean relationship. Draw a right triangle to connect points G and H. The legs of the triangle measure 5 and 12 spaces.
   $c^2 = a^2 + b^2$
   $c^2 = 5^2 + 12^2$
   $c^2 = 25 + 144$
   $c^2 = 169$
   $c = \sqrt{169}$
   $c = 13$

3. **9.1**   Let $(-2,-6) = (x_1,y_1)$. Let $(7,-5) = (x_2,y_2)$.
   Use the formula:
   $d = \sqrt{(x_2 - x_1)^2 + (y_2 - y_1)^2}$
   $d = \sqrt{(7 - (-2))^2 + (-5 - (-6))^2}$
   $d = \sqrt{9^2 + 1^2}$
   $d = \sqrt{81 + 1}$
   $d = \sqrt{82}$ Using a calculator, $\sqrt{82} \approx 9.0553851$.
   Round to the nearest tenth: $d \approx 9.1$.

4. **(4) between 10 and 11**
   Let $(2,6) = (x_1,y_1)$. Let $(-6,-1) = (x_2,y_2)$.
   Use the formula:
   $d = \sqrt{(x_2 - x_1)^2 + (y_2 - y_1)^2}$
   $d = \sqrt{(-6 - 2)^2 + (-1 - 6)^2}$
   $d = \sqrt{(-8)^2 + (-7)^2}$
   $d = \sqrt{64 + 49}$
   $d = \sqrt{113}$
   Think: $10^2 = 100$ and $11^2 = 121$, so $\sqrt{113}$ is between 10 and 11.

Skill Practice, page 291

1. **(3) -3 and -4**

$x^2 + 7x + 12 = 0$	$x^2 + 7x + 12 = 0$
$(-3)^2 + 7(-3) + 12 = 0$	$(-4)^2 + 7(-4) + 12 = 0$
$9 - 21 + 12 = 0$	$16 - 28 + 12 = 0$
$0 = 0$	$0 = 0$

2. **(2) -2 and 4**

$x^2 - 2x - 8 = 0$	$x^2 - 2x - 8 = 0$
$(-2)^2 - 2(-2) - 8 = 0$	$(4)^2 - 2(4) - 8 = 0$
$4 + 4 - 8 = 0$	$16 - 8 - 8 = 0$
$0 = 0$	$0 = 0$

3. **(4) -4 and 4**

$x^2 - 16 = 0$	$x^2 - 16 = 0$
$(-4)^2 - 16 = 0$	$(4)^2 - 16 = 0$
$16 - 16 = 0$	$16 - 16 = 0$
$0 = 0$	$0 = 0$

4. **(1) -2 only**
   $x^2 + 4x + 4 = 0$
   $(-2)^2 + 4(-2) + 4 = 0$
   $4 - 8 + 4 = 0$
   $0 = 0$

Problem Solver Connection, page 291

(3) 15   Substitute 15 for x: $\frac{4}{3}(15) - 7 = 28 - 15$.
The equation is true, so choice (3) is correct.

GED Practice, pages 292–294

1. **(1) $65t \geq 417$**   Using $d = rt$, you know that $417 = 65t$, or $\frac{417}{65} = t$. Solving this equation would give you the least amount of time the trip could take. The trip could take longer if Janet drives slower. Therefore, $t \geq \frac{417}{65}$ or $65t \geq 417$.

2. **(5) 48**   If the statement were an equation, x would equal 50: $3(50) = 150$. Since the inequality states that $3x$ is less than 150, x must be a number less than 50.

3. **(2) B**   Count over to 2 on the x-axis and down to -7 on the y-axis.

4. **(4) 3**   The fastest way to find slope is to count the number of spaces you need for the rise and the run and write a ratio. From point L, count up 9 spaces and 3 spaces to the right to reach point M. Write the ratio and express in lowest terms: $\frac{9}{3} = \frac{3}{1}$. The slope is 3.

5. **(4)**

```
 +--+--+--+--●--+--+--+--+--⊕--+
-5 -4 -3 -2 -1  0  1  2  3  4  5
```

A closed circle shows that the number is included in the solution set. An open circle means that the number is not included in the solution set.

6. **(3) 4 and -2**   You can solve by factoring the quadratic equation and setting each factor equal to zero: $x^2 - 2x - 8 = 0$, so $(x - 4)(x + 2) = 0$.
$$x - 4 = 0 \qquad x + 2 = 0$$
$$x = 4 \qquad x = -2$$
You can also solve by substituting the numbers from the answer choices for x to see which solutions make the equation true.

7. **(2) K**   The slope of a vertical line is undefined. (The slope of a horizontal line is zero.)

8. **(3) \$95**   Sharon's weekly costs are a function of the number of earrings she makes. Find 25 on the horizontal axis and move directly up to the corresponding point on the line. Read across to the scale. The point above 25 represents a cost of \$95.

9. **(2) $C = 20 + 3n$**   The fixed cost of \$20 is added to the number of earrings multiplied by \$3.

10. **(2) $3b + 8 \geq 29$**   Quickly substitute 10 for b in each answer choice, and you'll find choice (2) is true.

11. **(4) between 10 and 11**   Draw an imaginary right triangle with PQ as the hypotenuse. The lengths of the legs are 6 and 9. Use the Pythagorean relationship to find the length of the hypotenuse.
$$c^2 = a^2 + b^2$$
$$c^2 = 6^2 + 9^2$$
$$c^2 = 36 + 81$$
$$c^2 = 117$$
$$c = \sqrt{117}$$
Since $10^2 = 100$ and $11^2 = 121$, you know the hypotenuse must be between 10 and 11 units long.

12. **(2) $\frac{-3}{2}$**   Use the points P and Q and count the spaces for the rise and run. The rise is 9 and the run is -6. Write a ratio and express in lowest terms: $\frac{9}{-6} = \frac{-3}{2}$. *Note:* You do not have to use points P and Q. You can use any two convenient points on the line. You can also use the slope formula given on the GED formulas page, although this method tends to take more time.

13. **(5) (3,4)**   Remember, the x-coordinate is the first number, and the y-coordinate is the second number. Substitute the numbers from the coordinates for the x and y variables in the equation. Only choice (5) makes the equation true: $y = 3x - 5$, and $4 = 3(3) - 5$.

14. **(1) -3 and 1**   You can solve by factoring the quadratic equation and setting each factor equal to zero: $x^2 + 2x - 3 = 0$, so $(x + 3)(x - 1) = 0$.
$$x + 3 = 0 \qquad x - 1 = 0$$
$$x = -3 \qquad x = 1$$
You can also solve by substituting the numbers from the answer choices for x to see which solutions make the equation true.

15. **(1) 5**   Since you are asked to find *one* answer that is <u>not</u> in the solution set of the equation, and your answers are consecutive numbers, either 5 or 9 will be the correct choice. Substitute one of these two possibilities and you will know whether that choice or the only other possibility is correct.

16. **(5) $r + \frac{1}{2}$**   Only the love seat is one-half its regular price ($\frac{1}{2}$) when the recliner is purchased at its regular price (r).

17. **(2) $\frac{5 - (-2)}{6 - 1}$**   Use the formula for finding slope from the GED formulas page. Let $(1,-2) = (x_1,y_1)$ and $(6,5) = (x_2,y_2)$. Substitute and compare to the answer choices.

18. **(3) $\sqrt{[3-(-1)]^2 + (5 - 3)^2}$**   Find the coordinates for points M and N: $M = (-1,3)$ and $N = (3,5)$. Use the formula for finding the distance between two points in a plane from the GED formulas page. Let $M = (x_1,y_1)$ and $N = (x_2,y_2)$. Substitute and compare to the answer choices.

19. **(2) $(4,-2)$**   Start at the y-intercept, -4, and use the slope to plot the points on the new line. Since the slope is $\frac{1}{2}$, move up 1 and 2 to the right. Continue the pattern until you intersect line g.

20. **(5) $y = 5$**   By looking at the graph, we can see that for every point, $y = 5$. For all choices but choice (5), we can substitute different values for x and get solutions where y does not equal 5.

Alternate Math Formats, pages 295–296

21. and 22.

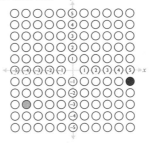

23. **4**   Use the slope formula or count spaces to write a ratio comparing rise over run. The line rises 4 spaces for every 1 space it moves to the right. Lines that rise moving from left to right have a positive slope.

24. $\frac{2}{9}$ Use the slope formula to find the distance between E $(-3,4)$ and D $(6,6)$.
$$4 - \frac{6}{-3} - 6 = \frac{-2}{-9} = \frac{2}{9}$$

25. **Any number greater than 2.5 and less than 3.4 is correct.**

26. **1**   Use the slope formula or calculate the ratio of rise over run by counting spaces. To find another point that the line passes through, use the information about the y-intercept of 2. This means that when $x = 0$, $y = 2$, or $(0,2)$. Find the slope using points $(3,5)$ and $(0,2)$.
$$5 - \frac{2}{3} - 0 = \frac{3}{3} = 1$$

27. **10**   Use the formula for finding the distance between points or draw a right triangle so that the segment connecting R and Q becomes the hypotenuse. Then use the Pythagorean relationship to solve for the hypotenuse:
$6^2 + 8^2 = c^2$, so $c = \sqrt{36 + 64} = 10$.

28. **5**   Use the formula for finding the distance between two points: $(-4,1)$ and $(0,-2)$.
$$(0 - (-4))^2 + (-2 - 1)^2$$
$$4^2 + (-3)^2$$
$$\sqrt{16 + 9}$$
$$\sqrt{25}$$
$$5$$

29. **24**   Use the formula $A = \frac{1}{2}bh$, substituting the known values.
$$336 = \frac{1}{2}(28)h$$
$$336 = 14h$$
$$24 = h$$
The height measures 24 inches.

30. **8**   Substitute the values for x and z, and solve for y.
$$4(9) = 7y - 5(4)$$
$$36 = 7y - 20$$
$$56 = 7y$$
$$8 = y$$

Math Handbook

Common Equivalencies

As you prepare to take the GED Math Test, you will find it helpful to memorize the basic equivalencies shown on this page.

COMMON FRACTIONS, DECIMALS, AND PERCENTS		
$\frac{1}{2}$	0.5	50%
$\frac{1}{3}$	about 0.33	$33\frac{1}{3}$%
$\frac{2}{3}$	about 0.67	$66\frac{2}{3}$%
$\frac{1}{4}$	0.25	25%
$\frac{3}{4}$	0.75	75%
$\frac{1}{5}$	0.2	20%
$\frac{2}{5}$	0.4	40%
$\frac{3}{5}$	0.6	60%
$\frac{4}{5}$	0.8	80%
$\frac{1}{8}$	0.125	$12\frac{1}{2}$%
$\frac{3}{8}$	0.375	$37\frac{1}{2}$%
$\frac{5}{8}$	0.625	$62\frac{1}{2}$%
$\frac{7}{8}$	0.875	$87\frac{1}{2}$%

Parts of a whole can be written as fractions, decimals, or percents. On the GED Math Test, use the form that is easiest for you to solve the problem.

You will not be asked to make conversions between the English and metric systems on the GED Math Test.

English Measurement Equivalencies

LENGTH
1 foot (ft) = 12 inches (in)
1 yard (yd) = 3 feet = 36 inches
1 mile (mi) = 5280 feet

TIME
1 minute (min) = 60 seconds (sec)
1 hour (hr) = 60 minutes
1 day = 24 hours
1 week (wk) = 7 days
1 year (yr) = 365 days

VOLUME
1 cup (c) = 8 fluid ounces (fl oz)
1 pint (pt) = 2 cups
1 quart (qt) = 2 pints = 4 cups
1 gallon (gal) = 4 quarts

WEIGHT
1 pound (lb) = 16 ounces (oz)
1 ton = 2000 pounds

Metric Measurement Equivalencies

LENGTH
1 meter (m) = 1000 millimeters (mm)
1 meter = 100 centimeters (cm)
1 centimeter = 10 millimeters
1 kilometer (km) = 1000 meters

VOLUME
1 liter (L) = 1000 milliliters (mL)

WEIGHT
1 gram (g) = 1000 milligrams (mg)
1 kilogram (kg) = 1000 grams

Using the CASIO® fx-260 on the GED Math Test

When you take the GED Math Test, you will be given a scientific calculator to use for the first part of the test. This calculator, the CASIO fx-260, has many more keys than you will actually need on the test. The keys that you will use most often are shown in the diagram below and on the next page.

You may have these same functions on a calculator that you have at home. Study the key locations on these diagrams. If possible, obtain this type of calculator in advance so that you can practice using it before you take the test.

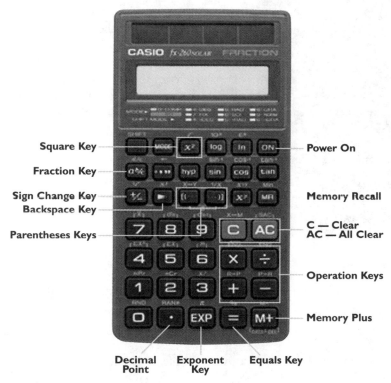

You will learn more about the fraction and memory keys on page 339.

Square Key
Fraction Key
Sign Change Key
Backspace Key
Parentheses Keys

Power On
Memory Recall
C — Clear
AC — All Clear
Operation Keys
Memory Plus

Decimal Point
Exponent Key
Equals Key

Basic Operations

The CASIO fx-260 follows the order of operations shown on page 57.

To evaluate an expression, enter the numbers and operations from left to right. Use parentheses to show that one operation must be performed before another.

Evaluate: 34 + 27 × 5 =
Enter: 3 4 + 2 7 × 5 = ⟨169.⟩

Evaluate: (34 + 27) × 5 =
Enter: [(- 3 4 + 2 7 -)] × 5 =
⟨305.⟩

In the first example, the multiplication step was performed first even though the addition step was entered first. In the second example, the parentheses instructed the calculator to add before multiplying.

Special Keys

If you make a mistake while entering a calculation, you can press:

▶ to backspace and delete digits
C to clear only the last operation performed
AC to clear everything and start the calculation over

Scientific Notation

You can enter a number in scientific notation using the **EXP** key. First, enter the mixed decimal portion of the number. Then press EXP and enter the power of ten by which the mixed decimal is multiplied.

Example: What is the value of 1.6×10^7?
Enter: 1 . 6 EXP 7 = ⟨16000000.⟩

Note: The EXP key replaces the multiplication symbol in the problem.

The CASIO *fx*-260 assigns two functions to some keys. The second function labels are written in yellow print above the keys. To use a second function, press SHIFT and then the desired key. The second functions you may need on the GED Math Test are shown in the diagram below.

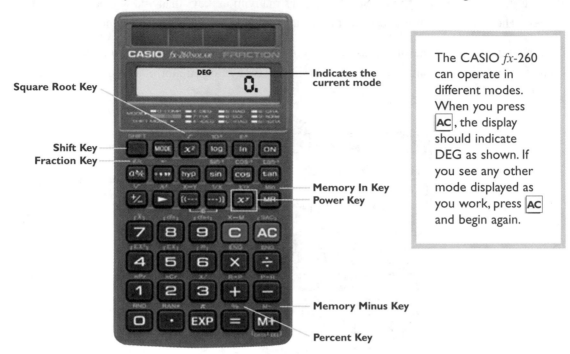

Square Root Key

DEG

0.

Indicates the current mode

Shift Key
Fraction Key

Memory In Key
Power Key

Memory Minus Key

Percent Key

The CASIO *fx*-260 can operate in different modes. When you press AC, the display should indicate DEG as shown. If you see any other mode displayed as you work, press AC and begin again.

Squares and Square Roots

While working with formulas and evaluating expressions, you may need to raise a number to a higher power.

To square a number, enter the number and press x^2.

Example: What is the square of 26?
Press: 2 6 x^2
Display: 676.

To raise a number to a higher power, enter the number, press x^y, and enter the power.

Example: What is the value of 6^5?
Press: 6 x^y 5 = 7776.

To find the square root of a number, enter the number and press SHIFT √.

Example: Find the square root of 576.
Press: 5 7 6 SHIFT √
Display: 24.

Percent

To access the percent function on this calculator, you must first press SHIFT. Study how the percent key is used in these examples.

Example: What is 42% of $1200?
Press: 1 2 0 0 × 4 2 SHIFT %
Display: 504.

Example: What percent of 224 is 56?
Press: 5 6 ÷ 2 2 4 SHIFT %
Display: 25.

Answer: 56 is **25%** of 224.

Example: A store paid $80 for a coat. The store sold the coat for the cost plus 40%. What was the selling price of the coat?

Press: 8 0 × 4 0 SHIFT % +
Display: 112.

Answer: The coat sold for **$112.**

Example: A $32 purchase is discounted 20%. What is the sale price of the purchase?
Press: 3 2 × 2 0 SHIFT % −
Display: 25.6

Answer: The sale price is **$25.60.**

Using the Fraction Keys

The fraction keys on your calculator can help you save time on the GED Math Test. The fraction keys allow you to enter fractions and whole numbers without first converting the fractions to decimals.

In the display window, the numerator and the denominator of a fraction are separated by the symbol ⌐.

The display shows the mixed fraction: $2\frac{4}{5}$.

Example: Reduce the fraction $\frac{85}{102}$ to lowest terms.
Press: [8] [5] [a%c] [1] [0] [2] [=]
Display: | 5⌐6. |

Answer: $\frac{85}{102}$ reduces to $\frac{5}{6}$.

You can also use the calculator to perform operations with fractions.

Example: $\frac{7}{10} + \frac{3}{4} = ?$

Press: [7] [a%c] [1] [0] [+] [3] [a%c] [4] [=] | 1⌐9⌐20. |
You can change the mixed fraction to an improper fraction.
Press: [SHIFT] [d/c]   **Display:** | 29⌐20. |

Answer: The sum of $\frac{7}{10}$ and $\frac{3}{4}$ is $1\frac{9}{20}$ or $\frac{29}{20}$.

Using the Memory Features

The memory keys on the CASIO *fx*-260 perform the following functions:

[SHIFT] [Min]	Memory In	Puts the displayed number in the memory.
[M+]	Memory Plus	Adds the displayed number to the memory.
[SHIFT] [M–]	Memory Minus	Subtracts the displayed number from the memory.
[MR]	Memory Recall	Displays the contents of the memory.

The memory features are useful when a problem has more than one part. To make sure the memory is empty before you begin, press the ON key.

Example: Zoila buys 3 jars of tomato sauce for $1.15 each and 2 pounds of ground beef for $2.79 each. She has a 75-cents-off coupon. What is the cost of the food?

1. Store the cost of the tomato sauce in the memory.

   Press: [1] [.] [1] [5] [×] [3] [=] [SHIFT] [Min]

2. Find the cost of the ground beef and add it to the memory.

   Press: [2] [.] [7] [9] [×] [2] [=] [M+]

3. Subtract the coupon amount.

   Press: [.] [7] [5] [SHIFT] [M–]

4. Use memory recall to find the answer.

   Press: [MR]   **Display:** | 8.28 |

Answer: The cost of the food is **$8.28.**

This page will be provided when you take the GED Math Test. Although you do not need to memorize these formulas, it is a good idea to be familiar with the contents of this page so that you will know when to use it.

FORMULAS

AREA of a:

square	Area = side^2
rectangle	Area = length × width
parallelogram	Area = base × height
triangle	Area = $\frac{1}{2}$ × base × height
trapezoid	Area = $\frac{1}{2}$ × (base$_1$ + base$_2$) × height
circle	Area = π × radius^2; π is approximately equal to 3.14.

PERIMETER of a:

square	Perimeter = 4 × side
rectangle	Perimeter = 2 × length + 2 × width
triangle	Perimeter = side$_1$ + side$_2$ + side$_3$

CIRCUMFERENCE of a:

circle	Circumference = π × diameter; π is approximately equal to 3.14.

VOLUME of a:

cube	Volume = edge^3
rectangular solid	Volume = length × width × height
square pyramid	Volume = $\frac{1}{3}$ × (base edge)^2 × height
cylinder	Volume = π × radius^2 × height; π is approximately equal to 3.14.
cone	Volume = $\frac{1}{3}$ × π × radius^2 × height; π is approximately equal to 3.14.

COORDINATE GEOMETRY

distance between points = $\sqrt{(x_2 - x_1)^2 + (y_2 - y_1)^2}$; (x_1,y_1) and (x_2,y_2) are two points in a plane.

slope of a line = $\frac{y_2 - y_1}{x_2 - x_1}$; (x_1,y_1) and (x_2,y_2) are two points on the line.

PYTHAGOREAN RELATIONSHIP

$a^2 + b^2 = c^2$; a and b are legs and c the hypotenuse of a right triangle.

MEASURES OF CENTRAL TENDENCY

mean = $\frac{x_1 + x_2 + ... + x_n}{n}$, where the x's are the values for which a mean is desired, and n is the total number of values for x.

median = the middle value of an odd number of <u>ordered</u> scores, and halfway between the two middle values of an even number of <u>ordered</u> scores.

SIMPLE INTEREST   interest = principal × rate × time
DISTANCE   distance = rate × time
TOTAL COST   total cost = (number of units) × (price per unit)

Reprinted with permission of the GED Testing Service. © 2001, GEDTS

340

Glossary

area: the measure of the surface of a flat figure

associative property: a law that states that when adding or multiplying more than two numbers, you can group the numbers in any order without affecting the result; for example,
$$2 + (3 + 4) = (2 + 3) + 4$$

bar graph: a graph that uses bars next to a scale to compare quantities

base: a number raised to a certain power

benchmark: a common object that can help you remember the relative size of a unit of measure

calculations: math processes—such as adding, subtracting, multiplying, and dividing—carried out to solve a problem

canceling: a shortcut procedure for multiplying fractions in which you factor out the same number from a numerator and denominator to make the multiplication simpler

chance: the likelihood of an event's occurrence

circle graph: a graph that uses sections of a circle to represent parts of a whole; also called a *pie chart*

circumference: the distance around a circle

cluster: a small group of values that is isolated from other values

common denominator: a number that each denominator in a problem can divide into evenly

commutative property: a law that states that the order in which you add or multiply numbers does not affect the result; for example, $2 \times 4 = 4 \times 2$

compatible numbers: numbers that are easy to work with in your mind

complementary angles: two angles whose sum measures 90°

compound inequality: a mathematical statement that combines two inequalities; for example, $3 < x < 10$

congruent figures: two shapes with identical measures of sides and angles

consecutive numbers: numbers in counting order

convenience sampling: selecting a portion of a population based on its availability

coordinate plane: a flat surface divided by a horizontal number line and a vertical number line in order to form four quadrants, or sections; the number lines intersect at right angles at the point of origin

corresponding angles: angles that are in the same position in the intersections formed when a transversal intersects parallel lines

cross products: the results of multiplying the denominator of the first ratio by the numerator of the second ratio and the denominator of the second ratio by the numerator of the first ratio. In a true proportion, cross products are equal.

cube: a 3-dimensional figure in which the length, width, and height are all equal and each face is a square

cylinder: a three-dimensional object with two circular bases

data: bits of information, often numerical

decimal: part of a whole expressed using digits written after a decimal point; for example, 0.75, 0.5, and 0.825

decimal point: the point that separates whole numbers from parts of a whole or dollars from cents

denominator: the number on the bottom of a fraction; tells you into how many parts the whole has been divided

dependent events: two events in which the outcome of the first event affects the outcome of the second

diameter: the distance across a circle through the center

digit: one of the symbols used to write numbers: 0, 1, 2, 3, 4, 5, 6, 7, 8, and 9

distributive property: a law that states that when a number is multiplied by a sum written in parentheses, you can find the result by multiplying the number outside the parentheses by each number in the parentheses and then adding; for example,
$$3 \times (5 + 6) = (3 \times 5) + (3 \times 6) = 15 + 18 = 33$$

dividend: the number being divided in a division problem; the number inside the long division bracket

divisor: the number you are dividing by

double-bar graph: a type of bar graph where multiple bars are shown for each date, event, or category; a key is needed to interpret the data

English system: the measurement system most commonly used in the United States

equation: a mathematical sentence in which two expressions or numbers are equal

equilateral triangle: a triangle with three equal sides and angles

equivalency: a statement that tells the number of one measurement unit that is equal to another measurement unit

equivalent fractions: different fractions that name the same number; for example, $\frac{3}{6}$ and $\frac{1}{2}$

estimate: to find an approximate value

evaluate: to find the value of an expression by substituting values for the variables and carrying out the operations according to the order of operations

experimental probability: a method of calculating probability in which chance is based on the results of a number of trials of an experiment

exponent: a small number written slightly above and to the right of a base number to specify the number of times to multiply the base by itself

factors: the numbers that are multiplied in a multiplication problem

favorable outcome: an event that you want to have happen

formula: an equation written with variables that shows the constant relationship among the variables

fraction: part of a whole expressed by showing the number of parts being discussed out of a total number of parts; for example, $\frac{1}{2}, \frac{2}{3}$, and $\frac{3}{4}$

frequency table: a method of organizing data in which tally marks are used to show how often each value occurs

front-end estimation: a method of estimating by using only the value of the first digits of the numbers in a problem

function: a constant relationship between quantities

gap: a space between values in a data set

horizontal axis: one of two perpendicular lines that define a graph; the line running left and right; called the *x*-axis

hypotenuse: the side opposite the right angle in a right triangle

improper fraction: a fraction that names a number equal to or greater than 1; the numerator is equal to or greater than the denominator

independent events: events in which one outcome does not affect the other

inequality: a mathematical statement that two expressions or numbers are not equal

integer: a signed number; a positive integer is greater than zero, and a negative integer is less than zero

inverse: opposite; for example, addition and subtraction are inverse, or opposite, operations

isosceles triangle: a triangle having two sides with the same length and two angles with the same measure

key: the information you need to read and interpret a graph; also called a *legend*

length: a measure of distance

like fractions: fractions that have the same denominator

like terms: terms that have identical variables; for example, $5xy$ and $3xy$ are like terms because the variable portions are alike

line graph: a graph used to display changes in data using points and line segments to represent the data

line plot: a method of organizing data in which Xs stand for data values

linear equation: an equation with two variables and multiple solutions; its solution set forms a line when graphed on a coordinate plane

lowest common denominator: the smallest number that two or more denominators will divide into evenly

margin of error: a percent that shows by how much the actual results in a statistical study may vary; for example, a margin of error of $\pm 3\%$ means that the actual results may be from 3% less to 3% greater than the reported results

mean: an approximate value that is typical of teh values in a group; the sum of a set of numbers divided by the number of values in the set; also called *average*

median: the middle value in a set of data arranged in order from least to greatest or from greatest to least

metric system: a measurement system based on the powers of ten; used outside the United States and in science and medicine

mixed number: a number that has both a whole number and a fractional part

mode: the value that occurs most often in a set of data

multiple: the product of any number multiplied by another number

negative numbers: the set of values less than zero

number line: a line used to show the order of numbers and their relationship to each other

number sense: common sense applied to mathematics and problem solving

numerator: the number on the top of a fraction; tells how many parts of the whole are used

order of operations: a set of rules that give the sequence for performing the mathematical operations in an expression

ordered pair: the pair of coordinates needed to locate a point on the coordinate plane; the coordinates are given in parentheses in the order (x, y)

origin: the point where the *x*-axis and *y*-axis cross on a coordinate plane; the coordinates of the point are $(0, 0)$

outcome: the result of a probability experiment

outlier: a data value that is much greater than or much less than the other values in a set of data

parallel: lines on the same flat surface that never meet or intersect

parallelogram: a closed figure with four straight sides; each pair of opposite sides is parallel

part: in a percent problem, a portion of the whole

partial product: the answer to part of a multiplication problem involving numbers with two or more digits; the sum of the partial products is the answer to the multiplication problem

pattern: an organized arrangement of numbers

percent: part of a whole number expressed as a part of 100

perimeter: the measure of the distance around the boundary of an object or figure

pi: the ratio of the circumference of a circle to its diameter; rounded to 3.14 on the GED Math Test

pictograph: a graph that uses pictures or symbols to represent data

place value: a system that shows how much a digit is worth by the location of the digit in the number

placeholder zero: a zero written between the decimal point and the start of a decimal number; for example: 4.02

population: the entire group from which a sample is taken

positive numbers: the set of values greater than zero

possible outcome: any event that could actually occur

power: the number of times a base is multiplied; a base is said to be raised to a certain power, which is indicated by an exponent

probability: the study of chance

product: the result when two or more numbers (factors) are multiplied together; the answer to a multiplication problem

projection: a prediction based on trends in data

proper fraction: a fraction that names a number less than 1; the numerator is less than the denominator

proportion: a mathematical statement that two ratios are equal

quadratic equation: an equation in which a variable is squared or written to the second power

quotient: the result when one number is divided by another; the answer to a division problem

radius: the distance from the center of a circle to any point on the circle

raising to higher terms: finding an equivalent fraction with a higher numerator and denominator by multiplying by a fraction equivalent to 1; for example, $\frac{2}{3} \times \frac{4}{4} = \frac{8}{12}$.

random sampling: selecting a portion of a population so that each member of the population has an equal chance of selection

range: the difference between the greatest and the least values in a set of data

rate: **1.** the element in a percent problem that is followed by the % sign: a ratio that compares some number to 100 **2.** a special kind of ratio that compares a number to one unit; the word *per* is often used in a rate

rate of change: the rate of increase or decrease over a period of time between an original amount and a new amount

ratio: a way to compare two numbers or quantities; can be written with the word *to*, with a colon (:), or as a fraction

reciprocal: the result of inverting the numbers in a fraction; for example, the reciprocal of $\frac{3}{4}$ is $\frac{4}{3}$

rectangular container: a three-dimensional object in which all angles are right angles (square corners)

reducing to lowest terms: writing an equivalent fraction using smaller numbers so that the numerator and denominator of the fraction have no common factors other than 1; for example, $\frac{6}{12} \div \frac{6}{6} = \frac{1}{2}$

regroup: when adding or subtracting, to carry or borrow a quantity from one place value column to another

remainder: the amount left over after dividing two numbers that do not divide evenly

right angle: a square corner; an angle having a measure of 90°

right triangle: a triangle having a right angle

rounding: expressing a number to the nearest ten, hundred, thousand, and so on

scalene triangle: a triangle with no sides the same length and no angles of equal measure

scientific notation: a useful system for writing a very large or a very small number as the product of a number between 1 and 10 and a power of 10

signed number: a number written with a positive sign ($+$) or a negative sign ($-$); a positive number is greater than zero, and a negative number is less than zero

similar figures: two shapes with identical angles whose corresponding sides are in proportion

simple interest: a percentage of an amount of money borrowed or invested that is paid for the use of the money

simplify: to reduce a ratio to lowest terms

slope: the measure of the steepness or incline of a line

square root: one of two equal factors of a number; for example, the square root of 9 is 3 because $3 \times 3 = 9$

stacked-bar graph: a type of bar graph in which each bar is divided into sections; a key is usually needed to interpret the data

statistics: the science or study of data

substitution: a method of solving a formula in which the variables are replaced with values and the indicated operations are completed

successive percents: a series of percent calculations in which the answer to each additional percent problem depends upon the previous calculation

sum: the results when two or more numbers are added together; the answer to an addition problem

supplementary angles: two angles whose sum measures 180°

systematic sampling: selecting a portion of a population according to a pattern

table: a presentation of data organized into columns (up and down) and rows (across)

term: in an expression or equation, a single number or a single variable or the product of a number and one or more variables

theoretical probability: a method of calculating probability in which chance is based on the ratio of desired outcomes to possible outcomes

transversal: a line that intersects two or more parallel lines

trend: an observed pattern of change in data

triangle: a closed figure with three straight sides

unit rate: a special kind of ratio that compares a number to one unit; often uses the word *per*

variable: a letter or symbol used to represent a numerical value in a formula; the value of a variable can change

vertex: the endpoint shared by the lines or segments that form an angle

vertical angle: either of two angles of the same measure that lie on opposite sides of two intersecting lines

vertical axis: one of two perpendicular lines that define a graph; the line running up and down; called the *y*-axis

volume: the measure of how much a solid object holds; capacity

weight: a measure of heaviness

whole: the base amount in a percent problem

whole number: a number that is used for counting

x-axis: the horizontal number line used to form the coordinate plane

y-axis: the vertical number line used to form the coordinate plane

y-intercept: the point at which the graph of a line crosses the *y*-axis on a coordinate plane

Index

Note to Reader: Vocabulary words appear in bold, and bold page numbers. following them contain their definitions.

adding and subtracting   46
algebra   247–268.
See also special topics in algebra and geometry
    equations   260–265
    expressions   256–259
    GED practice   266–268
    key points to think about   251
    objectives   247
    signed numbers   252–255
    Sneak Preview   247, 248–249
    vocabulary   250
approaches to learning math   28–29
area   132, 142–145, 156, 162–163, 338
associative property   44, 58

bar graphs   194, 200–201
base   132, 143
basic operations review
    adding and subtracting   46
    dividing   48–49
    multiplying   47
    solving one-step equations   50–51
    writing equations to solve problems   50
benchmarks   132, 134

calculations   66, 67
calculator skills
    decimals and calculators   70, 72–76
    general information on using a calculator   16–19
    scientific calculator (CASIO *fx*-260)   337–339
    signed numbers and calculators   255
canceling   88, 94
chance   230, 234
charts. *See* tables, charts, and graphs
circle graphs   192, 194, 204–207
circumference   172, 182, 340
cluster   214, 219
clustering   37
common denominator   88, 92
commutative property   44, 58
compatible numbers   44, 48
complementary angles   172, 174–**175**
compound inequality   272, 275, 277
congruent figures   172, 178
consecutive numbers   250, 263
content areas on GED Math Test
convenience sampling   214, 216
coordinate grids   21
coordinate plane   272, 282
corresponding angles   172, 176–177
cross products   110, 114
cube   152, 164
cylinders   172, 184

data   194
data analysis   211–226
    collection of data   216
    frequency tables and line plots   216–217
    GED Practice   224–226
    key points to think about   215
    mean, median, and mode   220–223
    normal distribution curve   218
    objectives   211

    Sneak Preview   211, 212–213
    vocabulary   214
decimal point   66, 68
decimals   63–84
    adding and subtracting   70–71
    comparing and ordering   69
    defined   26, 31
    dividing   74–75
    everyday decimals (money, time, distance)   76–79
    GED Practice   80–82
    key points to think about   67
    multiplying   72
    multi-step problems with   72–73
    objectives   63
    rounding   68
    Sneak Preview   63, 64–65
    vocabulary   66
denominator   88, 90
dependent events   230, 238
diameter   172, 182
digit   26, 30
distributive property   44, 59
dividend   66, 74
dividing   48–49
divisor   66, 74
double-bar graph   194, 200

English system   132, 134–137
equations   44, 50
    algebra   **250, 260**–265
    formulas   44, 54–55.
    See also formulas solving one-step   50–51
    writing equations to solve problems   50
equilateral triangle   172, 178
equivalency   132, 134
equivalent fractions   88, 90
estimate   26, 34–37
evaluate   250, 257
experimental probability   230, 235
exponents   132, 143, 250, 258

factors   44, 47
favorable outcomes   230, 234
formulas   149–168
    defined   **44, 54–55**
    GED formulas page   156–157, 340
    GED Practice   166–168
    geometry   162–165
    key points to think about   153
    objectives   149
    problem solving with   154–157
    Sneak Preview   149, 150–151
    solving for other variables   158–161
    vocabulary   152
fractions   85–106
    adding and subtracting   91–92
    defined   **26, 31**
    dividing   95
    everyday fractions (sale prices, finances, time, measurement)   100–103
    GED Practice   104–106
    key points to think about   89
    multiplying   94
    objectives   85
    problem solving with   96–99
    reducing   90
    Sneak Preview   85, 86–87
    vocabulary   88
frequency table   214, 216–217
front-end estimation   26, 34–35

MATHEMATICS

function
  defined   **152, 154, 272, 278**
  and formulas   152, 154
  graphing a   280–281
  & special topics in algebra & geometry **272, 278**–279

gap   214, 219
GED Math Test overview   14
  calculator skills   16–19, 337–339.
  See also calculator skills
  content areas   14
  coordinate grids   21
  graphing answers   22
  number grids   20
  practice test   297–310
  pretest   1–12
  purpose of test   13
  types of questions   14, 15
geometry   169–190.
See also special topics in algebra and geometry
  circles   182–185
  GED Practice   186–190
  key points to think about   173
  lines and angles   174–177
  objectives   169
  Sneak Preview   169, 170–171
  triangles   178–181
  vocabulary   172
geometry formulas   162–165
graphing test answers   22
graphs. *See* tables, charts, and graphs

horizontal axis   194, 200
hypotenuse   172, 178, 181

improper fractions   88, 93
independent events   230, 238
inequality   272, 274–277
integers   26, 30
inverse   44, 50–51
isosceles triangle   172, 178

key   194, 198

length   132, 134, 138, 334
like fractions   88, 91
like terms   250, 256
line graphs   194, 202–203
line plot   214, 216
linear equation   272, 284–285
lowest common denominator   88, 92

map scales   116
margin of error   230, 233
math questions
  concepts   14, 15
  problem solving   14, 15
  procedures   14, 15
math test overview   14
  calculator skills   16–19, 337–339.
  See also calculator skills
  content areas   14
  coordinate grids   21
  graphing answers   22
  number grids   20
  types of questions   14, 15
mean   214, 220, 340
measurement   129–148
  English system   134–137
  equivalencies   336
  GED Practice   146–148
  key points to think about   133
  metric system   138–141

  objectives   129
  perimeter and area   142–145, 162–163
  Sneak Preview   129, 130–131
  vocabulary   132
median   214, 221, 340
memory keys, calculator   18, 73, 339
metric system   132, 138–141
mixed numbers   88, 93, 96
mode   214, 221
multiples   26, 32
multiplying   47

negative numbers   250, 252
normal distribution curve   218
number grids   20
number line   26, 33
number sense   23–40
  applying   33
  approaches to learning math   28–29
  decimals, fractions, and percents   31
  defined   **23, 26, 28**
  estimating   34–37
  GED Practice   38–40
  integers   30–31
  key points to think about   27
  number relationships and patterns   32
  place value   30
  Sneak Preview   23, 24–25
  vocabulary   26
numerator   88, 90

order of operations   44, 56–57, **250, 254, 256**
ordered pair   272, 282
origin   272, 282
outcomes   230, 234
outlier   214, 219
overview of math test   14
  calculator skills   16–19, 337–339.
  See also calculator skills
  content areas   14
  coordinate grids   21
  graphing answers   22
  number grids   20
  practice test   297–310
  pretest   1–12
  purpose of GED Math Test   13
  types of questions   14, 15

parallel   152, 162
parallelogram   152, 156, 162
part   110, 118, 119
partial products   66, 72
passing GED Math Test   13–22
  calculator skills   16–19, 337–339.
  See also calculator skills
  content areas   14
  coordinate grids   21
  graphing answers   22
  number grids   20
  purpose of test   13
  types of questions   14, 15
patterns   26, 32
percent formula   120–121
percents
  defined   **26, 31, 110**
  and rate of change   122–123
  solving percent problems   118–123
  successive   122
perimeter   66, 78, 132, 156, 340
perimeter and area   142–145, 162–163
pi   172, 182, 183, 185

pictographs 194, 198–199
place value 26, 30, 66, 68
placeholder zeros 66, 68
population 214, 216
positive numbers 250, 252
possible outcomes 230, 234
power 132, 143
practice test 297–310
pretest 1–12
probability 230, 234.
See also statistics and probability
problem solving 41–62
    basic operations review 46–51
    GED Practice 60–62
    key points to think about 45
    multi-step problems 56–59
    objectives 41
    Sneak Preview 41, 42–43
    vocabulary 44
    word problems 52–55
product 44, 47
projections 194, 202–203
proper fractions 88, 93
proportions 110, 114–117
Pythagorean relationship 180–181, 340

quadratic equations 272, 290–291
questions, types of
    math concepts 14, 15
    math problem solving 14, 15
    math procedures 14, 15
quotient 44, 48

radius 172, 182
raising to higher terms 88, 92
random sampling 214, 216
range 214, 219
rate 110, 118, 119
rate of change 110, 122
ratio, proportion, and percent 107–128
    GED Practice 124–128
    key points to think about 111
    objectives 107
    percent 118–123
    proportions 114–117
    ratios 112–113
    Sneak Preview 107, 108–109
    vocabulary 110
ratios 110, 112–113
reciprocal 88, 95
rectangular container 152, 156, **164**
reducing to lowest terms 88, 90
regroup 88, 96
remainders 44, 48–49
right angles 152, 162
right triangle 172, 178
rounding 26, 34

scalene triangle 172, 178
scientific notation 250, 258–259
signed numbers 26, 30, 250, 252–255
similar figures 172, 178
simple interest 152, 154, 160, 340
simplify 110, 111, 112
slope 272, 286, 338
special topics in algebra and geometry 269–296
    coordinate geometry 282–291
    GED Practice 292–296
    inequalities 274–277
    key points to think about 273

    objectives 269
    patterns and functions 278–281
    Sneak Preview 269, 270–271
    vocabulary 272
square roots 172, 180
stacked-bar graphs 194, 201
statistics 214, 216
statistics and probability 227–246
    chance 234–237
    drawing conclusions with statistics 232–233
    GED Practice 242–246
    key points to think about 231
    objectives 227
    Sneak Preview 227, 228–229
    theoretical probability 236–237, 238–241
    vocabulary 230
substitution 152, 154–155
successive percents 110, 122
supplementary angles 172, 174–**175**
systematic sampling 214, 216

tables 194, 196
tables, charts, and graphs 191–210
    bar and line graphs 200–203
    circle graphs 204–207
    GED Practice 208–210
    key points to think about 195
    objectives 191
    reading 196–199
    Sneak Preview 191, 192–193
    vocabulary 194
term 250, 256
test overview 14
    calculator skills 16–19, 337–339.
    See also calculator skills
    content areas 14
    coordinate grids 21
    graphing answers 22
    number grids 20
    practice test 297–310
    pretest 1–12
    purpose of GED Math Test 13
    types of questions 14, 15
theoretical probability 230, **236**–237
transversals 172, 176
trends 194, 202–203
triangles 178–181
    defined **152, 156**
    equilateral 172, 178
    isosceles 172, 178
    right 172, 178
    scalene 172, 178
unit rate 110, 113

variable 44, 50, 250, 256
vertex 172, 174
vertical angles 172, 176
vertical axis 194, 200
volume 132, 134, 138, **152, 156, 164**, 336, 340

weight 132, 134, 138, 336
whole 110, 118, 120
whole numbers 26, 30
word problems 52–55, 262–265

x-axis 272, 282

y-axis 272, 282
y-intercept 272, 287